MOLECULAR BIOLOGY
OF THE GENE

BIOLOGY TEACHING
MONOGRAPH SERIES

CYRUS LEVINTHAL, *Editor*
Massachusetts Institute of Technology

Sidney Bernhard, *University of Oregon*   ENZYMES: STRUCTURE AND FUNCTION

Vernon M. Ingram, *Massachusetts Institute of Technology*   THE BIOSYNTHESIS OF MACROMOLECULES

Albert L. Lehninger, *Johns Hopkins University*   BIOENERGETICS

J. D. Watson, *Harvard University*   MOLECULAR BIOLOGY OF THE GENE

J. D. WATSON
Harvard University

MOLECULAR
BIOLOGY
OF THE GENE

1965

W. A. BENJAMIN, INC.   New York   Amsterdam

MOLECULAR BIOLOGY OF THE GENE

Library of Congress Catalog Card Number 65–19424
Manufactured in the United States of America

The final chapter of this manuscript was sent to the compositor on 26 January 1965; this volume was published on 21 July 1965.

W. A. BENJAMIN, INC.
New York, New York 10016

to S. E. LURIA

EDITOR'S FOREWORD

GREAT CHANGES HAVE TAKEN PLACE RECENTLY IN THE TEACHING OF undergraduate biology. To some extent, these changes are due, as they are in many other sciences, to the upgrading of high-school science education. However, the major factor for biology would seem to be the change that has taken place during the last 20 to 30 years in the science itself. Biology, which has in the past been taught primarily as a descriptive subject, is now changing to one that is primarily analytical. One result of this change is that the undergraduate biology courses are becoming more and more dependent on physics, mathematics, and chemistry, to enable the student to achieve a deeper understanding of this subject. The developments in molecular biology and biochemistry have not only become a part of the undergraduate biology curricula, but are increasingly necessary for a general understanding of our scientific culture.

This series of textbooks is designed to aid those biology teachers who are developing new programs for undergraduate biologists. We do not imagine a program lacking in the subject matter of "classical biology." Rather, we are thinking of a program in which the teaching of many of the more classical biological subjects will be firmly based on the student's background in biochemistry and molecular biology. Most introductory biology courses already include a section on molecular biology; however, it is our belief that future developments will see this section expand to the point where it can play a central role in the planning of the rest of biology program. Molecular biology is not a separate subject independent of "real biology"; rather it is fundamental for a serious understanding of any aspect of the subject.

We expect that this book will be useful as a supplementary text for courses at many different levels in a student's program. But its primary purpose is to enable the beginning students to gain enough background so that it will not be necessary to repeat the general and usually inadequate discussion of molecular biology at the beginning of each of the more advanced courses.

CYRUS LEVINTHAL

Cambridge, Massachusetts
June 1965

PREFACE

THIS BOOK HAS ITS ORIGINS IN A SERIES OF TEN LECTURES WHICH I have given for the past six years to introductory biology students at Harvard. In these lectures, I have not only attempted to convey the excitement of the recent discoveries of molecular genetics, but also to relate this new knowledge to the basic problem of biology—the nature of cells and how they divide. It has, therefore, been necessary to talk about ATP as well as DNA, a feature I have carried over into the text. I am aware, however, that some people may feel that I would have best restricted my discussion to the gene itself, with the expectation that the reader will learn the main principles of intermediary metabolism in another text. This, in fact, was my first intention. When I began to write the first draft, however, I was bothered by the artificial nature of the separation and so decided to start the book with two historically oriented chapters to help the reader see how our ideas about molecular genetics have developed out of the work of the classical geneticists and biochemists.

There may be readers troubled in another way. They could object that, in the later chapters, I have stated the arguments too strongly, in view of the rapidly developing nature of our ideas about the genetic code, the replication of viruses, and the control of protein synthesis. I do not believe this to be the case. Although a particular fact may later prove to be based on faulty evidence, I firmly believe that almost all the basic concepts I present are sound. This was not true five years ago; the writing of a molecular biology book for introductory students would have been unwise then. Now, however, I believe that biology has as sound a basis as was provided chemistry, about 1932, by the explosive development of the quantum theory of the atom. Therefore, it is time to reorient our teaching and to produce the new texts that will give the biologist of the future the rigor, the perspective, and the enthusiasm that will be needed to bridge the gap between the single cell and the complexities of higher organisms. Then we may expect hard facts about today's most challenging biological problems: the structure of cell membranes, the nature of cancer, the fundamental mechanism(s) of differentiation, and how the ability to think arises from the organization of the central nervous system.

It was my original intention to write a small book of about 125 pages. After writing a first draft of this length, I realized that I could not accomplish the task in this short space. Even at four times the original length, I am not completely satisfied. Often I present a fact, and, because of lack of space, I cannot outline the experiments that demonstrate its validity. Given the choice between deleting an important principle or giving an experimental detail, I am inclined to state the principle. This is partly because I have a preference for theory, but, more importantly, because a number of new laboratory manuals now exist which emphasize modern genetics and biochemistry.

Many of my friends have helped me in reading one or more of these chapters. Many useful comments were received from K. Bloch, M. Cohn, L. V. Crawford, J. Darnell, B. D. Davis, G. Edelman, J. T. Edsall, J. Hopkins, H. Latham, S. E. Luria, M. Meselson, N. A. Mitchison, M. Ptashne, H. Rubin, and H. Temin. Most particularly, I wish to thank Dick Roblin for his help with the index and Joan Argetsinger for her consistently intelligent comments throughout the preparation of the manuscript. Whenever possible, I have tried to follow their advice.

Sometimes, however, I took issue with their comments, and I alone am accountable for the errors in either fact or judgment. I am also greatly indebted to my secretaries, Margrit Hui and Jutta Binstock, for their cheerful competence, and to the Radcliffe students, Dolly Garter and Ellen Glass, for continual advice, not always followed, on what is a grammatical sentence. Most of the original drawings were done by Keith Roberts of St. John's College, Cambridge, England. I also wish to acknowledge the excellent artistic advice of Bill Prokos, who was responsible for the final version of the illustrations.

J. D. WATSON

Cambridge, Massachusetts
May, 1965

CONTENTS

EDITOR'S FOREWORD   vii

PREFACE   ix

One THE MENDELIAN VIEW OF
     THE WORLD   1

The Cell Theory   2
Mitosis Maintains the Parental Chromosome
    Number   4
Meiosis Reduces the Parental Chromosome
    Number   7
The Cell Theory Is Universally Applicable   8
Mendelian Laws   10
Principle of Independent Segregation   12
Some Genes Are Neither Dominant
    Nor Recessive   14
Principle of Independent Assortment   16
Chromosomal Theory of Heredity   16
Chromosomal Determination of Sex   18
The Importance of *Drosophila*   19
Gene Linkage and Crossing Over   20
Many Genes Control the Red Eye   24
Origin of Genetic Variability through Mutations   26
Early Speculation about What Genes Are and
    How They Act   27
Preliminary Attempts to Find a Gene-Protein
    Relationship   28

Summary   29
References   31

Two   CELLS OBEY THE LAWS OF
      CHEMISTRY   32
      The Concept of Intermediary Metabolism   38
      Energy Generation by Oxidation-Reduction
         Reactions   39
      Most Biological Oxidations Occur without Direct
         Participation of Oxygen   42
      The Breakdown of Glucose   43
      Involvement of Phosphorus and the Generation of
         ATP   48
      Most Specific Cellular Reactions Require a Specific
         Enzyme   50
      The Key Role of Pyruvate: Its Utilization via the
         Krebs Cycle   53
      Oxidation of Reduced Coenzymes by Respiratory
         Enzymes   54
      Synthesis of ATP in the Presence of Oxygen
         (Oxidative Phosphorylation)   56
      Generation of ATP during Photosynthesis   58
      Vitamins and Growth Factors   59
      The Lability of Large Molecules   60
      Implications of Chromatography   62
      The 25-Year Loneliness of the Protein
         Crystallographers   62
      Avery's Bombshell: Nucleic Acids Can Carry Genetic
         Specificity   64
      The Double Helix   66
      The Goal of Molecular Biology   67
      Summary   68
      References   69

Three   A CHEMIST'S LOOK AT THE
        BACTERIAL CELL   71
      Bacteria Grow under Simple, Well-Defined
         Conditions   71
      E. coli is the Best Understood Organism at the
         Molecular Level!   73
      Even Small Cells Are Complex   80
      Macromolecules Constructed by Linear Linking of
         Small Molecules   86
      Distinction between Regular and Irregular
         Polymers   93
      Metabolic Pathways   94
      Degradation Pathways Distinct from Biosynthetic
         Pathways   95
      The Significance of a Finite Amount of DNA   98
      One-Fifth to One-Third of the Chemical Reactions
         in E. coli Are known   99

Summary   100
References   101

Four   THE IMPORTANCE OF WEAK
       CHEMICAL INTERACTIONS   102

Definition and Some Characteristics of Chemical
    Bonds   103
Chemical Bonds Are Explainable in Quantum-
    Mechanical Terms   105
Chemical-Bond Formation Involves a Change in the
    Form of Energy   106
Equilibrium between Bond Making and
    Breaking   107
The Concept of Free Energy   107
K_{eq} Is Exponentially Related to ΔG 108
Covalent Bonds Are Very Strong   109
Weak Bonds Have Energies between 1 and 7
    kcal/mole   109
Weak Bonds Constantly Made and Broken at
    Physiological Temperatures   110
Enzymes Not Involved in Making (Breaking) of
    Weak Bonds   110
Distinction between Polar and Nonpolar Mole-
    cules   110
van der Waals Forces   112
Hydrogen Bonds   115
Some Ionic Bonds Are, in Effect,
    Hydrogen Bonds   118
Weak Interactions Demand Complementary
    Molecular Surfaces   119
H_2O Molecules Form Hydrogen Bonds   119
Weak Bonds between Molecules in Aqueous
    Solutions   121
Organic Molecules that Tend to Form Hydrogen Bonds
    Are Water Soluble   122
The Uniqueness of Molecular Shapes; The Concept
    of Selective Stickiness   122
The Advantage of ΔG's between 2 and 5
    kcal/mole   125
Weak Bonds Attach Enzymes to Substrates   126
Most Molecular Shapes Determined by Weak
    Bonds   126
Polymeric Molecules Are Sometimes Helical   128
Protein Structures Are Usually Irregular   130
DNA Can Form a Regular Helix   130
DNA Molecules Are Stable at Physiological
    Temperatures   131
Most Medium Size and Almost All Large Protein
    Molecules Are Aggregates of Smaller Polypeptide
    Chains   134
Subunits Are Economical   135
The Principle of Self Assembly   136

Summary   138
References   139

Five COUPLED REACTIONS AND GROUP
      TRANSFERS   141

Food Molecules Are Thermodynamically
    Unstable   142
Distinction between Direction and Rate of a
    Reaction   143
Enzymes Lower Activation Energies   145
A Metabolic Pathway Is Characterized by a
    Decrease in Free Energy   145
High-Energy Bonds Hydrolyze with Large
    Negative ΔG's   146
High-Energy Bonds Necessary for Biosynthetic
    Reactions   148
Peptide Bonds Hydrolyze Spontaneously   149
Coupling of Negative with Positive ΔG   150
Activation through Group Transfer   151
ATP Versatility in Group Transfer   152
Activation of Amino Acids by Attachment
    of AMP   154
Nucleic Acid Precursors Activated by Presence of
    Ⓟ ~ Ⓟ   155
Value of Ⓟ ~ Ⓟ Release in Nucleic Acid Syn-
    thesis   156
Ⓟ ~ Ⓟ Splits Characterize Most Biosynthetic
    Reactions   157
Summary   158
References   159

Six THE CONCEPT OF TEMPLATE
     SURFACES   160

Synthesis of Small Molecules   161
Synthesis of a Large "Small Molecule"   165
Synthesis of a Regular, Very Large Polymeric
    Molecule   168
A Deeper Look into Protein Structure   168
The Primary Structures of Proteins   172
Secondary Structures of Proteins May Be Sheets or
    Helices   174
Tertiary Structures of Proteins Are Exceedingly
    Irregular   175
S–S Bonds Form Spontaneously between Correct
    Partners   176
Enzymes Cannot Be Used to Order Amino Acids in
    Proteins   178
Template Interactions Are Based on Relatively
    Weak Bonds   180
Attraction of Opposites versus Self-Attraction   180
A Chemical Argument against the Existence of
    Protein Templates   181

Summary   182
References   183

Seven THE ARRANGEMENT OF GENES
       ON CHROMOSOMES   184

Much Remains to Be Learned about the Molecular
    Aspects of Chromosome Structure   185
The Genetic Cross   186
Chromosome Mapping   189
Importance of Work with Microorganisms   193
The Value of Mutagens   194
Bacterial Mutations: The Use of Growth
    Factors   195
Viruses Also Contain Chromosomes   198
Viruses Do Not Grow by Gradual Increase
    in Size   199
Bacterial Viruses (Phages) Are Often Easy to
    Study   201
Phages Form Plaques   203
Virus Chromosomes Are Sometimes Inserted into
    the Chromosomes of Their Host Cells   204
Bacterial-Chromosome Mapping by Mating   207
Bacterial Chromosomes Are Circular   209
Phages Occasionally Carry Bacterial Genes   215
Transfer of Purified Chromosome Fragments   218
Phages Also Mutate   220
Phage Crosses   222
Viral Crosses Involve Multiple Pairings   226
Summary   227
References   228

Eight GENE STRUCTURE AND
       FUNCTION   230

Recombination within Genes Allows Construction
    of a Gene Map   231
The Complementation Test Determines if Two
    Mutations Are in the Same Gene   235
Genetic Control of Protein Function   237
One Gene—One Polypeptide Chain   240
Recessive Genes Frequently Do Not Produce
    Functional Products   241
Genes with Related Functions Are Often
    Adjacent   241
Proof That Genes Control Amino Acid Sequences
    in Proteins   244
Colinearity of the Gene and its Polypeptide
    Product   245
A Mutable Site Can Exist in Several Alternative
    Forms   246
Single Amino Acids Are Specified by Several
    Adjacent Mutable Sites   247

Unique Amino Acid Sequences Are Not Required for
    Enzyme Activity   251
"Reverse" Mutations Sometimes Cause a Second
    Amino Acid Replacement   252
Summary   253
References   254

Nine THE REPLICATION AND GENETIC
      ORGANIZATION OF DNA   255

The Gene Is (Almost Always) DNA   257
The Amount of Chromosomal DNA Is Constant   259
Viral Genes Are Also Nucleic Acids   259
DNA Is Usually a Double Helix   261
The Complementary Shape Immediately Suggests
    Self-Replication   266
Base Pairing Should Permit Very Accurate
    Replication   268
DNA Replication Does Not Involve Synthesis of
    Specific Proteins   269
Solid Evidence in Favor of DNA Strand
    Separation   271
Replication Goes Hand in Hand with Strand
    Separation   273
Single-Stranded DNA Also Is Replicated by Base
    Pairing   273
Single DNA Molecules Are the Chromosomes of
    Viruses and E. coli   276
DNA Molecules Sometimes Have a Circular
    Shape   277
The Average Gene Contains about 1500 Nucleotide
    Pairs   279
Crossing Over Is Due to Breakage and Rejoining
    of Intact DNA Molecules   281
The Genetic Code Is Carried by the Sequence of
    Bases   285
Genetic Fine Structure Reflects the Base-Pair
    Arrangement   286
The Genetic Code Is Read in Groups of Three   291
Summary   295
References   296

Ten THE TRANSCRIPTION OF RNA
     UPON DNA TEMPLATES   297

The Central Dogma   297
Protein Synthesis in Absence of DNA   298
RNA Is Chemically Very Similar to DNA   302
RNA Is Usually Single-Stranded   302
Enzymatic Synthesis of RNA upon DNA
    Templates   305
Only One DNA Strand Acts as an RNA
    Template   308

Synthesis of RNA Chains Occurs in a Fixed
   Direction   311
Genetic Messages Must Be Given to Start (Stop)
   the Synthesis of Specific RNA Molecules   312
Summary   313
References   313

Eleven   INVOLVEMENT OF RNA IN
         PROTEIN SYNTHESIS   315

Amino Acids Have No Specific Affinity for RNA   315
Amino Acids Attach to RNA Templates by Means
   of Adaptors   316
Specific Enzymes Recognize Specific
   Amino Acids   316
The Adaptor Molecules Are Themselves RNA
   Molecules   318
Yeast Alanine sRNA Contains 77 Nucleotides   319
The 3-D Shape of sRNA Is Not Yet Known   320
Addition of the Adaptor Also Activates the Amino
   Acid   322
Peptide Bond Formation Occurs on Ribosomes   324
Ribosome-Associated RNA Does Not Usually
   Carry Genetic Information   325
Template RNA (mRNA) Reversibly Associates with
   Ribosomes   326
rRNA Exists in Two Size Classes   327
The Function of rRNA Is Not Yet Known   328
All Three Forms of RNA Are Made on DNA
   Templates   329
mRNA Molecules Exist in a Large Variety of
   Sizes   330
Ribosomes Attach to mRNA at Specific Points   330
The Direction of mRNA Reading is 5′ to 3′   331
An mRNA Molecule Works on Several Ribosomes
   Simultaneously   332
Stepwise Chain Growth Begins with the Amino
   Terminal End   333
Two Different Enzymes Are Needed to Form the
   Peptide Bond   337
Much More Must Be Learned about Ribosomes   339
Summary   339
References   340

Twelve   THE REPLICATION OF VIRUSES   342

The Core and Coating of Viruses   343
Nucleic Acid: The Genetic Component of All
   Viruses   345
Viral Nucleic Acid May Be Either Single- or
   Double-Stranded   346
Viral Nucleic Acid and Protein Syntheses Occur
   Independently   347
Synthesis of Viral Specific Proteins   350

Viral Nucleic Acids Code for Both Enzymes and
    Coat Proteins   350
Viral Infection Often Radically Changes Host
    Cell Metabolism   350
Replication of Double-Helical Viral DNA   351
Replication of Single-Stranded DNA Viruses   355
Viral RNA Self-Replication: Requirements for a
    New Viral Specific Enzyme   355
A Lower Size Limit Exists for Dividing Cells   357
The Lower Size Limit of a Virus Is Very Much
    Smaller   359
The Simplest Known Viruses Contain Three to
    Five Genes   359
More Complex Viruses Have More Genetic Material
    Than Simple Ones   360
Summary   361
References   362

Thirteen THE GENETIC CODE   363

Addition of mRNA Stimulates in vitro Protein
    Synthesis   363
Viral RNA Is mRNA   366
Specific Protein Can Be Made in Cell-Free
    Systems   366
Stimulation of Amino Acid Incorporation by
    Synthetic mRNA   367
Poly U Codes for Polyphenylalanine   369
Mixed Copolymers Allow Additional Codon
    Assignments   369
Ordering Codons by sRNA Binding   371
Codon Assignment from Regular Copolymers   372
The Code Is Degenerate   373
Nonsense versus Missense Mutations   374
Code Signals Must Be Given to Start and Stop
    Chain Growth   376
Reading Mistakes Can Occur in Cell-Free
    Protein Synthesis   378
Suppressor Genes Upset the Reading of the
    Genetic Code   378
Specific Codons Are Misread by Specific
    Suppressor Genes   381
Suppressor Genes Also Misread Good Genes   383
Streptomycin Also Causes Misreading   385
The Code Is Largely, if Not Entirely,
    Universal   386
Summary   387
References   388

Fourteen REGULATION OF PROTEIN SYN-
          THESIS AND FUNCTION   390

All Proteins Are Not Produced in the Same
    Numbers   390

Variations in the Amounts of Different *E. coli*
    Proteins   391
Relation between Amount of and Need for Specific
    Proteins   393
Variation in Protein Amount Can Reflect the
    Number of Specific mRNA Molecules   394
Repressors Control the Rate of Much mRNA
    Synthesis   395
Corepressors and Inducers Determine the
    Functional State of Repressors   396
Repressors Can Control More Than One Protein   397
Operators Control the Functioning of Operons   399
mRNA Synthesis May Begin near the Operator   401
Unequal Production of Proteins Coded by a Single
    mRNA Molecule   402
Bacterial mRNA Is Often Metabolically
    Unstable   404
Many Stable RNA Molecules Can Exist in
    Differentiated Cells   405
Some Proteins May Not Be under Control of
    Repressors   407
Repressor Synthesis Must Also Be Regulated   408
Regulation of Protein Function by Feedback
    Inhibition   408
Summary   412
References   413

Fifteen   CELL DIFFERENTIATION AND THE
          PROBLEM OF ANTIBODY
          SYNTHESIS   414

Amount of DNA per Cell Increases about a
    Thousandfold from *E. coli* to Mammals   415
The Heart of Embryology Is the Problem of Cell
    Differentiation   416
Differentiation Is Usually Irreversible   417
Differentiation Is Not Due to Chromosome Gain
    or Loss   417
Multicellular Organisms Must Have Devices to
    Control When Genes Act   418
Genes of Higher Organisms Differ in the Rates at
    Which They Produce Their Specific mRNA
    Products   419
Necessity of Finding a Model System for
    Studying Differentiation   421
Antibody Synthesis May Present a System for
    Studying Cell Differentiation   422
Antibodies Are Always Proteins   425
Antibody Specificity Resides in Amino Acid
    Sequence   426
Light and Heavy Chains Both Influence the
    Specificity of Antibodies   429
Plasma Cell Site of Antibody Synthesis   429

A Given Plasma Cell Usually Produces One Type
    of Antibody Molecule   430
Second Injection of Antigen Increases the
    Number of Antibody-Producing Cells   433
Antibody-Producing Cells Need Not Contain
    Antigens   433
Theory of Clonal Selection   434
Immunological Tolerance   436
Inability to Induce Antibodies in vitro   437
Summary   438
References   439

Sixteen **A GENETICIST'S VIEW OF
CANCER**   441

Cancer Can Arise in Almost All Differentiated
    Cells   443
Cancer Cells Grow where They Should Not   443
Contact Inhibition   444
Malignancy as a Loss of Cellular Affinities   446
Search for Chemical Differences between Normal
    and Cancer Cells   446
Cancer Induction by Radiation and Chemicals   447
Cancer as a Hereditary Change   448
Somatic Mutations as Possible Causes of
    Cancer   449
Viruses as a Cause of Cancer   449
Two Fates of a Polyoma Particle   450
Absence of Infectious Polyoma Particles from
    Transformed Cells; Search for a Provirus   453
Tumor-Specific Antigens   455
Virus-Infected Cells Need to Synthesize Nucleic
    Acids   456
Rous sarcoma Is Caused by a Myxovirus   459
Infection by a Single RSV Particle Leads to a
    Cancer Cell   461
Cancer Cells Produced by Single Infection Do Not
    Produce Progeny RSV Particles   462
Nonproducing Tumor Cells Produce RSV When
    Superinfected with a Related Virus   463
RSV Is a Defective Virus   464
A DNA Provirus Stage for RSV?   465
Can the Rous sarcoma System be Generalized to
    Other Cancers?   467
Study of Cancer at the Molecular Level   467
Summary   468
References   470

GLOSSARY   471

INDEX   483

1

THE
MENDELIAN
VIEW OF
THE WORLD

IT IS EASY TO CONSIDER MAN UNIQUE among living organisms. He alone has developed complicated languages that allow meaningful and complex interplay of ideas and emotions. Great civilizations have developed and changed our world's environment in ways inconceivable for any other form of life. Thus there has always been a tendency to think that something special differentiates man from everything else. This belief has found expression in man's religions, by which he tries to find an origin for his existence and, in so doing, to provide workable rules for conducting his life. It seemed natural to think that, just as every human life begins and ends at a fixed time, man had not always existed but was created at a fixed moment, perhaps the same moment for man and for all other forms of life.

This belief was first seriously questioned just over 100 years ago when Darwin and Wallace proposed their theories of evolution, based upon selection of the most fit. They stated that the various forms of life are not constant, but are continually giving rise to slightly different animals and plants, some of which are adapted to survive and to multiply more effectively. At the time of this theory, they did not know the origin of this continuous variation, but they did correctly realize that these new characteristics must persist in the progeny if such variations were to form the basis of evolution.

1

At first, there was a great deal of furor against Darwin, most of it coming from people who did not like to believe that man and the rather obscene-looking apes could have a common ancestor, even if this ancestor had occurred some 50 to 100 million years in the past. There was also initial opposition from many biologists, who failed to find Darwin's evidence convincing. Among these was the famous Swiss-born naturalist Agassiz, then at Harvard, who spent many years writing against Darwin and Darwin's champion, T. H. Huxley, the most successful of the popularizers of evolution. But by the end of the nineteenth century, the scientific argument was almost finished; both the current geographic distribution of plants and animals and their selective occurrence in the fossil records of the geologic past were explicable only by postulating that continuously evolving groups of organisms had descended from a common ancestor. Today, the theory of evolution is an accepted fact for everyone but a fundamentalist minority, whose objections are based not on reasoning but on doctrinaire adherence to religious principles.

An immediate consequence of the acceptance of Darwinian theory is the realization that life first existed on our Earth some 1 to 2 billion years ago in a simple form, possibly resembling the bacteria—the simplest variety of life now existing. Of course, the very existence of such small bacteria tells us that the essence of the living state is found in very small organisms. Nonetheless, evolutionary theory further affects our thinking by suggesting that the basic principles of the living state are the same in all living forms.

THE CELL THEORY

The same conclusion is independently given by the second great principle of nineteenth century biology, the *cell theory*. This theory, first put forward convincingly in 1839 by the German microscopists Schleiden and Schwann, proposes that all the larger plants and animals are constructed from small fundamental units called cells. All cells are surrounded by a membrane, and usually contain an inner body, the nucleus, which is

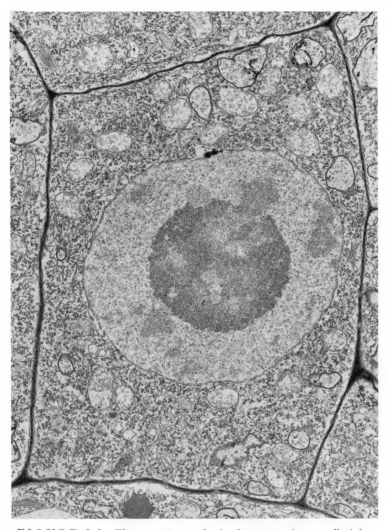

FIGURE 1–1   *Electron micrograph of a thin section from a cell of the African violet. The thin primary cellulose cell wall and the nucleus, containing a prominent nucleolus, are clearly visible. The cytoplasmic ground substance is heavily laden with spherical particles, the ribosomes, visible as small black dots. The profiles of a network of hollow membranes, the endoplasmic reticulum, can be seen scattered throughout the cell (courtesy of Drs. K. R. Porter and M. C. Ledbetter, Biological Laboratories, Harvard University).*

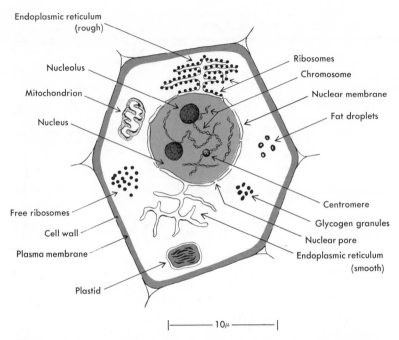

Endoplasmic reticulum
(rough)

Nucleolus

Mitochondrion

Nucleus

Free ribosomes

Cell wall

Plasma membrane

Plastid

Ribosomes

Chromosome

Nuclear membrane

Fat droplets

Centromere

Glycogen granules

Nuclear pore

Endoplasmic reticulum
(smooth)

|———— 10μ ————|

FIGURE 1–2   *A schematic view of the plant cell shown in Figure 1–1. The various components are not always drawn to scale. The plastid shown in the bottom of the cell will eventually transform into a chloroplast, the chlorophyll-containing site of photosynthesis.*

also surrounded by a membrane, called the nuclear membrane (Figures 1–1 and 1–2). Most important, cells arise only from other cells by the process of cell division. Most cells are capable of growing and of splitting roughly equally to give two daughter cells. At the same time, the nucleus divides so that each daughter cell can receive a nucleus.

MITOSIS MAINTAINS THE PARENTAL CHROMOSOME NUMBER

Each nucleus encloses a fixed number of linear bodies, called chromosomes (Figure 1–3). Before cell division, each chromosome divides to form two chromosomes identical to the parental body. This process, first accurately observed by Flemming in

1879, doubles the number of nuclear chromosomes. During nuclear division, one of each pair of daughter chromosomes moves into each daughter nucleus (Figure 1–4). As a result of these events (now collectively termed *mitosis*), the chromosomal complement of daughter cells is usually identical to that of the parental cells.

During most of a cell's life, its chromosomes exist as highly extended linear objects. Prior to cell division, however, they condense into much more compact bodies. The duplication of chromosomes occurs chiefly when they are in the extended state characteristic of interphase (the various stages of cell division are defined in Figure 1–4). One part of the chromosome, however, always duplicates during the contracted metaphase state; this is the *centromere*, a body that controls the movement of the chromosome during cell divisions. The centromere always has a fixed location on a given chromosome. Its specific location,

FIGURE 1–3   *The haploid complement of chromosomes from the leopard frog (Rana pipens), magnified 2125 times. This photograph was taken with a light microscope by T. E. Powell, of the Biological Laboratories, Harvard University. It shows the chromosomes when they have duplicated to form two chromatids held together by a single centromere.*

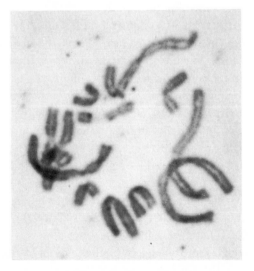

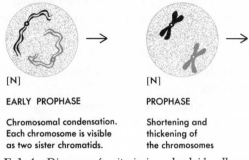

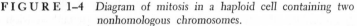

[N]

EARLY PROPHASE

Chromosomal condensation.
Each chromosome is visible
as two sister chromatids.

[N]

PROPHASE

Shortening and
thickening of
the chromosomes

FIGURE 1-4   *Diagram of mitosis in a haploid cell containing two nonhomologous chromosomes.*

however, varies with the specific chromosome; in some it is near one end, and in others it occupies an intermediate region.

When a chromosome is completely duplicated except for the centromere, it is said to consist of two *chromatids.* A chromatid is transformed into a chromosome as soon as its centromere has divided and is no longer shared with another chromatid. As soon as one centromere becomes two, the two daughter chromosomes begin to move away from each other.

The regular lining up of chromosomes during the metaphase stage is accompanied by the appearance of the *spindle.* This is a cellular region, shaped like a spindle, through which the chromosomes of higher organisms move apart during the anaphase stage. Much of the spindle region is filled with long, thin, protein molecules, which some people think are similar to the contractile proteins of muscles. If this resemblance is genuine, then perhaps the same mechanism that underlies the contraction of muscles also underlies the movement of chromosomes through the spindle.

Objects called the *nucleoli* are also present in the nucleus of practically every plant and animal cell. There is at least one nucleolus per haploid set of chromosomes, and in some cells the nucleolus is connected to a specific chromosome. Until recently, the functional role of the nucleolus was completely obscure, though some biologists originally thought that it might be related to the formation of the spindle. Now, however,

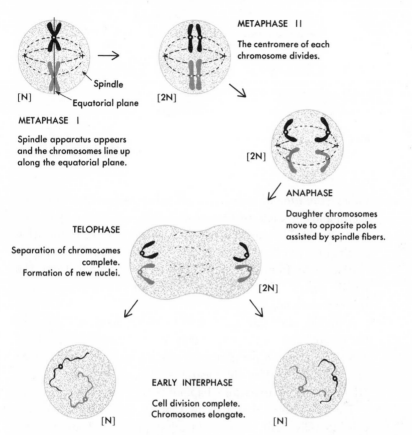

METAPHASE II

The centromere of each
chromosome divides.

Spindle

[N]

Equatorial plane   [2N]

METAPHASE I

Spindle apparatus appears
and the chromosomes line up
along the equatorial plane.

[2N]

ANAPHASE

Daughter chromosomes
move to opposite poles
assisted by spindle fibers.

TELOPHASE

Separation of chromosomes
complete.
Formation of new nuclei.

[2N]

EARLY INTERPHASE

Cell division complete.
Chromosomes elongate.

[N]   [N]

there are some strong hints that the nucleolus is involved in
the synthesis of ribosomes, small cellular particles upon which
all proteins are synthesized.

MEIOSIS REDUCES THE PARENTAL CHROMOSOME NUMBER

One important exception was found to the mitotic process. After
the conclusion of the two cell divisions that form the sex cells,
the sperm, and the egg (*meiosis*), the number of chromosomes
is reduced to one-half of its previous number (Figure 1–5).
In higher plants and animals each specific type of chromosome
is normally present in two copies: the homologous chromo-

PROPHASE I

Two pairs of homologous chromosomes
are shown in this imaginary diploid cell.
Chromosomes become visible as single
strands.

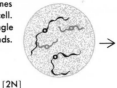

[2N]

FIGURE 1–5   *Schematic diagram of mitosis in the cell of an organism containing two pairs of homologous chromosomes.*

somes (the *diploid* state). In sex-cell formation the resulting sperm and egg each usually encloses only one of each type (the *haploid* state). Union of sperm and egg during fertilization results in a fertilized egg (*zygote*) containing one homologous chromosome from the male parent and another from the female parent. Thus the normal diploid chromosome constitution is restored.

Although most cells are diploid in higher plants and animals, the haploid state is the most frequent condition in lower plants and bacteria, the diploid number existing only briefly following sex-cell fusion. Usually meiosis occurs almost immediately after fertilization to produce haploid cells (Figure 1–6).

The cell theory thus tells us that all cells come from pre-existing cells. All the cells in adult plants and animals are derived from the division and growth of a fertilized egg, itself formed by the union of two other cells, the sperm and the egg. All growing cells contain chromosomes, usually two of each type, and here again, new chromosomes always arise through division of previously existing bodies.

THE CELL THEORY IS UNIVERSALLY APPLICABLE

Although the cell theory developed from observations about higher organisms, it holds with equal force for the more simple forms of life, such as protozoa and bacteria. Each bacterium or protozoan is a single cell, whose division ordinarily produces a new cell identical to its parent, from which it soon separates. In the higher organisms, on the other hand, the daughter cells

PROPHASE Ia

Homologous chromosomes undergo pairing. Later, each chromosome becomes visible as two chromatids (crossing over occurs at this point).

[2N]

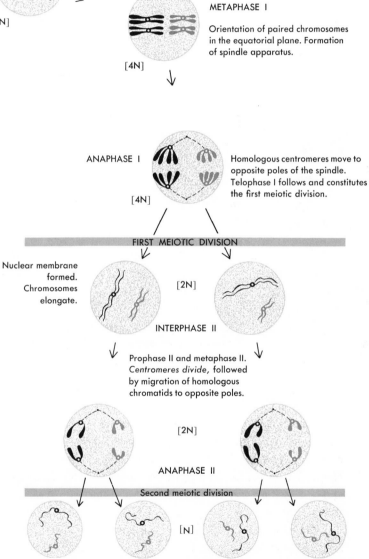

METAPHASE I

Orientation of paired chromosomes in the equatorial plane. Formation of spindle apparatus.

[4N]

ANAPHASE I

[4N]

Homologous centromeres move to opposite poles of the spindle. Telophase I follows and constitutes the first meiotic division.

FIRST MEIOTIC DIVISION

Nuclear membrane formed. Chromosomes elongate.

[2N]

INTERPHASE II

Prophase II and metaphase II. *Centromeres divide,* followed by migration of homologous chromatids to opposite poles.

[2N]

ANAPHASE II

Second meiotic division

[N]

Final result is four haploid cells.

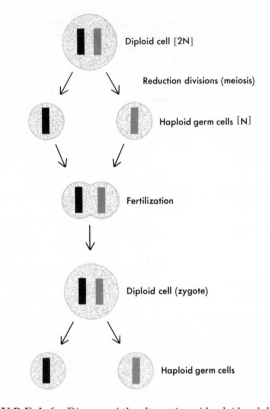

FIGURE 1–6   Diagram of the alternation of haploid and diploid states,
which comprise the sexual cycle. The chromosome set
derived from one parent is shown in black, that from
the other parent in color.

not only often remain together, but also frequently differentiate
into radically different cell types (such as nerve or muscle cells),
while maintaining the chromosome complement of the zygote.
Here, new organisms arise from the highly differentiated sperm
and egg, whose union initiates a new cycle of division and
differentiation.

Thus, although a complicated organism like man contains a
large number of cells (up to 5×10^{12}), all these cells arise initially from a single cell. The fertilized egg contains all the information necessary for the growth and development of an adult

plant or animal. Again the living state per se does not demand the complicated interactions that occur in complex organisms; but its essential properties can be found in single growing cells.

MENDELIAN LAWS

The most striking attribute of a living cell is its ability to transmit hereditary properties from one cell generation to another. The existence of heredity must have been noticed by early man as he witnessed the passing of characteristics, like eye or hair color, from parents to their offspring. Its physical basis, however, was not understood until the first years of the twentieth century, when, during a remarkable period of creative activity, the chromosomal theory of heredity was established.

Hereditary transmission through the sperm and egg became known by 1860, and in 1868 Haeckel, noting that sperm consisted largely of nuclear material, postulated that the nucleus was responsible for heredity. Almost 20 years passed before the chromosomes were singled out as the active factors, because the details of mitosis, meiosis, and fertilization had to be worked out first.

When this was accomplished, it could be seen that, unlike other cell constituents, the chromosomes were equally divided between daughter cells. Moreover, the complicated chromosomal changes which reduce the sperm and egg chromosome number to the haploid number during meiosis became understandable as necessary for keeping the chromosome number constant. These facts, however, merely suggested that chromosomes carry heredity.

Proof came at the turn of the century with the discovery of the basic rules of heredity. These rules, named after their original discoverer, Mendel, had in fact been first proposed in 1865, but the climate of scientific opinion had not been ripe for their acceptance. They were completely ignored until 1900, despite some early efforts on Mendel's part to interest the prominent biologists of his time. Then de Vries, Correns, and Tschermak, all working independently, realized the great importance of Mendel's forgotten work. All three were plant breeders, doing experiments related to Mendel's, and each reached similar conclusions before they knew of Mendel's work.

PRINCIPLE OF INDEPENDENT SEGREGATION

Mendel's experiments traced the results of breeding experiments (genetic crosses) between strains of peas differing in well-defined characteristics, like seed shape (round or wrinkled), seed color (yellow or green), pod shape (inflated or wrinkled), and stem length (long or short). His concentration on well-defined differences was of great importance; many breeders had previously tried to follow the inheritance of more gross qualities, like body weight, and were unable to discover any simple rules about their transmission from parents to offspring. After ascertaining that each type of parental strain bred true (that is, produced progeny with particular qualities identical to those of the parents), Mendel made a number of crosses between parents (P) differing in single characteristics (such as seed shape *or* seed color). All the progeny (F_1 = first filial generation) had the appearance of *one* parent. For example, in a cross between peas having yellow seeds and peas having green seeds, all the progeny had yellow seeds. The trait that appears in the progeny is called *dominant*, whereas that not appearing in F_1 is called *recessive*.

The meaning of these results became clear when Mendel made genetic crosses between F_1 offspring. These crosses gave the most important result that the recessive trait reappeared in approximately 25 per cent of the progeny, whereas the dominant trait appeared in 75 per cent of them. For each of the seven traits he followed, the ratio in F_2 of dominant to recessive traits was always approximately 3:1. When these experiments were carried to a third (F_3) progeny generation, all the F_2 peas with recessive traits bred true (produced progeny with the recessive traits). Those with dominant traits fell into two groups: one-third bred true (produced only progeny with the dominant trait); the remaining two-thirds again produced mixed progeny in a 3:1 ratio of dominant to recessive.

Mendel correctly interpreted his results as follows (Figure 1–7): The various traits are controlled by pairs of factors (which we now call *genes*), one factor derived from the male parent, the other from the female. For example, pure-breeding strains of round peas contain two genes for roundness (RR), whereas pure-breeding wrinkled strains have two genes for wrinkledness (rr). The round-strain gametes each have one gene for roundness; the wrinkled-strain gametes each have one gene for wrinkledness (r). In a cross between RR and rr, fertilization produces an F_1 plant with both genes (Rr). The

FIGURE 1–7 *Representation of how Mendel's first law (independent segregation) explains the 3:1 ratio of dominant to recessive phenotypes among the F_2 progeny. (A) represent the dominant gene and (a) the recessive gene. The shaded circles represent dominance, the unshaded circles the recessive phenotype.*

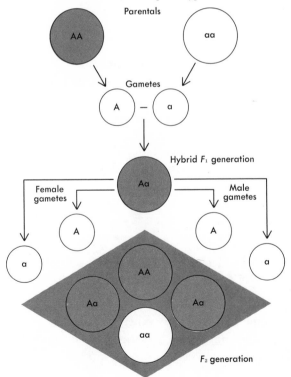

plant looks round because R is dominant over r. We refer to the appearance (physical structure) of an individual as its *phenotype*, and to its genetic composition as its *genotype*. Individuals with identical phenotypes may possess different genotypes; thus, to determine the genotype of an organism, it is frequently necessary to perform genetic crosses for several generations. The term *homozygous* refers to a gene pair in which both the maternal and paternal genes are identical (e.g., RR or rr). In contrast, those gene pairs in which paternal and maternal genes are different (e.g., Rr) are called *heterozygous*.

It is important to notice that a given gamete contains only one of the two genes present in the organism it comes from (for example, either the R or the r, but never both) and that the two types of gamete are produced in equal numbers. Thus there is a 50:50 chance that a given gamete from an F_1 pea will contain a particular gene (R or r). This choice is purely random. We do not expect to find *exact* 3:1 ratios when we examine a limited number of F_2 progeny. The ratio will sometimes be slightly higher and other times slightly lower. But as we look at increasingly larger samples, we expect that the ratio of peas with the dominant trait to peas with the recessive trait will approximate the 3:1 ratio more and more closely.

The reappearance of the recessive character in the F_2 generation indicates that recessive genes are neither modified nor lost in the *hybrid* (Rr) generation, but that the dominant and recessive genes are independently transmitted, and so are able to segregate independently during the formation of sex cells. *This principle of independent segregation is frequently referred to as Mendel's first law.*

SOME GENES ARE NEITHER DOMINANT NOR RECESSIVE

In the crosses reported by Mendel, one of each gene pair was clearly dominant, and the other recessive. Such behavior, however, is not universal. Sometimes the heterozygous phenotype is intermediate between the two homozygous phenotypes.

For example, the cross between a pure-breeding red snapdragon (*Antirrhinum*) and a pure-breeding white variety gives
F_1 progeny of the intermediate pink color. If these F_1 progeny
are crossed among themselves, the resulting F_2 progeny contain
red, pink, and white flowers in the proportion of 1:2:1 (Figure
1-8). Thus it is possible here to distinguish heterozygotes
from homozygotes by their phenotype. We furthermore see
that Mendel's laws do not depend for their applicability on
whether one *gene* of a gene pair is dominant over the other.

FIGURE 1-8 *The inheritance of flower color in the snapdragon.
One parent is homozygous for white flowers (AA) and
the other homozygous for white flowers (aa). No
dominance is present, and the heterozygous flowers
are pink. The 1:2:1 ratio of red:pink:white flowers
is shown by appropriate coloring.*

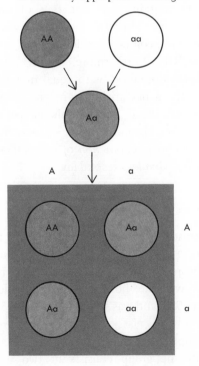

PRINCIPLE OF INDEPENDENT ASSORTMENT

Mendel extended his breeding experiments to peas differing by more than one character. As before, he started with two strains of peas, each of which bred pure when mated with itself. One of the strains had round yellow seeds, the other, wrinkled green seeds. Since round and yellow are dominant over wrinkled and green, the entire F_1 generation produced round, yellow seeds. The F_1 generation was then crossed within itself to produce a number of F_2 progeny, which were examined for seed appearance (phenotype). In addition to the two original phenotypes (round yellow; wrinkled green), two new types (*recombinants*) emerged: wrinkled yellow and round green.

Again Mendel found he could interpret the results by the postulate of genes, if he assumed that, during sex-cell formation, each gene pair was independently transmitted to the sex cell (gamete). This interpretation is shown in Figure 1–9. Any one gamete contains only one type of inherited factor from each gene pair. Thus the gametes produced by an F_1 (RrYy) will have the composition RY, Ry, rY, or ry, but never Rr, Yy, YY, or RR. Furthermore, in this example, all four possible gametes are produced with equal frequency. There is no tendency of the genes arising from one parent to stay together. As a result, the F_2 progeny phenotypes appear in the ratio: 9 round yellow, 3 round green, 3 wrinkled yellow, and 1 wrinkled green. *This phenomenon of independent assortment is frequently called Mendel's second law.*

CHROMOSOMAL THEORY OF HEREDITY

A principal reason for the original failure to appreciate Mendel's discovery was the absence of firm facts about the behavior of chromosomes during meiosis and mitosis. This knowledge was available, however, when Mendel's laws were reannounced in 1900, and was seized upon in 1903 by the American Sutton. In his classic paper, *The Chromosomes in Heredity*, he emphasized the importance of the fact that the diploid chromosome group consists of two morphologically

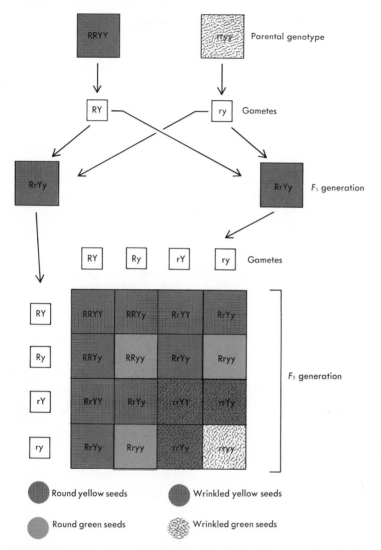

FIGURE 1–9 Schematic drawing of how Mendel's second law (independent assortment) operates. In this example, the inheritance of yellow (Y) and green (y) seed color is followed together with the inheritance of round (R) and wrinkled (r) seed shapes. The (R) and (Y) alleles are dominant over (r) and (y). The genotypes of the various parents and progeny are indicated by letter combinations, and four different phenotypes distinguished by appropriate shading.

similar sets and that, during meiosis, every gamete receives only one chromosome of each homologous pair. He then used this fact to explain Mendel's results by the assumption that genes are parts of the chromosome. He postulated that the yellow-and-green-seed genes are carried on a certain pair of chromosomes, and that the round- and wrinkled-seed genes are carried on a different pair. This hypothesis immediately explains the experimentally observed 9:3:3:1 segregation ratios. Though Sutton's paper did not prove the chromosomal theory of heredity, it was immensely important; it brought together for the first time the independent disciplines of genetics (the study of breeding experiments) and cytology (the study of cell structure).

CHROMOSOMAL DETERMINATION OF SEX

There exists one important exception to the rule that all chromosomes of diploid organisms are present in two copies. It was observed as early as 1890 that one chromosome (then called an accessory chromosome and now the x chromosome) does not always possess a morphologically identical mate. The biological significance of this observation was clarified by the American cytologist Wilson and his student Stevens, in 1905. They showed that, although the female contains a pair of x chromosomes, the x chromosome is present only once in the male. In addition, in some species (including man), the male cells contain a unique chromosome, not found in females, called the y chromosome. They pointed out how this situation provides a simple method of sex determination; whereas every egg will contain one x chromosome, only half the sperms will carry one. Fertilization of an ovum by an x-bearing sperm leads to an xx zygote, which becomes a female; fertilization by a sperm cell lacking an x chromosome gives rise to male offspring (Figure 1–10). These observations provided the first clear linking of a definite chromosome to a hereditary property. In addition they elegantly explained how male and female zygotes are created in equal numbers.

Mendelian view of the world

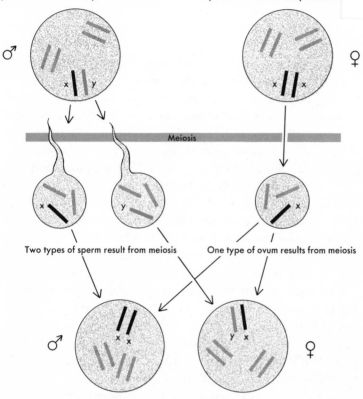

Diploid chromosome complement of male   Diploid chromosome complement of

♂   ♀

Meiosis

Two types of sperm result from meiosis   One type of ovum results from meiosis

♂   ♀

Sex determined by the type of sperm entering the ovum

FIGURE 1-10   *Schematic representation of how sex chromosomes operate.   Here is shown a case in which males contain one x and one y chromosome, and females, two x chromosomes.   This is the situation in both humans and Drosophila.   In some other species there is no y chromosome, so that diploid male cells contain one less chromosome than diploid female cells.*

THE IMPORTANCE OF DROSOPHILA

Initially, all breeding experiments used genetic differences already existing in nature.   For example, Mendel used seeds obtained from seed dealers who must have obtained them from farmers.   The existence of alternative forms of the same gene (alleles) raises the question of how they arose. One obvious hypothesis states that genes can change (mutate) to give rise to new genes (mutant genes). This hypothesis was first seriously tested, beginning in 1908, by the great American biologist Morgan and his young collaborators, the geneticists Bridges, Muller, and Sturtevent. They worked with the tiny fly *Drosophila*. This fly, which normally lives on fruit, was found to be easily maintained under laboratory conditions, where a new generation can be produced every 14 days. Thus by using *Drosophila* instead of more slowly multiplying organisms like peas, it was possible to work at least 25 times faster, and also much more economically. The first mutant found was a male with white eyes instead of the normal red eyes. It spontaneously appeared in a culture bottle of red-eyed flies. Because essentially all *Drosophila* found in nature have red eyes, the gene leading to red eyes was referred to as the *wild-type* gene; the gene leading to white eyes was called a *mutant gene* (allele).

The white-eye mutant gene was immediately used in breeding experiments (Figure 1–11a and b), with the striking result that the behavior of the allele completely paralleled the distribution of an x chromosome (i.e., was sex linked). This immediately suggested that this gene might be located on the x chromosome, together with those genes controlling sex. This hypothesis was quickly confirmed by additional genetic crosses using newly isolated mutant genes. Many of these additional mutant genes also were sex linked.

GENE LINKAGE AND CROSSING OVER

Mendel's principle of independent assortment is based on the fact that genes located on different chromosomes behave independently during meiosis. Often, however, two genes do not assort independently, because they are located on the same chromosome (*linked genes*). Numerous examples of nonrandom assortment were found as soon as a large number of mutant genes became available for breeding analysis. In every well-studied case, the number of linked groups was identical with the haploid chromosome number. For example, there are four groups of linked genes in *Drosophila* and four morphologically distinct chromosomes in a haploid cell.

Linkage, however, is in effect never complete. The probability that two genes on the same chromosome will remain together during meiosis ranges from just less than 100% to about 50%.

This means that a mechanism must exist for exchanging genes on homologous chromosomes. This mechanism is called *crossing over*. Its cytological basis was first described by the Danish cytologist Janssens. At the start of meiosis, the homologous chromosomes form pairs (*synapse*) with their long axes parallel. At this stage, each chromosome has duplicated to form two chromatids. Thus synapsis brings together four chromatids (a tetrad), which coil about each other. Janssens postulated that, possibly because of tension resulting from this coiling, two of the chromatids might sometimes break at a corresponding place on each. This could create four broken ends, which might rejoin crossways, so that a section of each of the two chromatids would be joined to a section of the other (Figure 1–12). Thus recombinant chromatids might be produced that contain a segment derived from each of the original homologous chromosomes.

Morgan and his students were quick to exploit the implication of Janssens' still unproved theory: that genes located close to each other on a chromosome would assort with each other much more regularly (close linkage) than genes located far apart on a chromosome. This immediately suggested a way to locate (map) the relative positions of genes on the various chromosomes (see Chapter 7 for details). By 1915, more than 85 mutant genes in *Drosophila* had been assigned locations, each a distinct spot on one of the four linkage groups or chromosomes (Table 1–1). The definitive volume which Morgan then published, *The Mechanism of Mendelian Heredity*, showed the general validity of the chromosomal basis of heredity, a concept ranking with the theories of evolution and the cell as one of the main achievements of the biologist's attempt to understand the nature of the living world.

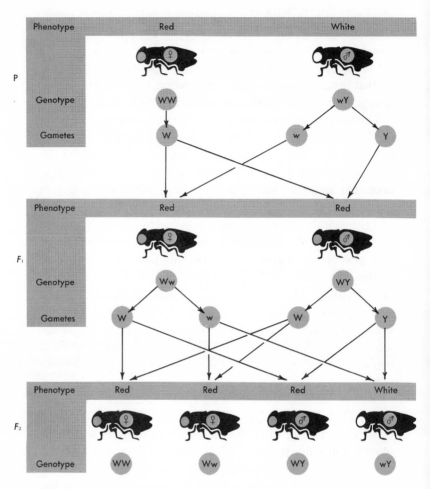

(a)

FIGURE 1-11   *The inheritance of a sex-linked gene in Drosophila. Genes located on sex chromosomes can express themselves differentially in male and female progeny because, if there is only one x chromosome present, recessive genes present on this chromosome are always expressed. Here are shown two crosses, both involving a recessive gene (w, for white eye) located on the x chromosome. In (a) the male parent is a white-eyed*

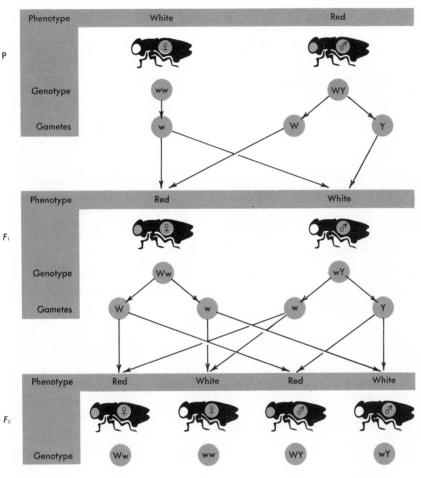

P

Phenotype   White   Red

Genotype   ww   WY

Gametes   w   W   Y

F₁

Phenotype   Red   White

Genotype   Ww   wY

Gametes   W   w   w   Y

F₂

Phenotype   Red   White   Red   White

Genotype   Ww   ww   WY   wY

(b)

(wY) fly, and the female, homozygous for red eye
(WW). In (b) the male has red eyes (WY) and
the female, white eyes (ww). The letter (Y) stands,
here, not for an allele, but for the y chromosome,
present in male *Drosophila* in place of a homologous
x chromosome. There is no gene on the y chromosome corresponding to the (w) or (W) gene on the
x chromosome.

MANY GENES CONTROL THE RED EYE

Mere inspection of the list of mutant genes in Table 1–1 reveals an important fact; many different genes act to influence a single character. For example, 13 of the genes discovered by

T A B L E   1–1   *The eighty-five mutant genes reported in Drosophila melanogaster in 1915*[a]

Group I

Name	Region affected	Name	Region affected
Abnormal	Abdomen	Lethal, 13	Body, death
Bar	Eye	Minature	Wing
Bifid	Venation	Notch	Venation
Bow	Wing	Reduplicated	Eye color
Cherry	Eye color	Ruby	Leg
Chrome	Body color	Rudimentary	Wing
Cleft	Venation	Sable	Body color
Club	Wing	Shifted	Venation
Depressed	Wing	Short	Wing
Dotted	Thorax	Skee	Wing
Eosin	Eye color	Spoon	Wing
Facet	Ommatidia	Spot	Body color
Forked	Spine	Tan	Antenna
Furrowed	Eye	Truncate	Wing
Fused	Venation	Vermilion	Eye color
Green	Body color	White	Eye color
Jaunty	Wing	Yellow	Body color
Lemon	Body color		

Group II

Name	Region affected	Name	Region affected
Antlered	Wing	Jaunty	Wing
Apterous	Wing	Limited	Abdominal band
Arc	Wing	Little crossover	II chromosome
Balloon	Venation	Morula	Ommatidia
Black	Body color	Olive	Body color
Blistered	Wing	Plexus	Venation
Comma	Thorax mark	Purple	Eye color
Confluent	Venation	Speck	Thorax mark
Cream II	Eye color	Strap	Wing
Curved	Wing	Streak	Pattern
Dachs	Leg	Trefoil	Pattern
Extra vein	Venation	Truncate	Wing
Fringed	Wing	Vestigial	Wing

T A B L E 1–1 (continued)

Group III

Name	Region affected	Name	Region affected
Band	Pattern	Pink	Eye color
Beaded	Wing	Rough	Eye
Cream III	Eye color	Safranin	Eye color
Deformed	Eye	Sepia	Eye color
Dwarf	Size of body	Sooty	Body color
Ebony	Body color	Spineless	Spine
Giant	Size of body	Spread	Wing
Kidney	Eye	Trident	Pattern
Low crossing over	III chromosome	Truncate intensf.	Wing
Maroon	Eye color	Whitehead	Pattern
Peach	Eye color	While ocelli	Simple eye

Group IV

Bent	Wing	Eyeless	Eye

a The mutations fall into four linkage groups. Since four chromosomes were cytologically observed, this indicated that the genes are situated on the chromosomes. Notice that mutations in various genes can act to alter a single character, such as body color, in different ways.

1915 affect eye color. When a fly is homozygous for a mutant form of any of these genes, the eye color is not red, but a different color, distinct for the mutant gene (e.g., carnation, vermillion). Thus there is no one-to-one correspondence between genes and complex characters like eye color or wing shape. Instead, the development of each character is controlled by a series of events, each of which is controlled by a gene. We might make a useful analogy with the functioning of a complex machine like the automobile: There are clearly a number of separate parts, like the motor, the brakes, the radiator, and the fuel tank, all of which are essential for its proper operation. Although a fault in any one part may cause the car to stop functioning properly, there is no reason to believe that the presence of that component alone is sufficient for proper functioning.

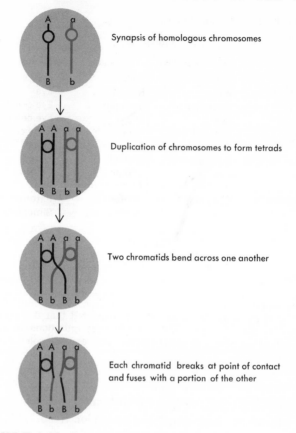

Synapsis of homologous chromosomes

Duplication of chromosomes to form tetrads

Two chromatids bend across one another

Each chromatid breaks at point of contact and fuses with a portion of the other

FIGURE 1–12 *Janssens' theory of crossing over.*

ORIGIN OF GENETIC VARIABILITY THROUGH MUTATIONS

It now became possible to understand the hereditary variation that is found throughout the biological world and that forms the basis of the theory of evolution. Genes are normally copied exactly during chromosome duplication. Rarely, however, changes (*mutations*) occur in genes to give rise to altered forms most, *but not all*, of which function less well than the wild-type alleles. This process is necessarily rare; otherwise many genes would be changed during every cell cycle, and offspring would not ordinarily resemble their parents. There is instead a strong advantage in there being a small but finite mutation rate; it provides a constant source of new variability, necessary to allow plants and animals to adapt to a constantly changing physical and biological environment.

Surprisingly, however, the results of the Mendelian geneticists were not avidly seized upon by the classical biologists, then the authorities on the evolutionary relations between the various forms of life. Doubts were raised about whether genetic changes of the type studied by Morgen and his students were sufficient to permit the evolution of radically new structures, like wings or eyes. Instead, they believed that there must also exist more powerful "macromutations," and that it was these which allowed great evolutionary advances.

Gradually, however, doubts vanished, largely as a result of the efforts of the mathematical geneticists Wright, Fisher, and Haldane. Considering the great age of the earth, they showed that the relatively low mutation rates found for *Drosophila* genes, together with only mild selective advantages, would be sufficient to allow the gradual accumulation of new favorable attributes. By the 1930s, biologists themselves began to re-evaluate their knowledge on the origin of species, and to understand the work of the mathematical geneticists. Among these new Darwinians were the biologist Julian Huxley (a grandson of Darwin's original publicist T. H. Huxley), the geneticist Dobzhansky, the paleontologist Simpson, and the ornithologist Mayr. In the 1940s, all four wrote major works, each showing from his special viewpoint how Mendelianism and Darwinism were indeed compatible.

EARLY SPECULATIONS ABOUT WHAT GENES ARE AND HOW THEY ACT

Almost immediately after the rediscovery of Mendel's laws, geneticists began to speculate about both the chemical structure of the gene and how it acts. No real progress could be made, however, since the chemical identity of the genetic material remained unknown. Even the realization that both nucleic acids and proteins are present in chromosomes did not really help, since the structure of neither was at all understood. The most fruitful speculations focused attention on the fact that genes must be, in some sense, self-duplicating: Their structure must be exactly copied every time one chromosome becomes two. This fact immediately raised the profound chemical ques: tion of how a complicated molecule could be precisely copied to yield exact replicas.

Some physicists also became intrigued with the gene, and when quantum mechanics burst on the world in the late 1920s, the possibility arose that perhaps to understand the gene it would be necessary to master the subtleties of the most advanced theoretical physics. Such thoughts, however, never really took root, since it was obvious that even the best physicists or theoretical chemists could not worry about a substance whose structure still awaited elucidation. There was only one fact which they might ponder: Muller's 1927 discovery that x rays induce mutation. Since there is a greater probability that an x ray will hit a larger gene than a smaller one, the frequency of mutations induced in a given gene by an x rays yields an estimate of the size of this gene. But even here so many special assumptions had to be made that virtually no one, not even the estimators themselves, took the estimates very seriously.

PRELIMINARY ATTEMPTS TO FIND A GENE–PROTEIN RELATIONSHIP

The most fruitful endeavors to find a relationship between genes and proteins examined the ways in which gene changes affect what proteins are present in the cell. At first this study was difficult, since no one really knew anything about the proteins that were present in structures such as the eye or the wing. It soon became obvious that genes with simple metabolic functions would be easier to study than genes affecting gross structures. One of the first useful examples came from a study of an hereditary disease affecting amino acid metabolism. Spontaneous mutations occur in humans, affecting the ability to metabolize the amino acid phenylalanine. When individuals homozygous for the mutant trait eat food containing phenylalanine, their inability to break it down allows a toxic level of phenylalanine to build up in the blood stream. The existence of such diseases, an example of the so-called "inborn errors of metabolism," suggested as early as 1909 to the physician Garrod that the wild-type gene is responsible for the presence of a particular enzyme and that, in a homozygous mutant, the enzyme is congenitally absent.

Garrod's general hypothesis of a gene-enzyme relationship was extended in the 1930s by work on flower pigments and the pigments of insect eyes. In both cases evidence was obtained that a particular gene affected a particular step in the formation of the pigment. However, the absence of fundamental knowledge about the structures of the relevant proteins ruled out deeper examination of the gene-protein relationship, and no assurance could be given either that most genes control the synthesis of proteins (by then it was suspected that all enzymes were proteins), or that all proteins are under gene control.

As early as 1935, it became obvious to the Mendelian geneticists that future experiments of the sort successful in elucidating the basic features of Mendelian genetics were unlikely to yield productive evidence about how genes act. Instead it would be necessary to find biological objects more suitable for chemical analysis. They were aware, however, that the contemporary state of nucleic acid and protein chemistry was completely inadequate for a fundamental chemical attack on even the most suitable biological systems. Fortunately, however, the limitations in chemistry did not deter them from learning how to do genetic experiments with chemically simple molds, bacteria, and viruses. As we shall see, the necessary chemical facts became available almost as soon as the geneticists were ready to use them.

SUMMARY

The study of living organisms at the biological level has led to three great generalizations: (1) Darwin's and Wallace's theory of evolution by natural selection, which tells us that today's complex plants and animals are derived by a continuous evo-

lutionary progression from the first primitive organisms; (2) the cell theory, the realization that all organisms are built up of cells; (3) the chromosomal theory of heredity, the understanding that the function of chromosomes is the control of heredity.

All cells contain chromosomes, which are normally duplicated prior to a cell-division process (mitosis) which produces two daughter cells, each with a chromosomal complement identical to that of the parental cell. In haploid cells there is usually just one copy of each type of chromosome; in diploid cells there are usually two copies (pairs of homologous chromosomes). A diploid cell arises by fusion of a male and a female haploid cell (fertilization), whereas haploid cells are formed from a diploid cell by a distinctive form of cell division (meiosis), which reduces the chromosome number to one-half of its previous number.

Chromosomes control heredity because they are the cellular locations of genes. Genes were first discovered by Mendel in 1865, but their importance was not realized until the start of the twentieth century. Each gene can exist in a variety of different forms called alleles. Mendel proposed that a gene for each hereditary trait is given by each parent to each of its offspring. The physical basis for this behavior is in the distribution of homologous chromosomes during meiosis: One (randomly chosen) of each pair of homologous chromosomes is distributed to each haploid cell. When two genes are on the same chromosome, they tend to be inherited together (linked genes). Genes affecting different characters are sometimes inherited independently of each other: this is because they are located on different chromosomes. In any case, linkage is seldom complete, because homologous chromosomes attach to each other during meiosis and often break at identical spots and rejoin crossways (crossing over). This attaches genes initially found on a paternally derived chromosome to gene groups originating from the maternal parent.

Different alleles of the same gene arise by inheritable changes (mutations) in the gene itself. Normally genes are extremely stable and are exactly copied during chromosome duplication; mutation normally occurs only rarely and usually has harmful consequences. It does, however, play a positive role, since the accumulation of the rare favorable mutations provides the basis for the genetic variability that the theory of evolution presupposes.

For many years the structure of the genes and the chemical way in which they control cellular characteristics were a mystery. As soon as large numbers of spontaneous mutations had been described, it became obvious that a one genome character relationship does not exist, but that all complex characters are under the control of many genes. The most sensible idea, postulated clearly by Garrod as early as 1909, was that genes affect the synthesis of enzymes. However, in general, the tools of the Mendelian geneticists, organisms such as the corn plant, the mouse, and even the fruit fly, Drosophila, were not suitable for chemical investigations of gene-protein relations. For this type of analysis, work with much simpler microorganisms became indispensable.

REFERENCES

Swanson, C. P., *The Cell*, 2nd ed., Prentice-Hall, Englewood Cliffs, N.J., 1964. An introductory survey of the cell theory.

Moore, J. A., *Heredity and Development*, Oxford, New York, 1963. An elegant introduction to genetics and embryology, with emphasis on the historical approach.

Sturtevant, A. H., and G. W. Beadle, *An Introduction to Genetics*, Dover, New York, 1962. Now available in paperback form, this book, originally published in 1939, remains a classic statement of the results of *Drosophila* genetics.

Levine, R. P., *Genetics*, Holt, New York, 1962. A rapid survey of genetics, with emphasis on the use of microorganisms in establishing a chemical basis of genetics.

Srb, A., and R. Owen, *General Genetics*, Freeman, San Francisco, 1952. Though now somewhat out of date, this book remains an excellent introduction to the many aspects of genetics which have not changed significantly since 1952.

Peters, J. A., *Classic Papers in Genetics*, Prentice-Hall, Englewood Cliffs, N. J., 1959. A collection of reprints of many of the most significant papers in the history of genetics, up to Benzer's fine-structure analysis of the gene.

Mayr, E., *Animal Species and Evolution*, Harvard University Press, Cambridge, 1963. The most complete statement of the facts supporting the theory of evolution.

2

CELLS OBEY
THE LAWS OF
CHEMISTRY

IN DARWIN'S TIME CHEMISTS WERE ALready asking whether living cells worked by the same chemical rules as nonliving systems. By then, cells had been found to contain no atoms peculiar to living material. Also recognized early was the predominant role of carbon, a major constituent of almost all types of biological molecules. A reflection of the initial tendency to distinguish between carbon compounds like those in living matter and all other molecules is retained in the division of modern chemistry into organic chemistry (the study of most compounds containing carbon atoms) and inorganic chemistry. Now we know that this distinction is artificial and has no biological basis. There is no purely chemical way to decide whether a compound has been synthesized in a cell or in a chemist's laboratory.

Nonetheless, through the first quarter of this century, a strong feeling existed in many biological and chemical laboratories that some vital force outside the laws of chemistry differentiated between the animate and the inanimate. Part of the reason for the persistence of this "vitalism" was that the success of the biologically oriented chemists (now usually called biochemists) was limited. Although the techniques of the organic chemists were sufficient to work out the structures of relatively small molecules like glucose (Table 2–1), there was increasing awareness that many of the most important molecules in the cell were very large—the so-called macromolecules—too large to be pursued by even the best of organic chemists.

The most important group of macromolecules was for many years believed to be the proteins, because of the growing evidence that all enzymes are proteins. Initially, there was controversy as to whether enzymes were small molecules or macromolecules. It was not until 1926 that the enzymatic nature of a crystalline protein was demonstrated by the American biochemist Sumner; the controversy was then practically settled. But even this important discovery did not dispel the general aura of mystery about proteins. Then, the complex structures of proteins were undecipherable by available chemical tools, so it was still possible, as late as 1940, for some scientists to believe that these molecules would eventually be shown to have features unique to living systems.

The general belief also existed that the genes, like the enzymes, might be proteins. There was no direct evidence, but the high degree of specificity of genes suggested to most people who speculated on their nature that they could only be proteins, by then known to occur in the chromosomes. Another class of molecules, the nucleic acids, were also found to be a common chromosomal component, but these were thought to be relatively small and incapable of carrying sufficient genetic information.

Besides general ignorance of the structures of the large molecules, the feeling was often expressed that something unique about the three-dimensional organization of the cell gave it its living feature. This argument was sometimes phrased in terms of the impossibility of ever understanding all the exact chemical interactions of the cell. More frequently, however, it took the form of the prediction that some new natural laws, as important as the cell theory or the theory of evolution, would have to be discovered before the essence of life could be understood. But these almost mystical ideas never led to meaningful experiments and, in their vague form, could never be tested. Progress was made instead only by biologically oriented chemists and physicists patiently at-

TABLE 2–1 *Some important classes of small biological molecules*

Class	Characteristics	Example
Aliphatic hydrocarbon	Linear or branched molecules containing only carbon and hydrogen	
Aromatic hydrocarbon	Ring-shaped hydrocarbons containing alternating single and double bonds	
Pyrimidine	An aromatic compound of the formula $C_4H_4N_2$ (or a derivitive thereof)	

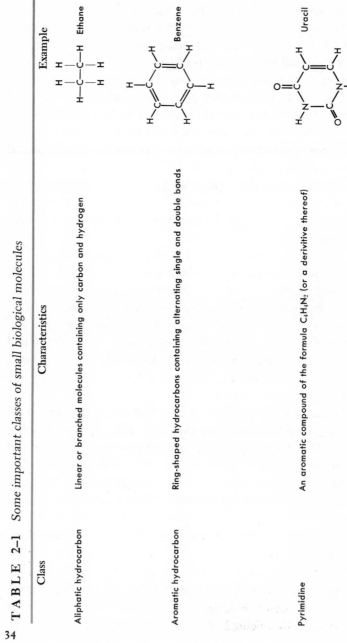

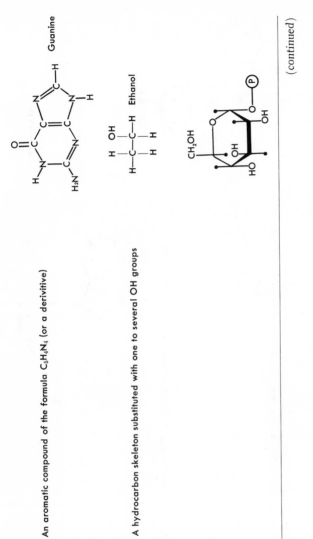

Purine

An aromatic compound of the formula $C_5H_4N_4$ (or a derivitive)

Alcohol

A hydrocarbon skeleton substituted with one to several OH groups

(continued)

T A B L E 2-1 (continued)

Class	Characteristics	Example
Phosphate ester	Molecule formed from alcohols and phosphoric acids with the elimination of H_2O.	
Nucleoside	Contains a pentose sugar linked to either a purine or pyrimidine base, through a C—N bond	
Nucleotide	Phosphate ester of a nucleoside	

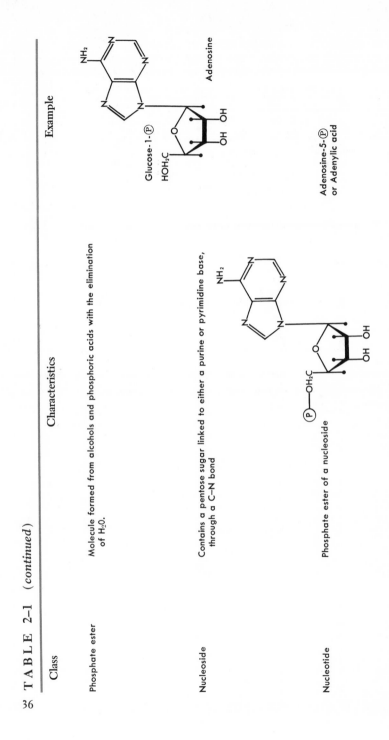

Glucose-1-Ⓟ

Adenosine

Adenosine-5-Ⓟ
or Adenylic acid

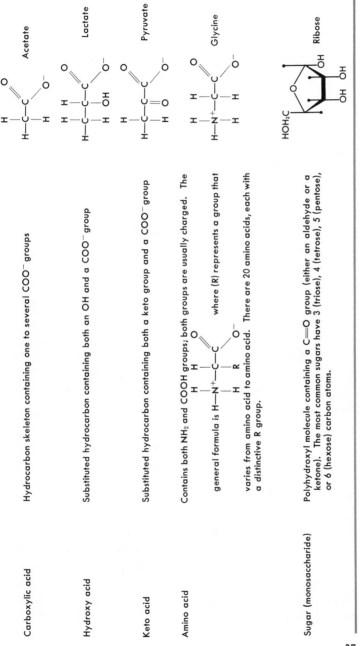

Carboxylic acid	Hydrocarbon skeleton containing one to several COO^- groups
Hydroxy acid	Substituted hydrocarbon containing both an OH and a COO^- group
Keto acid	Substituted hydrocarbon containing both a keto group and a COO^- group
Amino acid	Contains both NH_2 and COOH groups; both groups are usually charged. The general formula is [structure] where (R) represents a group that varies from amino acid to amino acid. There are 20 amino acids, each with a distinctive R group.
Sugar (monosaccharide)	Polyhydroxyl molecule containing a C=O group (either an aldehyde or a ketone). The most common sugars have 3 (triose), 4 (tetrose), 5 (pentose), or 6 (hexose) carbon atoms.

37

tempting to devise new ways of solving more and more complex biological structures. But for many years, there were no triumphs to shout. The chemists and biologists usually moved in different and sometimes hostile worlds, the biologist often denying that the chemist would ever provide the real answers to the important riddles of biology. Always not too far back in some biologists' minds was the feeling, if not the hope, that something more basic than mere complexity and size separated biology from the bleak, inanimate world of a chemical laboratory.

THE CONCEPT OF INTERMEDIARY METABOLISM

As soon as the organic chemists began to identify some of the various cellular molecules, it became clear that food molecules are extensively transformed after they enter an organism. In no case does a food source contain all the different molecules present in a cell. On the contrary, in some cases practically all the organic molecules within an organism are synthesized inside it. This point is easily seen by observing cellular growth on well-defined food sources: for example, the growth of yeast cells using the simple sugar glucose as the sole source of carbon. Here, soon after its cellular entry, glucose is chemically transformed into a large variety of molecules necessary for the building of new structural components. Usually these chemical transformations do not occur in one step; instead intermediate compounds are produced. These intermediate compounds often have no cellular function besides forming part of a pathway leading to the synthesis of a necessary structural component like an amino acid.

The sum total of all the various chemical reactions occurring in a cell is frequently referred to as the *metabolism* of the cell. Correspondingly, the various molecules involved in these transformations are often called *metabolites*. *Intermediary metabolism* is the term used to describe the various chemical reactions involved in the transformation of food molecules into essential cellular building blocks.

ENERGY GENERATION BY OXIDATION–
REDUCTION REACTIONS

By the middle of the nineteenth century, it was known that the food (initially of plant origin) eaten by animals and bacteria is only in part transformed into new cellular building blocks, some of it being burned by combustion with oxygen to yield CO_2 and H_2O and energy. At the same time it was becoming clear that the reverse cycle also operates in green plants.

Respiration:

$C_6H_{12}O_6 + 6O_2 \rightarrow 6CO_2 + 6H_2O$ + energy in form of heat
                                        (occurs both in plants and animals)   (2–1)

Photosynthesis:

$6CO_2 + 6H_2O$ + energy (from the sun) $\rightarrow C_6H_{12}O_6$ (glucose) + $6O_2$
                                        (occurs only in plants)   (2–2)

Both these equations can be thought of as the sum total of a lengthy series of oxidation-reduction reactions.

In respiration, organic molecules such as glucose are oxidized by molecular oxygen to form C=O bonds (Table 2–2), which contain *less* usable energy (energy which can do work) than the starting C—H, C—OH, and C—C bonds. Energy is given off in respiration, just as it is when glucose burns at high temperatures outside the cell to produce CO_2, H_2O, and energy in the form of heat. In contrast, during photosynthesis, the energy from the light quanta of the sun is used to reduce CO_2 to molecules which contain *more* usable energy.

When these relationships were first worked out, no one knew how the energy obtained during respiration was put to advantage. It was clear that somehow a useful form of energy had to be available to enable living organisms to carry out a variety of forms of work, such as muscular contraction and selective transport of molecules across cell membranes. Even then it seemed unlikely that the energy obtained from food was first released as heat, since, at the temperature at which life exists, heat energy cannot be effectively used to synthesize new

TABLE 2-2 *Important functional groups in biological molecules*

Group	Molecular Example	Biological Significance
—C—H Methyl	Methyl group of alanine	Highly insoluble in water; does not form hydrogen bonds
—OH Hydroxyl	Ethanol (ethyl alcohol)	Water soluble; forms hydrogen bonds
Carboxyl	Acetic acid	Usually charged: good acceptor of hydrogen bonds
Amino	Glycine	Often charged: $NH_2 + H^+ \rightleftharpoons NH_3^+$ forms hydrogen bonds
Carbonyl	Acetaldehyde	Forms hydrogen bonds; usually exists in keto form:

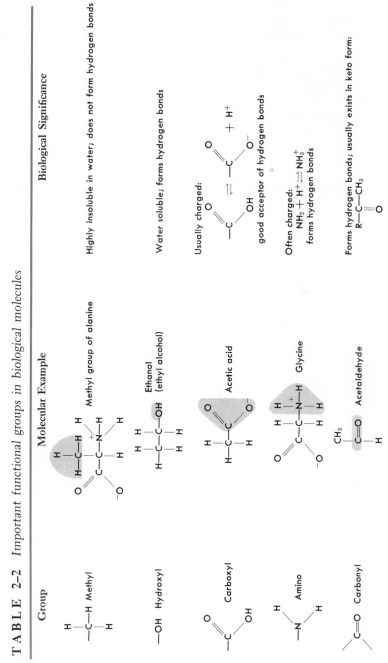

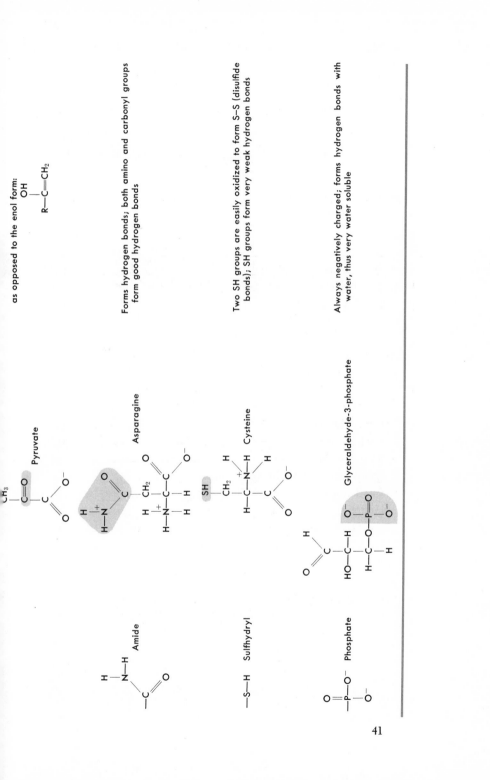

as opposed to the enol form:

$$R-\overset{\overset{\displaystyle OH}{|}}{C}=CH_2$$

Pyruvate

Asparagine

Forms hydrogen bonds; both amino and carbonyl groups form good hydrogen bonds

Cysteine

Two SH groups are easily oxidized to form S—S (disulfide bonds); SH groups form very weak hydrogen bonds

Glyceraldehyde-3-phosphate

Always negatively charged; forms hydrogen bonds with water, thus very water soluble

Amide

Sulfhydryl   —S—H

Phosphate

41

chemical bonds. Thus since the awakening of an interest in the chemistry of life, a prime challenge has been to understand the generation of energy in a useful form.

MOST BIOLOGICAL OXIDATIONS OCCUR
WITHOUT DIRECT PARTICIPATION OF OXYGEN

Because oxygen is so completely necessary for the functioning of animals, it was natural to guess that oxygen would participate directly in all oxidations of carbon compounds. Actually, most biological oxidations occur in the absence of oxygen. This is possible because, as first proposed around 1912 by the German biochemist Wieland, most biological oxidations are actually dehydrogenations. A compound is oxidized when we remove a pair of hydrogen atoms from it (Figure 2–1). It is not possible, however, merely to remove the hydrogen atoms: They must be transferred to another molecule, which is then said to be reduced (Figure 2–2). In these reactions, as in all other oxidation-reduction reactions, every time one molecule is oxidized, another must be reduced. There are several different molecules whose role is to receive hydrogen atoms. All are medium-sized (MW ~ 500) organic molecules that associate with specific proteins to form active enzymes. The protein components alone have no enzymatic activity. Only when the small molecule partner is present will activity be present. Hence these small molecules are named *coenzymes* (we should note that not all coenzymes participate in oxidation-reduction reactions; some coenzymes function in other types of metabolic reactions).

FIGURE 2–1   *Oxidation of an organic molecule by removal of a pair of hydrogen atoms. This figure shows the oxidation of lactate to pyruvate.*

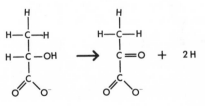

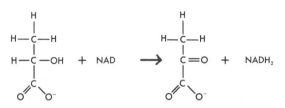

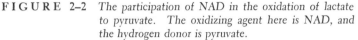

FIGURE 2–2   *The participation of NAD in the oxidation of lactate to pyruvate. The oxidizing agent here is NAD, and the hydrogen donor is pyruvate.*

Although the involvement of coenzymes in oxidative reactions was hinted at by 1910, it was not until the early 1930s that their cardinal significance was appreciated. Then the work of the great German biochemist, Otto Warburg, and the Swedish chemists, von Euler and Theorell, established the structure and action of several of the most important coenzymes: nicotinamide adenine dinucleotide (NAD, earlier called diphosphopyridine nucleotide or DPN, Figure 2–3), flavin mononucleotide (FMN), and flavin adenine dinucleotide (FAD).

Coenzymes, like enzymes, function many different times and are not used up in the course of functioning. This is because the hydrogen atoms transferred to them do not remain permanently attached, but are transferred by a second oxidation-reduction reaction, usually to another coenzyme, or to oxygen itself (Figure 2–4). Coenzymes are thus being continually oxidized and reduced. Furthermore, we see that, although oxygen is not directly necessary for a given reaction, it is often necessary indirectly, since it must be available to oxidize the coenzyme molecules to make them available for accepting additional pairs of hydrogen atoms (or electrons).

THE BREAKDOWN OF GLUCOSE

Much of the early work in intermediary metabolism dealt with the transformation of glucose into other molecules. Glucose was emphasized, not only because it played a central role in the economy of cells, but also for a practical reason: The ethyl alcohol (ethanol) produced when wine is made from grapes is derived from the breakdown of glucose. As early as 1810, the chemist Gay-Lussac demonstrated the production of ethyl alcohol by this process, and by 1837 the essential role of yeast was established. The production of the alcohol in wine is not a spontaneous process but normally requires the presence of living yeast cells.

Also important in the initial work with glucose was the French microbiologist Pasteur, who discovered that the process does not require air; to distinguish it from reactions requiring oxygen, he used the term *fermentation*. He also showed that

FIGURE 2-3   *The oxidation and reduction of a coenzyme. Shown here are both the oxidized and reduced forms of the very important coenzyme nicotinamide adenine dinucleotide, NAD (the oxidized form), an acceptor of hydrogen atoms, and NADH₂ (the reduced form), a donor of hydrogen atoms. The release of hydrogen atoms decreases the free energy of a molecule; the acceptance of them increases its free energy.*

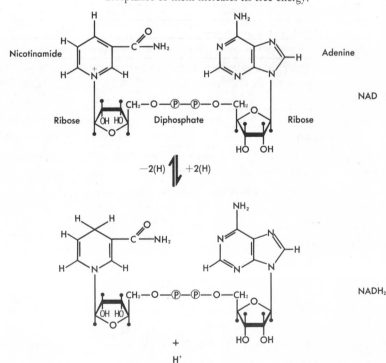

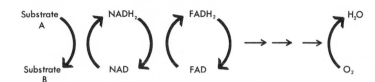

FIGURE 2–4 *The transfer of a pair of hydrogen atoms from one coenzyme to another. In this series of reactions, the final hydrogen acceptor is oxygen (O_2). FAD is flavin adenine dinucleotide, which exists not free, but usually in combination with a specific protein, to form a flavoprotein.*

ethanol is not the only product of glucose fermentation, but that there are other products, such as lactic acid and glycerol.

The next great advance came with Buchner's discovery in 1897 that the living cell per se is not necessary for fermentation, but that a cell-free extract from yeast can, by itself, transform glucose into ethanol. This step was not only conceptually important, but also provided a much more practical system for studying the chemical steps of fermentation. When working with cell-free systems, it is relatively easy to add or subtract components thought to be involved in the reaction; when living cells are being used, it is often very difficult, and sometimes impossible, to transfer specific compounds in an unmodified form across the cell membrane.

Over the next 40 years, cell-free extracts were used by a large number of distinguished biochemists, including the Englishmen Harden and Young, and the Germans Embden and Meyerhof, to work out the exact chemical pathways of glucose degradation (Figure 2–5). During this period, the important generalization emerged that the reactions involved (collectively called the Embden-Meyerhof pathway) were not peculiar to alcoholic fermentation in yeast, but occurred in many other cases of glucose utilization as well. Perhaps the most significant discovery was made by Meyerhof. He showed that, when muscles contract in the absence of oxygen, the carbohydrate food reserve of glycogen is broken down, via glucose, to lactic acid (anaerobic *glycolysis*). Thus it became clear that, not only can microorganisms obtain their energy and carbon

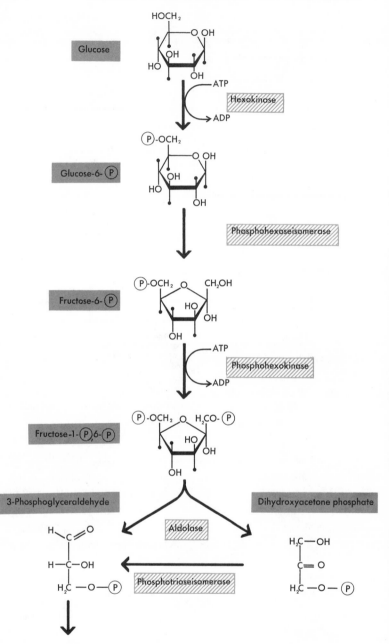

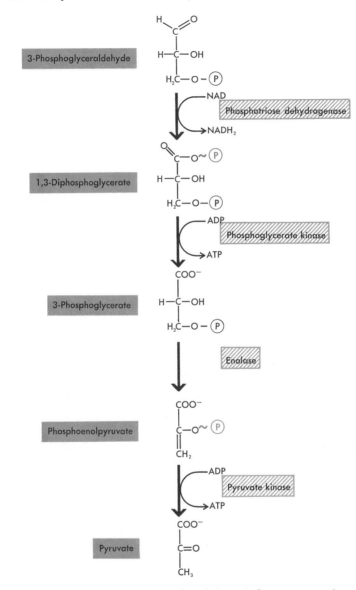

FIGURE 2–5 *The stepwise degradation of glucose to pyruvic acid. This collection of consecutive reactions is often called the Embden-Meyerhof pathway.*

via the Embden-Meyerhof pathway, but energy involved in the contraction of muscles is also generated by the same pathway. A feeling often expressed as "the unity of biochemistry" began to develop. By this we mean the realization that the basic biochemical reactions upon which cell growth and division depend are the same, or very similar, in all cells, those of microorganisms as well as of higher plants and animals. This unity was not surprising to the more astute biologists, many of whom were largely preoccupied with the consequences of evolutionary theory: Given that a man and a fish are descended from a common ancestor, it should not be surprising that many of their cell constituents are similar.

INVOLVEMENT OF PHOSPHORUS
AND THE GENERATION OF ATP

As early as 1905 the phosphorus atom was implicated in a vital role in metabolism. Then Harden and Young found that alcoholic fermentation occurs only when inorganic phosphate (PO_4^{3-}) is present. This discovery was followed by the eventual isolation of a large number of intermediary metabolites containing PO_4^{3-} (Ⓟ) groups attached to carbon atoms by

phosphate ester linkages $\left(\begin{array}{c} | \\ -C-O-Ⓟ \\ | \end{array}\right)$.

The significance of phosphorylated intermediates was unclear for 25 years. Then, about 1930, Meyerhof and Lipmann realized the crucial fact that it is by means of the phosphate esters that cells are able to trap some of the energy of the chemical bonds present in their food molecules. During fermentation several intermediates (Figure 2–6) are created (e.g., D-1,3-diphosphoglyceric acid), which contain what are popularly known as high-energy phosphate bonds (see Chapter 5 for more details). These high-energy phosphate groups are usually transferred to acceptor molecules, where they can serve as sources of chemical energy for vital cellular processes, such as motion, generation of light, and (as we shall see in Chapters 5 and 6) the efficient biosynthesis of necessary cellular molecules. The most important of the acceptor molecules is adenosine diphosphate (ADP, Figure 2–7). Addition of a high-energy ℗ group to ADP forms *adenosine triphosphate* (ATP).

ADP + ℗ ⇌ ATP

The discovery of the role of ADP as an acceptor molecule and that of ATP as a donor of high-energy phosphate groups was one of the most important discoveries of modern biology. Until the roles of these molecules were known, there was complete mystery about how cells obtained energy. There was constant speculation about how cellular existence was compatible with the second law of thermodynamics [in a closed system the amount of disorder (entropy) invariably increases]. What was conceivably a paradox ceased to exist as soon as it was seen how animal cells could trap and utilize the energy in food molecules. At that time the mechanism by which the sun's energy was trapped in photosynthesis was not known. Here again, the primary action of the sun's energy is now known to be the generation of ATP.

FIGURE 2–6 *The formation of an energy-rich phosphate ester bond, coupled with the oxidation of 3-phosphoglyceraldehyde by NAD.*

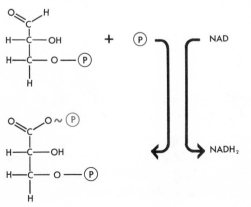

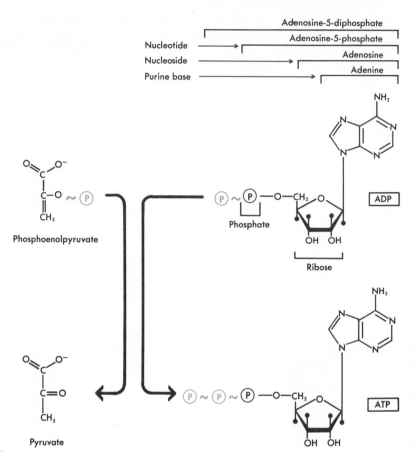

FIGURE 2-7   *The formation of ATP (adenosine-5'-triphosphate) from ADP and an energy-rich phosphate bond. Here the donor of the high-energy bond is phosphoenolpyruvate. The symbol ~ signifies that the bond is of the high-energy variety.*

MOST SPECIFIC CELLULAR REACTIONS REQUIRE A SPECIFIC ENZYME

The idea that most specific metabolic steps require a specific enzyme was realized only when a number of specific reactions were unraveled.   As the Embden-Meyerhof pathway was being worked out, it became clear that each step required a separate enzyme (see Figure 2–5). Each of the enzymes acts by combining with the molecules involved in the particular reaction (the substrates of the enzymes). For example, glucose and ATP are substrates for the enzyme hexokinase. When these molecules interact on the surface of hexokinase, the terminal P of ATP is transferred to a glucose molecule to form glucose-6-Ⓟ.

The essence of an enzyme is its ability to speed up (catalyze) a reaction involving the making or breaking of a specific covalent bond (a bond in which atoms are held together by the sharing of electrons). In the absence of enzymes, most of the covalent bonds of biological molecules are very stable, and decompose only under high nonphysiological temperatures; only at several hundred degrees centigrade is glucose, for example, appreciably oxidized by O_2 in the absence of enzymes. Enzymes must therefore act by somehow lowering the temperature at which a given bond is unstable. A physical chemist would say that an enzyme lowers the "activation energy." How this is done is not yet understood at the molecular level, since the 3-D structure of not one enzyme is yet known. This is no reason to suspect, however, that still undiscovered laws of chemistry underlie enzyme action. Numerous examples already exist where well-defined molecules speed up reactions between other molecules.

A very important characteristic of enzymes is that they are never consumed in the course of reaction; once a reaction is complete, they are free to adsorb new molecules and function again (Figure 2–8). On a biological time scale (seconds to years), enzymes can work very fast, some being able to catalyze as many as 10^6 reactions per minute; often no successful collision of substrates will occur in this time interval when enzymes are absent.

Not all enzymatic reactions, however, are specific. There exist, for example, various enzymes which break down a variety of different proteins to their component amino acids. They are specific only in the sense that they catalyze the breakdown of a specific type of covalent bond, the peptide bond, and will not, for example, degrade the phosphodiester linkages of the nucleic acids.

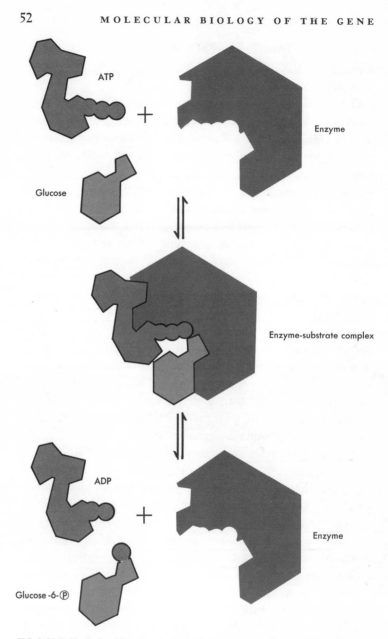

FIGURE 2–8 *The formation of an enzyme-substrate complex, followed by catalysis.*

THE KEY ROLE OF PYRUVATE*: ITS
UTILIZATION VIA THE KREBS CYCLE

Attempts to understand the generation of ATP in the presence of oxygen occurred parallel with the study of fermentation and glycolysis. It was immediately obvious from consideration of the amounts of ATP generated by fermentation and glycolysis that these processes could account for only a small fraction of total ATP production in the presence of oxygen. This means that ATP production in the presence of oxygen does not cease once glucose has been degraded as far as pyruvic acid (pyruvate), but that pyruvic acid itself must be further transformed, via energy-yielding reactions requiring the presence of oxygen.

The first real breakthrough in understanding how this happens came with the discoveries made by the biochemists Szent-Györgyi, Martius, and Krebs. Their work revealed the existence of a cyclic series of reactions (now usually called the Krebs cycle) by which pyruvate is oxidatively broken down to yield carbon dioxide (CO_2) and a series of pairs of hydrogen atoms that attach to oxidized coenzyme molecules. Before pyruvate enters the Krebs cycle, it is transformed into a key molecule called acetyl-CoA (Figure 2–9), known before its chemical identification as "active acetate." This important intermediate, discovered in 1949 by Lipmann, working in Boston, then combines with oxaloacetate to yield citrate. A series of at least nine additional steps (see Figure 2–10) then occur to yield four pairs of H atoms and two molecules of CO_2. The pairs of hydrogen atoms never exist free, but are transferred to specific coenzyme molecules.

The Krebs cycle should be viewed as a mechanism for breaking down acetyl-CoA to two types of products: the completely oxidized CO_2 molecules, which cannot be used as energy sources, and the reduced coenzymes, whose further oxidation yields most of the energy used by organisms growing in the presence of oxygen.

---

* The terms pyruvic acid and pyruvate are used interchangeably. Technically, pyruvate refers to the negatively charged ion. Likewise, lactic acid is often called lactate, glutamic acid–glutamate, citric acid–citrate, etc.

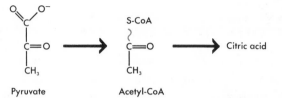

Pyruvate   Acetyl-CoA

FIGURE 2–9   *The transformation of pyruvate to acetyl-CoA. CoA refers to coenzyme A. The transformation, as written, is greatly simplified. Several steps are required in which the coenzymes thiamine pyrophosphate and lipoic acid are both involved. Acetyl-CoA is an extremely important intermediate, for it is formed not only from glucose via pyruvate, but also by the degradation of fatty acids.*

OXIDATION OF REDUCED COENZYMES BY RESPIRATORY ENZYMES

During the functioning of the Krebs cycle there is no direct involvement of molecular oxygen. Oxygen is involved only after the hydrogen atoms (or electrons) have been transferred through an additional series of oxidation-reduction reactions that involve a series of closely linked enzymes, all of which contain iron atoms. These enzymes are often collectively called the respiratory enzymes.

Their existence was hinted at late in the nineteenth century, but it was not until the period of 1925 to 1940 that their significance was appreciated, largely as a result of the work of Warburg and the Polish-born David Keilin, who spent most of his scientific life in England. Even today there remains uncertainty about the exact number of enzymes involved. Nevertheless, the correctness of the general picture is not disputed. Figure 2–11 shows the general features of the respiratory chain.

The chain operates by a series of coupled oxidation-reduction reactions, during each of which energy is released. Thus the energy present in the reduced coenzymes is released not all at once but in a series of small packets. If $NADH_2$ were instead directly oxidized by molecular oxygen, a great amount of energy would be released, which it would be impossible to couple efficiently with the formation of the high-energy bonds of ATP.

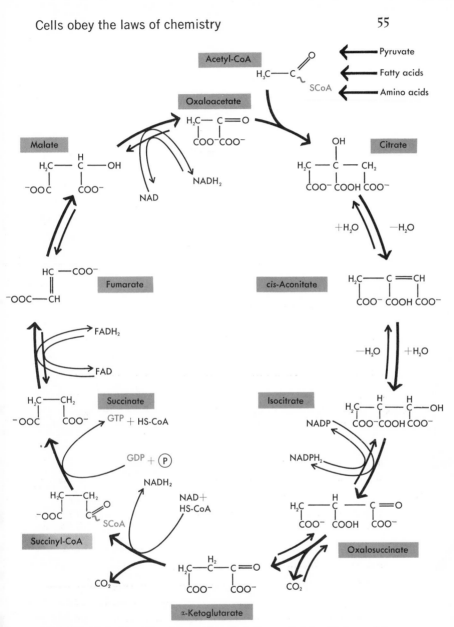

FIGURE 2–10 *The citric acid cycle (often called the Krebs cycle).*

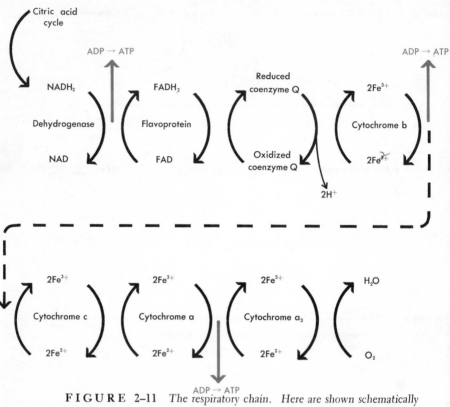

FIGURE 2-11   *The respiratory chain. Here are shown schematically the successive oxidation-reduction reactions which release, in small packets, the energy present in NADH₂ molecules. Whether all the cytochromes operate in a single cycle is not known. The exact sites of ATP formation have not been unambiguously determined.*

SYNTHESIS OF ATP IN THE PRESENCE OF OXYGEN (OXIDATIVE PHOSPHORYLATION)

During the period 1925 to 1940, most biochemists concentrated on following the path of hydrogen atoms (or electrons) through the linked, energy-yielding oxidation-reduction reactions. Until the end of this period, only slight attention was given to how the energy was released in a useful form. Then the Dane, Kalckar, and the Russian, Belitzer, observed ATP formation coupled with oxidation-reduction reactions in cell-free systems (1938–1940).

Further understanding did not come quickly, since most of the enzymes involved could not be obtained in pure soluble form. These troubles were not resolved until it was realized that the normal sites of *oxidative phosphorylation in plant and animal cells are large, highly organized subcellular particles, the mitochondria.* When intact mitochondria are employed, it is easy to observe the oxidative generation of ATP; this was first demonstrated in 1947 by the Americans Lehninger and Kennedy. Now there is evidence for the generation of three ATP molecules for each passage of a pair of hydrogens through the respiratory chain. There are believed to exist, however, at least six separate oxidation-reduction steps in the chain. Future work may reveal that one ATP molecule is generated during each distinct oxidation-reduction step.

Roughly 20 times more energy is released by the respiratory chain than by the initial breakdown of glucose to pyruvate. This explains why growth of cells under aerobic conditions is

FIGURE 2–12   The fermentation of glucose to yield lactate. Here the NADH₂ produced during pyruvate formation is oxidized to reduce pyruvate to lactate. When oxygen is present, the NADH₂ is oxidized through the respiratory chain, and no lactate is produced.

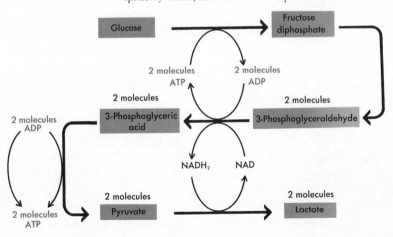

so much more efficient than growth without air: If oxygen is not present, pyruvate cannot accumulate, since its formation (see Figure 2–5) demands a supply of unreduced NAD. The amount of NAD within cells, like that of other coenzymes, is, however, very small. In the absence of oxygen, it is rapidly converted to NADH₂ as glucose is oxidized by the Embden-Meyerhof pathway. Thus for the continued generation of ATP without oxygen (fermentation), a device must be used to oxidize the reduced NADH₂. This is often achieved by reducing pyruvate itself, using NADH₂ as the hydrogen donor. This explains the appearance of lactic acid both during the anaerobic contraction of muscles and during the anaerobic growth of many bacteria (Figure 2–12).

GENERATION OF ATP DURING PHOTOSYNTHESIS

Today the ultimate source of the various food molecules used by microorganisms and animals is the photosynthetic plants. Thus the energy of the sun's light quanta must somehow be converted into the energy present in covalent bonds. How this happens chemically did not become clear until the basic energy relations within animals and bacteria were understood. Largely as a result of the work of the American biochemist Arnon, it was discovered in 1959 that the primary action of the sun's light quanta is to phosphorylate ADP to ATP.

This phosphorylation takes place in the chloroplasts, which are complicated, chlorophyll-containing cellular particles found in all cells capable of usefully trapping the energy of the sun. Thus we realize that the controlled release of energy in plants depends upon the same energy carrier important in bacterial and animal cells, ATP. The details of the process remain unclear. An initial step must be the capture of the light quantum by the green pigment molecule chlorophyll, to excite one of its electrons to a high-energy state. What happens between this initial energy adsorption and the phosphorylation of ATP remains to be elucidated.

It is most important to realize the uniqueness of photosynthesis. It is the only significant cellular event that utilizes any energy source other than the covalent bond. All other important cellular reactions are accompanied by a decrease in the energy included in covalent bonds. Superficially, we might thus guess that the ability to photosynthesize must have been a primary feature of the first forms of life. It is, however, difficult to imagine that very early forms possessed the complicated chloroplast structures necessary for photosynthesis. Instead there is good reason to believe that, early in the history of the earth, a unique chemical environment allowed the creation of a large number of carbon-containing compounds using the energy of light quanta originating from the sun. These spontaneously formed organic molecules then served as the energy (food) supply for the first forms of life. As these original organic molecules were depleted and living matter increased, a strong selective advantage developed for those cells which evolved a photosynthetic structure to provide a means of increasing the amount of organic molecules. Today essentially all glucose molecules are formed using chemical energy originating in photosynthesis.

VITAMINS AND GROWTH FACTORS

Although some microorganisms, such as the bacteria *Escherichia coli*, can use glucose as their sole carbon and energy source, not all bacteria and none of the higher animals can use glucose to synthesize all the necessary metabolites. For example, rats are unable to synthesize 11 of the 20 amino acids present in their proteins; thus their food supply must contain substantial amounts of these molecules.

In addition to dietary requirements (necessary growth factors) for compounds with important structural roles, requirements often exist for very small amounts of certain specific organic molecules. These molecules, needed in just trace amounts, are called vitamins (vital molecules). For many years they seemed quite mysterious. Now we realize that the vitamins are closely related to the coenzymes. Some are precursors of coenzymes and some are coenzymes themselves. For example, the vitamin niacin is used in the synthesis of NAD. The fact that coenzymes, like enzymes, are able to function over and over explains why they are needed only in trace amounts.

Thus there is nothing unusual about the fact that a molecule is sometimes required as a growth factor or a vitamin; such requirements are fully explicable in chemical terms. It seems most likely that the genes necessary for the synthesis of certain molecules were lost during evolution, bringing specific growth-factor requirements into existence. There would be no selective advantage to an organism's retaining a specific gene if the corresponding metabolite were always available in its food supply.

THE LABILITY OF LARGE MOLECULES

In striking contrast with the splendid success of biochemists in understanding the behavior of small molecules like the amino acids and nucleotides, scientists interested in the large molecules had arrived at only partial answers before 1950. Their only real success involved a number of polysaccharide molecules (e.g., glycogen). They were relatively easy to understand, because they are built up by the regular polymerization of a smaller subunit (e.g., glucose). Their understanding, however, had no real biological impact because molecules like glycogen are, in most respects, structurally uninteresting. Their sole purpose is to serve as a reserve form of energy-yielding glucose residues. The molecules that people most wanted to unravel were the proteins, because many of them are enzymes, and the nucleic acids, because they were thought to be involved in the hereditary mechanism. Both these classes of molecules were, however, initially refractory to investigation.

One major reason why they were difficult to study was that they appeared to be much less stable (more labile) than most small molecules. Extremes of temperature and pH (acidity or alkalinity) cause them to lose their natural shapes (*denaturation*) and sometimes to precipitate irreversibly out of solution in an inactive form. Thus great care had to be taken in their isolation; sometimes it was necessary to perform the entire isolation process at temperatures near 0°C. At first it was thought that only proteins were subject to denaturation, but now it is clear that nucleic acid molecules also denature during isolation if proper precautions are not taken.

Until 1945 (after the Second World War), the commonly used techniques of organic chemistry were the main tools for studying most of the small molecules. Thus the success of a biochemist working on intermediary metabolism often depended on his ability as an organic chemist. In work with proteins and nucleic acids, however, most of the initial stages of research did not rely on the analytical techniques of the organic chemist. Instead the protein chemist, before he could even start worrying about the detailed structure of a protein, needed to work very hard to be sure his protein was both chemically pure and biologically active. He had to devise gentle techniques for isolation, which avoided the usual strong acids and alkalies of organic analysis. Then he needed techniques to reveal whether his product was homogeneous, and hopefully, also to provide data on molecular size. For this sort of answer, the help of physical chemists was indispensable, and there developed a well-recognized new line of research investigating the physical-chemical properties of macromolecules in solution. It concerned itself with topics like the osmotic properties of macromolecular solutions and the movement of macromolecules under electrical and centrifugal forces.

Perhaps the most striking contribution of physical chemistry to the study of biological macromolecules was the development, in the 1920s, of centrifuges that rotated at high speed (ultracentrifuges) and that could cause the rapid sedimentation of proteins and nucleic acids. The development of the ultracentrifuge was the work of the Swede Svedberg, after whom the unit of sedimentation (S = Svedberg) was named. Ultracentrifuges equipped with optical devices to observe exactly how fast the molecules sedimented were extremely valuable in obtaining data on the molecular weight of proteins and establishing the concept that proteins, like smaller biological molecules, are of discrete molecular weights and shapes. This work revealed that the sizes of proteins vary greatly, with a continuous range in weights between the extremes of approximately 10,000 and 1,000,000.

IMPLICATIONS OF CHROMATOGRAPHY

Early in the twentieth century, the work of the great German chemist Emil Fischer had established that protein molecules are largely composed of amino acids linked together by peptide bonds. The determination of the exact way in which the amino acids are linked together to form proteins remained, however, a great puzzle until 1951. This was partly because there are 20 different amino acids and their proportions vary from one type of protein to another. Until about 1942, the methodological problems involved in amino acid separation and identification were formidable, and most organic chemists chose to work with simpler molecules.

This state of affairs changed completely in 1942, when the Englishmen Martin and Synge developed separation methods that depended on the relative solubilities of the several amino acids in two different solvents (partition chromatography). Particularly useful were separation methods by which the amino acids were separated on strips of paper. With these new tricks, it became a routine matter to separate quantitatively the 20 amino acids found in proteins. These methods were quickly seized upon by the English biochemist Sanger, who used them to establish all the covalent linkages in the protein hormone insulin (see Chapter 6 for details of the insulin structure). Sanger's work was a milestone in the study of proteins, for it demonstrated that each type of protein contains a specific arrangement of amino acids.

THE 25-YEAR LONELINESS OF THE PROTEIN CRYSTALLOGRAPHERS

An equally significant step in understanding macromolecules was the effective extension of x-ray crystallographic techniques to their study. This approach utilizes the diffraction of x rays by crystals to give precise data about the three-dimensional arrangement of the atoms in molecules. The first successful use of x-ray diffraction was in 1912, when the Englishman Bragg solved the NaCl structure. This success immediately initiated research on the structures of molecules of increasing complexity.

The technique used in the initial x-ray diffraction studies of small molecules consisted of guessing the structure, calculating the theoretical diffraction pattern predicted by this structure, and comparing the calculated with the observed pattern. This method was practical for studying relatively simple structures, but was not usually useful in the study of larger structures. It took much insight on the part of Bragg and the great American chemist Pauling, in the 1920s, to solve the structures of some complicated inorganic silicate molecules. Clearly, however, proteins were too complicated for even the best chemist to guess their 3-D structures. Thus the early protein crystallographers knew that, until new methods for structural determination were found, they would have no results to present to the impatient biochemists, who were increasingly anxious to know what proteins actually looked like.

The first serious x-ray diffraction studies on proteins began in the mid-1930s in Bernal's Cambridge, England, laboratory. Here it was found that although dry protein crystals gave very poor x-ray patterns, wet crystals often gave beautiful pictures. Unfortunately, however, there was no logical method available for their interpretation. Nonetheless, Bernal's student Perutz, an Austrian then in England, slowly increased the pace of his work (begun in 1937) with the oxygen-carrying blood protein, hemoglobin. He had chosen hemoglobin for several reasons: Not only is it one of the most important of all animal proteins, but it is also easy to obtain, and forms crystals that lend themselves well to crystallographic analysis. For many years, however, no very significant results emerged either from Perutz's work on hemoglobin structure or from that begun in 1947 by Kendrew, on the structure of the muscle protein myoglobin. This protein, which, like hemoglobin, combines with oxygen, had the added advantage of being four times smaller (MW = 17,000) than hemoglobin.

During the lonely period of no real results there was only one triumph. Pauling correctly guessed from stereochemical considerations that amino acids linked together by peptide bonds would sometimes tend to assume helical configurations, and proposed in 1951 that a helical configuration, which he called the alpha helix (see Chapter 4 for details), would be an important element in protein structure. Support for Pauling's α-helix theory came soon after its announcement, when Perutz demonstrated that several synthetic polypeptide chains containing only one type of amino acid exist as α-helices.

It was not until 1959 that Perutz and Kendrew got their answers. An essential breakthrough, which occurred in 1953, showed how the attachment of heavy atoms to protein molecules could logically lead from the diffraction data to the correct structures. For the next several years, these heavy-atom methods were exploited at a pace undreamed of 20 years before, largely thanks to the availability of high-speed electronic computers. Then, to everyone's delight, the x-ray diffraction measurements could at last be translated into the arrangement of atoms in myoglobin and (in somewhat less detail) in hemoglobin. Both molecules were found to be enormously complicated, with their amino acid chains folded as α-helices in some regions, and very irregularly in others. Furthermore, their molecular configurations were found to obey in every respect the chemical laws that govern the shape of smaller molecules. Absolutely no new laws of nature are involved in the construction of proteins; this was no surprise to the biochemists.

AVERY'S BOMBSHELL: NUCLEIC ACIDS CAN CARRY GENETIC SPECIFICITY

Until 1944, the number of chemists working on the nucleic acids was but a tiny fraction of the number attempting to understand proteins. Two nucleic acids, DNA (*deoxyribonucleic acid*) and RNA (*ribonucleic acid*), were known to exist, but the general features of their chemical structures had not been elucidated. Although DNA was found only in nuclei (hence the name nucleic acids), there was general agreement that it probably was not a genetic substance, since chemists thought that its four types of nucleotide (see Chapter 3 for details of their structures) were present in equal amounts, giving DNA a repetitive structure like that of glycogen (the tetranucleotide hypothesis).

In the middle 1930s, the Swedish chemists Hammarsten and Caspersson found by physical-chemical techniques that DNA molecules, prepared by gentle procedures, have molecular weights even larger (>500,000) than most proteins. At the same time, chemical analysis of purified plant viruses by the American Stanley and the Englishmen Bawden and Pirie suggested the generalization that all viruses contain nucleic acid, hinting that nucleic acids might have a genetic role.

The first real proof, however, of the genetic role for nucleic acids came from the work of the noted American microbiologist Avery and his colleagues MacLeod and McCarty at the Rockefeller Institute in New York. They made the momentous discovery in 1944 that the hereditary properties of pneumonia bacteria can be specifically altered by the addition of carefully prepared DNA of high molecular weight.

Even though there was momentary hesitation in accepting its implications, their discovery provided great stimulation for a detailed chemical investigation of nucleic acids. Here also paper chromatography became immensely useful, and quickly allowed the biochemist Chargaff, then working in New York, to analyze the nucleotide composition of DNA molecules from a number of different organisms. In 1947, his experiments showed not only that the four nucleotides are not present in equal amounts, but also that exact ratios of the four nucleotides varied from one species to another. This finding meant that much more variation was possible among DNA molecules than the tetranucleotide hypothesis had allowed, and immediately opened up the possibility that the precise arrangement of nucleotides within a molecule is related to its genetic specificity.

It also became obvious from Chargaff's work in the next several years that the relative ratios of the four bases were not random. The amount of adenine in a DNA sample was always found to be equal to the amount of thymine, and the amount of guanine equal to the amount of cytosine. The fundamental significance of these relationships did not become clear, however, until serious attention was given to the 3-D arrangement of DNA.

THE DOUBLE HELIX

Parallel with work on the x-ray analysis of protein structure, a still smaller number of scientists concentrated on trying to solve the x-ray diffraction pattern of DNA. The first diffraction patterns were taken in 1938 by the Englishman Astbury and used DNA supplied by Hammarsten and Caspersson. It was not until after the war (1948–1950), however, that high quality photographs were taken, by Wilkins and Franklin, working in London at King's College. Even then, however, the chemical bonds linking the various nucleotides were not unambiguously established. This was accomplished in 1952 by a group of organic chemists working in the Cambridge, England, laboratory of Alexander Todd.

Because of interest in Pauling's α-helix, in 1951 an elegant theory of the diffraction of helical molecules was developed. The existence of this theory made it easy to test possible DNA structures on a trial and error basis. The correct solution, a complementary double helix (see Chapter 9 for details), was found in 1953 by Crick and Watson, then working in England in the laboratory of Perutz and Kendrew. Their arrival at the correct answer was in large part dependent on finding the stereochemically most favorable configuration compatible with the x-ray diffraction data of the King's College group.

The establishment of the double helix immediately initiated a profound revolution in the way in which many geneticists analyzed their data. The gene was no longer a mysterious entity whose behavior could be investigated only by breeding experiments. Instead it quickly became a real molecular object about which chemists could think objectively in the same manner as smaller molecules, such as pyruvate or NAD. Most of the excitement, however, came not merely from the fact that the structure was solved, but also from the nature of the structure. Before the answer was known, there had always been the mild fear that it would turn out to be dull, and reveal nothing about how genes replicate and function. Fortunately, however, the answer was immensely exciting. The structure appeared to be two intertwined strands of complementary structures, suggesting that one strand serves as the specific surface (*template*) upon which the other strand is made. If this hypothesis were true (which it is now known to be!), then the fundamental problem of gene replication, about which the geneticists had puzzled for so many years, was, in fact, solved.

There were thus initiated over the past 12 years a variety of experiments designed to study, at a molecular level, how DNA molecules control what a cell is like. These studies have brought many discoveries, unforeseen in 1953, about how the genetic material functions. Because these answers are, for the first time, consistently at the molecular level, it is convenient to refer to the subject matter at this level as molecular genetics.

THE GOAL OF MOLECULAR BIOLOGY

Until recently, heredity has always seemed the most mysterious of life's characteristics. The current realization that the structure of DNA already allows us to understand practically all its fundamental features at the molecular level is thus most significant. We see not only that the laws of chemistry are sufficient for understanding protein structure, but also that they are consistent with all known hereditary phenomena. Complete certainty now exists among essentially all biochemists that the other characteristics of living organisms (for example, selective permeability across cell membranes, muscle contraction, nerve conduction, and the hearing and memory processes) will all be completely understood in terms of the coordinative interactions of small and large molecules. Much is already known about the less complex features, enough to give us confidence that further research of the intensity recently given to genetics will eventually provide man with the ability to describe with completeness the essential features that constitute life.

SUMMARY

The growth and division of cells are based upon the same laws of chemistry that control the behavior of molecules outside of cells. Cells contain no atoms unique to the living state; they can synthesize no molecules which the chemist, with inspired, hard work, cannot some day make. Thus there is no special chemistry of living cells. A biochemist is not someone who studies unique types of chemical laws, but a chemist interested in learning about the behavior of molecules found within cells (biological molecules).

The growth and division of cells depend upon the availability of a usable form of chemical energy. This energy now initially comes from the energy of the sun's light quanta, which is converted by photosynthetic plants into cellular molecules, some of which are then used as food sources by various microorganisms and animals. The most striking initial triumphs of the biochemists told us how food molecules are transformed into other cellular molecules and into useful forms of chemical energy. The energy within food molecules largely resides in the covalent bonds of reduced carbon compounds; it is released when these molecules are transformed by oxidation-reduction reactions to carbon compounds of a higher degree of oxidation. For most forms of life, the ultimate oxidizing agent is molecular O_2. The products of the complete oxidation of organic molecules like glucose are CO_2 and H_2O.

Most organic molecules, however, are not oxidized directly by oxygen. They are oxidized instead by diverse organic molecules, often coenzymes, such as the coenzyme NAD. The reduced coenzyme (for example, $NADH_2$) is itself oxidized by another molecule (such as FAD) to yield a new reduced coenzyme ($FADH_2$) and the original coenzyme, in the oxidized form (NAD). After several such cycles, molecular oxygen directly participates, to end the oxidation-reduction chain, giving off water (H_2O).

The energy released during the oxidation-reduction cycles is not released entirely as heat. Instead, more than half the energy is converted into new chemical bonds. Phosphorus atoms play a key role in this transformation. *Phosphate esters are formed that have a higher usable energy content than most covalent bonds.* These phosphate groups are transferred in a high-energy form to acceptor molecules. The most important acceptor of such groups is ADP; *a phosphate group is added to ADP to yield ATP.* Very recently, experiments revealed that the phosphorylation of ADP to ATP is a primary step in photosynthesis, where it is called photophosphorylation. The ADP → ATP transformation is at the heart of energy relations in all cells.

Until a few years ago, the chemists' understanding of the cell's very large molecules, the proteins and nucleic acids, was much less firm than it is now. Most of these molecules are in a size range several orders of magnitude larger than the largest "small molecules" studied by organic chemistry (molecules of protein and nucleic acid run from MW 10^4 to 10^8). Both proteins and nucleic acids are complex, and only recently have physical and chemical techniques been developed to allow a concerted attack on their structure. *Among the most important techniques have been partition chromatography, analytical ultracentrifugation, and x-ray crystallography as extended to the study of large molecules.* Now practically all the important features of the protein myoglobin and the primary genetic material DNA are known. In both cases the chemical laws applicable to small molecules also apply. So far the greatest impact on biological thought has come from the realization that DNA has a complementary double-helical structure. This structure immediately suggested a mechanism for the replication of the gene, and initiated a revolution in the way biologists think of heredity. These successes have created a firm belief that the current extension of our understanding of biological phenomena to the molecular level (molecular biology) will soon enable us to understand all the basic features of the living state.

REFERENCES

McElroy, W. D., *Cell Physiology and Biochemistry*, 2nd ed., Prentice-Hall, Englewood Cliffs, N.J., 1964. A concise introductory statement of many of the important principles of biochemistry.

Lehninger, A. L., *Energy of the Living Cell: Molecular Basis of Energy Transformations in the Cell*, Benjamin, New York, 1965. An introduction to the chemical reactions by which cells trap, store, and utilize chemical energy. Emphasis is placed on generation of ATP in mitochondria and chloroplasts.

Baldwin, E., *Dynamic Aspects of Biochemistry*, 3rd ed., Cambridge, New York, 1959. This is one of the few texts in biochemistry deserving to be called a classic. Now it is best read for the way in which coenzymes participate in hydrogen transfers.

Conn, E. E., and P. K. Stumpf, *Outlines of Biochemistry*, Wiley, New York, 1963. An introductory text that emphasizes metabolic pathways.

Kamen, M. D., *Primary Processes in Photosynthesis*, Academic, New York, 1963. A concise statement, available in paperback form, about what we do and do not understand about photosynthesis.

3

A CHEMIST'S
LOOK AT THE
BACTERIAL
CELL

THE MOST IMPORTANT ASPECT OF LIVING cells is their tendency to grow and divide. In this process, food molecules are absorbed from the external environment and transformed into cellular constituents. The rates of cell growth vary tremendously, but in general the smallest cells grow the fastest. Under optimal conditions some bacteria double their number every 20 minutes, whereas most larger mammalian cells can divide only once about every 24 hours. But, independent of the length of the time interval, growth and division necessarily demand that the number of cellular molecules double with each cell generation. One way, therefore, of asking the question, "What is life?" is to ask how a cell doubles its molecular content, that is, how biological molecules are replicated as a cell grows.

BACTERIA GROW UNDER SIMPLE, WELL-DEFINED CONDITIONS

Today most serious questions about cell growth and division are studied by using microorganisms, especially the bacteria. The tendency to concentrate on microorganisms does not arise from a belief that bacteria are fundamentally more important than higher organisms. The converse is obviously true to human beings, naturally curious to know about themselves and anxious to use information about their own

71

chemical makeup to combat the various diseases threatening their existence. Nonetheless, upon even a superficial examination, the difficulties of thoroughly mastering the chemical events in a higher organism are staggering. There are about 5×10^{12} cells in a human being, each of whose existence is intimately related to the behavior of many other cells. It is therefore difficult to study the growth of a single cell within a multicellular organism without taking into consideration the influence of its surrounding cells.

Much effort has been devoted to learning how to grow the cells of multicellular organisms in an isolated system. In this work (often called *tissue culture*) small groups of cells, or sometimes single cells, are removed from a plant or animal and placed under controlled laboratory conditions in a solution containing a variety of food molecules. In the first experiments, the isolated cells almost invariably died, but now, partly because of a better understanding of the nutritional requirements of cells, they often grow and divide to form large numbers of new cells. Such freely growing plant and animal cells have been of much value in showing how cells aggregate to form organized groups of similar cells (tissues), and even more striking, how tissues unite in the test tube to form bodies morphologically identical to small regions of organs, such as the liver or the kidney. On the other hand, tissue culture cells are not ideal objects for studying cell growth and division. Even though many cells of higher organisms will grow in isolation, it must be remembered that this is not their normal way of existence, and, unless precautions are taken, they tend to aggregate quickly into multicellular groups. Thus even today the isolated growth of cells from higher organisms can be difficult and time consuming.

In contrast, the cells of many microorganisms normally grow free, as single cells, separating from each other as soon as cell division occurs. It is thus fairly easy to grow such single-celled organisms under well-defined laboratory conditions, since the conditions of growth in the scientist's test tube are not radically different from the conditions under which they normally grow outside the laboratory. In contrast to mammalian cells, which require a large variety of growth supplements, many bacteria will grow on a simple, well-defined diet or medium. For ex-

T A B L E 3–1   *A simple synthetic growth medium for E. coli*[a]

NH_4Cl	1.0	g
$MgSO_4$	0.13	g
KH_2PO_4	3.0	g
Na_2HPO_4	6.0	g
Glucose	4 0	g
Water	1000	ml

[a] Traces of other ions (e.g., Fe^{2+}) are also required for growth. Usually these are not added separately, since they are normally present as contaminants in either the added inorganic salts or the water itself.

ample, the bacteria *Escherichia coli* will grow on an aqueous solution containing just glucose and several inorganic ions (Table 3–1).

The growth of a specific bacterium is usually not dependent on the availability of a specific carbon source. Most bacteria are highly adaptable as to which organic molecules they can use as their carbon and energy sources. Glucose can be replaced by a variety of other organic molecules, and the greater the variety of food molecules supplied, the faster a cell generally grows. For example, if *E. coli* grows upon only glucose, about 60 minutes are required at 37°C to double the cell mass. But if glucose is supplemented by the various amino acids and purine and pyrimidine bases (the precursors of nucleic acids), then only 20 minutes are necessary for the doubling of cell mass. This effect is due to the direct incorporation of these components into proteins and nucleic acids, sparing the cell the task of carrying out the synthesis of the building blocks. There is a lower limit, however, to the time necessary to double the cell mass (often called the *generation time*): No matter how favorable the growth conditions, bacteria are unable to divide more than once every 20 minutes.

E. COLI IS THE BEST UNDERSTOOD ORGANISM AT THE MOLECULAR LEVEL!

Over the past 20 years there has been an increasing polarization of effort toward work with the bacterium *E. coli* and evolutionarily related organisms. Because of its small size, normal lack of pathogenicity to any common organism, and ease of growth under laboratory conditions, *E. coli* is now the most intensively studied organism except for man. Many other bacteria besides *E. coli* possess the same favorable attributes, and the original reasons for choosing *E. coli* are essentially accidental. Once serious work had started on *E. coli*, however, it obviously made no sense to switch to another organism if *E. coli* could be used. Even now the tendency to concentrate on *E. coli* is increasing, because parallel with the chemical studies, extensive successful genetic analysis has also been carried out. Our knowledge of the genetics of *E. coli* is thus much more complete than our knowledge of that of any other bacterium or lower plant. As we shall see, the combined methods of genetics and biochemistry are so powerful that it is often just not sensible to use in biochemical studies an organism with which genetic analysis is not possible.

The average *E. coli* cell (Figure 3–1) is rod-shaped and about 2μ in length and 1μ in diameter. It grows by increasing in length, followed by a fission process that generates two cells of equal length. Growth occurs best at temperatures about 37°C, perhaps to suit it for existence in the intestines of higher mammals, where it is frequently found as a harmless parasite. It will, however, regularly grow and divide at temperatures as low as 20°. Cell growth proceeds much more slowly at these low temperatures; the generation time under otherwise optimal conditions is about 120 minutes at 20°C.

Cell number and size are often measured by observation under the light microscope (and occasionally the electron microscope). Such observation, however, cannot reveal whether a visible cell is alive or dead. This can be determined only by seeing whether a given cell forms daughter cells. This determination is usually made by spreading a small number of cells on top of a solid agar surface (Figure 3–2), which has been supplemented with the nutrients necessary for cell growth. If a cell is alive, it will grow to form two daughter cells which in turn give rise to subsequent generations of daughter cells. The net result after 12 to 24 hours of incubation at 37°C is discrete masses (*colonies*) of bacterial cells. Provided that the colonies do not overlap, each must have arisen from the initial presence of a single bacterial cell.

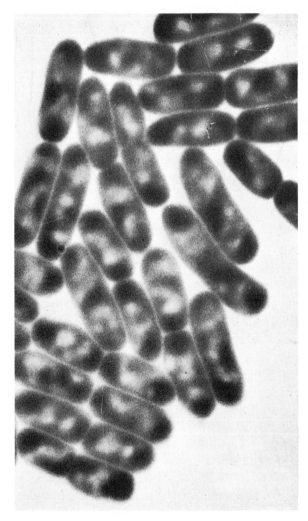

FIGURE 3–1 *Electron micrograph of a group of E. coli cells. The light regions inside the bacteria represent areas where DNA is concentrated. Magnification is 12,000. This photograph was taken in the laboratory of E. Kellenberger, University of Geneva (reproduced with permission).*

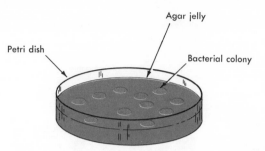

F I G U R E 3–2   *The multiplication of single bacterial cells to form colonies. E. coli cells are usually not motile. Thus when a cell has divided on a solid surface, the two daughter cells and all their descendants will tend to remain next to each other. After 24 hours at 37°C, each initial living cell has given rise to a solid mass of cells.*

The growth of bacteria may also be followed in liquid nutrient solutions. If a nutrient medium is inoculated with a small number of rapidly dividing bacteria from a similar medium, the bacteria will continue dividing with a constant division time, doubling the number of bacteria each generation time. Thus the number of bacteria increases in an exponential (logarithmic) fashion (Figure 3–3). *Exponential growth* continues until the number of cells reaches such a high level that the initial optimal nutritional conditions no longer exist. One of the first factors that usually limits growth is the supply of oxygen. When the number of cells is low, the oxygen available by diffusion from the liquid interface is sufficient, but as the number of cells rises additional oxygen is needed. It is often supplied either by bubbling oxygen through the solution or by shaking the solution rapidly. Even with violent aeration, the growth rates begin to slow down after the cell density reaches about 10^9 cells per milliliter, and a tendency develops for the cells being produced to be shorter. Finally, at cell densities of about 5×10^9 cells per milliliter, cell growth is discontinued, for still unclear nutritional reasons. The term *growth curve* is frequently used to describe the increase of cell numbers as a function of time.

In most growing bacterial cultures, the exact division time of the cells varies, so that even if a culture has started from a single cell, after a few generations, cells can be found at various stages of the division cycle at any given moment. Such growth is frequently called *unsynchronized growth*. Over the past 10 years, tricks have been developed to isolate bacterial cells at the same stage of the cell cycle. These can be used to obtain several generations of *synchronized cell growth* (Figure 3–4). Then, because of slightly unequal divisions, the resulting growth curve again acquires an unsynchronized appearance.

During exponential growth each cell contains between two and four chromosomes. All these chromosomes have identical genetic compositions since they are all descendants of the same parental chromosome. Why each healthy cell contains several

FIGURE 3–3 Growth curve of E. coli cells at 37°C. The gray line shows the increase in cell number following the inoculation of a sterile, nutrient-rich solution (glucose, salts, amino acids, purines, pyrimidines) with 10^5 cells from an E. coli culture in an exponential phase of growth. If this growth curve had been started, instead, from cells in a slow-multiplying, nearly saturated culture, the growth would not have begun immediately, but rather (colored curve) a lag period of approximately 1 hour would have preceded exponential growth.

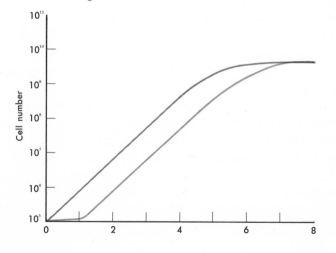

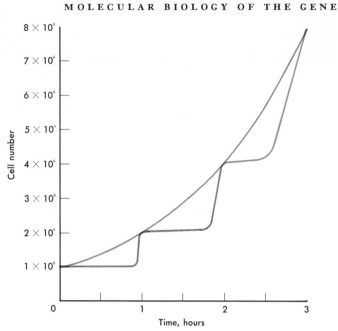

FIGURE 3-4   *The growth curve (colored line) of a synchronized E.
coli culture growing upon glucose as the sole carbon
source. The gray line shows the increase in cell number of an unsynchronized culture. Here we show an
example in which the degree of synchronization noticeably lessens in the second and third cycles of growth.*

identical chromosomes is not known.   It is not an intrinsic
feature of the *E. coli* life cycle, since when the nutritional conditions are poor, chromosome duplication sometimes lags behind
cell division (Figure 3–5), resulting in viable cells with just one
chromosome apiece.

In *E. coli*, as in most if not all bacteria, the chromosome is
not enclosed within a nuclear membrane.   There is no structural
distinction between the nucleus and the cytoplasm.   Nonetheless, bacterial cytologists often refer to the region occupied by
the chromosomes as the *nuclear region*.   This term, however, is
a misnomer.   It is still very unclear what separates the chromosomes during cell division.   There is no evidence of a spindle-
like region even under the electron microscope, which hints

that the spindle is a specialized structure developed at the point in evolution when the nuclear and cytoplasmic regions were differentiated. Thus the only essential parallel between mitotic divisions in higher organisms and in the bacteria is that in both the accurate duplication and partition of the chromosomes is essential.

For many years it was believed that bacteria, including *E. coli*, had no sexual process involving cell fusion. Since 1947, however, it has been known that male and female cells do exist, and that there is a very rare cell-fusion process which produces diploid cells (see Chapter 7 for details). These diploid cells do not exist long, but quickly segregate out, giving rise to haploid cells within one or two cell division cycles. Here, as in the case of bacterial mitosis, no evidence is available about the me-

FIGURE 3-5 *The life cycle of E. coli cells. Under optimal growth conditions the average cell contains from two to four chromosomes, depending upon its exact stage in the division cycle. All these chromosomes are descended from the same parental chromosome, and so are genetically identical.*

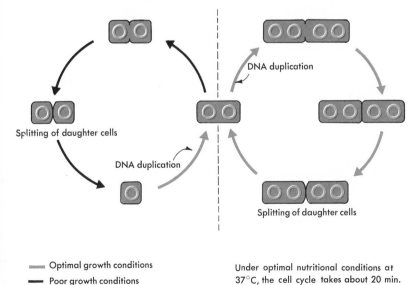

DNA duplication

Splitting of daughter cells

DNA duplication

Splitting of daughter cells

▬▬▬ Optimal growth conditions

▬▬ Poor growth conditions

Under optimal nutritional conditions at 37°C, the cell cycle takes about 20 min.

chanics of chromosome separation, which must underlie the reduction of chromosome number back to the haploid condition.

EVEN SMALL CELLS ARE COMPLEX

Even cells as small as those of *E. coli* present great difficulties when we study them at the molecular level. At first sight, the problem of soon, if ever, understanding the essential features of *E. coli* should seem insuperable to an honest chemist. He realizes immediately that, on a chemical scale, even the smallest cells are fantastically large. Although an *E. coli* cell is about 500 times smaller than an average cell in a higher plant or animal (which has a diameter of approximately 10μ), it nonetheless weighs approximately 2×10^{-12} gram (MW $\sim 10^{12}$ daltons; a dalton has a MW $= 1$). This number, which initially may seem very small, is immense on the chemist's scale, since it is 6×10^{10} times greater than the weight of a water molecule (MW $= 18$). Furthermore, this mass reflects the highly complex arrangement of a large number of different carbon-containing molecules.

There is also seemingly infinite variety in the chemical nature of these molecules. But fortunately, it is possible to distribute most molecules in terms of mass into several well-defined classes possessing common arrangements of some atoms. These classes are the carbohydrates, lipids, proteins, and nucleic acids (Table 3–2). Many molecules possess chemical groups common to several of these categories, so that the classification of such molecules is necessarily arbitrary. Also in the cell are many smaller molecules, such as amino acids, purine and pyrimidine nucleotides, various coenzymes, very small molecules (e.g., O_2 and CO_2), and numerous electrically charged inorganic ions, (e.g., Na^+, K^+ and PO_4^{3-}). Finally, there is H_2O, the most common molecule in all cells, and a solvent for most biological molecules, through which diffusion from one cellular location to another can occur quickly.

A glimpse into the cellular organization of *E. coli* is shown in an electron micrograph of a very thin section cut from a rapidly growing cell (Figure 3–6). On the outside is the rigid cell wall,

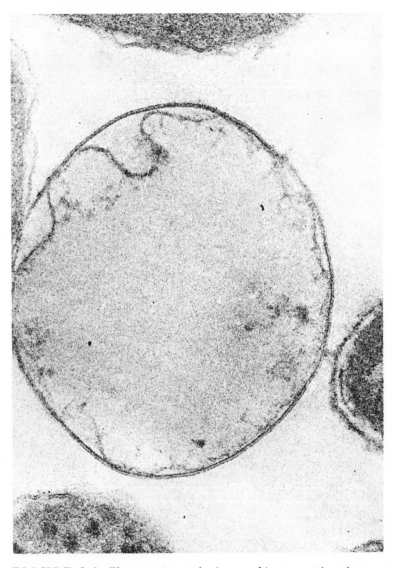

FIGURE 3-6   Electron micrograph of a very thin cross section of an
E. coli cell. The magnification is ×105,000. The
outer membrane is the protective cell wall; inside this
is the cell membrane, which controls permeability.
Normally the cell membrane lies tightly next to the
cell wall; here, for illustrative purposes, we show an
accidental situation in which the membrane has in a
few places separated from the cell wall. (Supplied by
E. Kellenberger; reproduced with permission.)

T A B L E   3–2   *The main classes of biological molecules*

	General description	Functions
Proteins	Molecules containing C, H, O, N, and sometimes S, which are built up from amino acids.	Most proteins are enzymes— some, usually present in very large numbers per cell, are used to build up essential structures, such as the cell wall, the cell membrane, the ribosomes, muscle fiber, nerves, etc.
Lipids	Molecules insoluble in water, that are sometimes built up by the combination of glycerol and three long-chain fatty acids (triglycerid). Sometimes one fatty acid is replaced by choline (lecithins). Sometimes glycerol is replaced by sphingosine. Phosphorus is present in a large number of the lipids (phospholipids).	Triglycerids are a main storehouse of energy-rich food. They degrade to give acetyl-CoA. Phospholipids are an essential component of all membranes. Their insolubility in water is related to their control of permeability.
Carbohydrates	Molecules containing C, H, and O, usually in ratios near 1:2:1; polysaccharides are built up from simple sugars (monosaccharides) such as glucose and galactose. In some cases the sugars contain amino groups (e.g., glucosamine).	Some, such as cellulose and pectin, are used to construct strong, protective cell walls; others, such as glycogen, provide a form of storing glucose.
Nucleic acids	Long, linear molecules containing P, as well as C, H, O, and N, which are built up from pentose (5-carbon) nucleotides.	There are two main classes of nucleic acids in cells: DNA is the primary genetic component of all cells; RNA usually functions in the synthesis of proteins. In some viruses, RNA is the genetic material.

a 100-A thick mosaic structure built up of protein, polysaccharide, and lipid molecules. Just inside the cell wall is a flexible, 100-A thick cell membrane, largely composed of protein and lipid. This membrane is semipermeable and controls which molecules enter and leave the cell. Of vital importance is its ability to maintain a concentration gradient, since most molecules, both small and large, are present at much higher levels

TABLE 3–2 (*continued*)

Building blocks

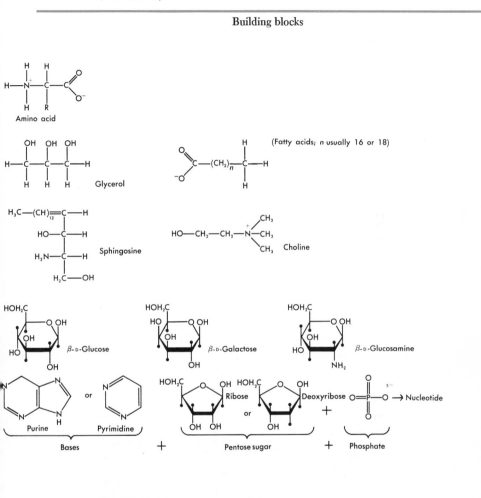

Amino acid

Glycerol

(Fatty acids; *n* usually 16 or 18)

Sphingosine

Choline

β-D-Glucose

β-D-Galactose

β-D-Glucosamine

Purine or Pyrimidine

Bases

Ribose or Deoxyribose

Pentose sugar

Phosphate → Nucleotide

inside than outside the cell membrane. This is true for both inorganic ions (e.g., K⁺ and Mg²⁺) and most important organic molecules. The membrane must actively prevent molecules from diffusing into the outside area of very much lower concentrations.

A schematic view of a typical *E. coli* cell is shown in Figure 3–7. About one-fifth of the interior of the cell is occupied by deoxyribonucleic acid (DNA), the compound responsible for the transmission of genetic material from one cell to another. Immediately surrounding the DNA there occur some 20,000 to 30,000 spherical particles, 200-A thick, the ribosomes. These are the cellular sites of protein synthesis, and contain approximately 40 per cent protein and 60 per cent ribonucleic acid (RNA). The remainder of the cell's interior is filled with water, water-soluble enzymes, and a large number of various small molecules.

At present we can make only an approximate guess of the number of chemically different molecules within a single E. coli cell. Each year many new molecules are discovered. The best guess is that between 3000 and 6000 different types of molecules are present (Table 3–3). Some of these, such as H_2O and CO_2, are chemically simple. Others, like the common sugar glucose or the nitrogen-containing purine and adenine, are more complex but nonetheless rather easily studied by current chemical

FIGURE 3–7   *Schematic view of an E. coli cell containing two identical chromosomes.*

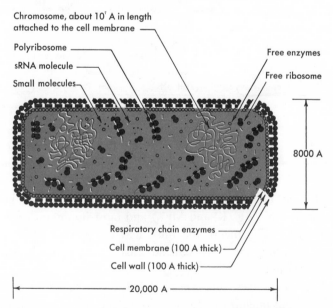

Chromosome, about 10^7 A in length
attached to the cell membrane

Polyribosome

sRNA molecule

Small molecules

Free enzymes

Free ribosome

8000 A

Respiratory chain enzymes

Cell membrane (100 A thick)

Cell wall (100 A thick)

20,000 A

techniques. Still other cellular molecules, in particular the proteins and nucleic acids, are very large, and even today their chemical structures are immensely difficult to unravel. Most of these macromolecules are not being actively studied, since their overwhelming complexity has forced chemists to concentrate on relatively few of them. Thus we must immediately admit that the structure of a cell will never be understood in the same way as that of water or glucose molecules. Not only will the exact structures of most macromolecules remain unsolved, but their relative locations within cells can be only vaguely known.

It is thus not surprising that many chemists, after brief periods

T A B L E 3–3 *Approximate chemical composition of a rapidly dividing Escherichia coli cell*[a]

Component	Per cent of total cell weight	Average MW	Approximate number per cell	Number of different kinds
H_2O	70	18	4×10^{10}	1
Inorganic ions (Na^+, K^+, Mg^{2+}, Ca^{2+}, Fe^{2+}, Cl^-, PO_4^{4-}, SO_4^{2-}, etc.)	1	40	2.5×10^8	20
Carbohydrates and precursors	3	150	2×10^8	200
Amino acids and precursors	0.4	120	3×10^7	100
Nucleotides and precursors	0.4	300	1.2×10^7	200
Lipids and precursors	2	750	2.5×10^7	50
				200
Other small molecules (heme, quinones, breakdown products of food molecules, etc.)	0.2	150	1.5×10^7	
Proteins	15	40,000	10^6	2000 to 3000
Nucleic acids				
DNA	1	2.5×10^9	4	1
RNA	6			
16s rRNA		500,000	3×10^4	1 (?)
23s rRNA		1,000,000	3×10^4	1 (?)
sRNA		25,000	4×10^5	40
mRNA		1,000,000	10^3	1000

[a] Weight 10^{12} daltons.

T A B L E 3–4 *Structural organization of several important biological macromolecules*

Macromolecule	Monomeric units	Number of different monomers	General monomer formula	Fixed or irregular chain length	Linkage between monomers
Glycogen (a polysaccharide)	Glucose	One	$6CH_2OH$ ... OH ... OH ... HO ... 5 4 OH 3 ... 1 2	Indefinite— may be > 1000	1–4-Glycosidic linkage C—O—C $_1$ $_4$
DNA (deoxyribo-nucleic acid)	Deoxynucleotides	Four: deoxyadenylate deoxyguanylate deoxythymidilate deoxycytidilate	Purine-deoxyribose-P (or pyrimidine-deoxyribose-P)	Genetically fixed—may be $> 10^7$	3–5-Phosphodiester linkage
RNA (ribonucleic acid)	Ribonucleotides	Four: adenylate guanylate uradylate cytidylate	Purine-ribose-P (or pyrimidine-ribose-P)	Genetically fixed, often > 3000	3–5-Phosphodiester linkage
Protein	L-Amino acids	Twenty: glycine, alanine, serine, etc.	side group	Genetically fixed, usually varies between 100 and 1000	Peptide linkage

of enthusiasm for studying "life," silently return to the world of pure chemistry. Others, however, become more optimistic when they understand (1) that all macromolecules are polymeric molecules built up from smaller monomers, (2) that there exist well-defined chains of successive chemical reactions in cells (metabolic pathways), and (3) that a limit is placed on the number of enzymes (and hence small molecules) that can exist in a cell by the fact that each contains a finite amount of DNA.

MACROMOLECULES CONSTRUCTED
BY LINEAR LINKING OF SMALL MOLECULES

Most of the mass of E. coli (excluding water), like that of all other cells, is composed of macromolecules. Most of these large molecules are proteins, about half of which function as enzymes. The remainder of the proteins are used to help construct the ribosomes, the cell wall, etc. Table 3–3 shows that the number of atoms in a macromolecule is 25 to 50 times the number in a small molecule. Thus one might initially guess that most biochemists concerned with synthesis would be directly concerned with the frightfully complicated task of understanding the atom by atom growth of big molecules. Furthermore, one might also guess that their relatively immense size would lead to a very slow pace of research. Fortunately, however, the existence of three simplifying structural generalizations reduces the problem to a difficult, but not impossible, task.

First, all macromolecules are polymeric molecules formed by the condensation of small molecules. Macromolecule biosynthesis thus occurs in two stages: (1) the formation of the smaller subunits, and (2) the systematic linking together of these subunits. An analogy can be made to the building of a house from preconstructed bricks.

Second, the building blocks for a given macromolecule have common chemical groupings as illustrated in Table 3–4, which describes the main structural features of several important macromolecules. For example, proteins form by the condensation of nitrogen-containing organic molecules called amino

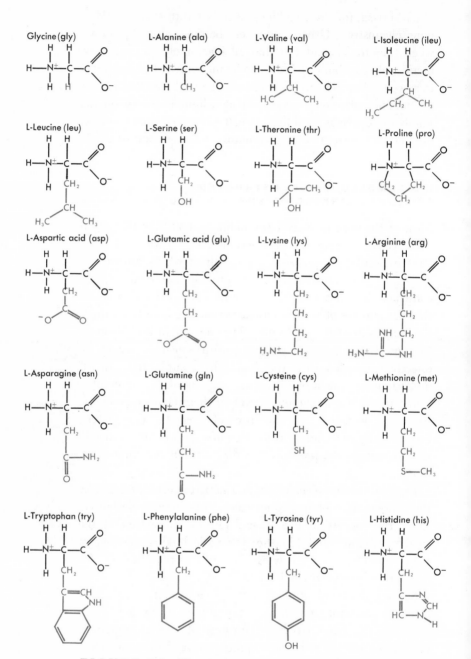

FIGURE 3–8 *The twenty common amino acids found in proteins.*

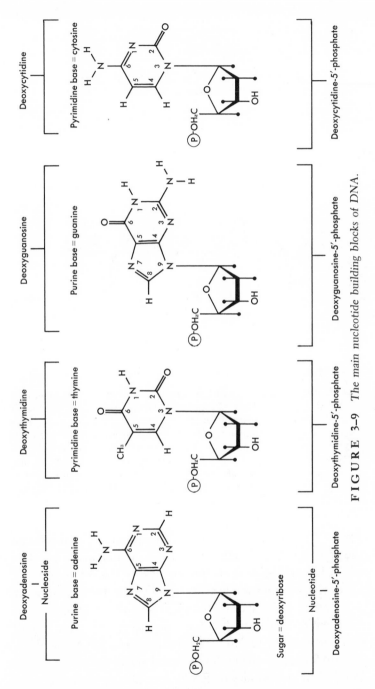

FIGURE 3-9 *The main nucleotide building blocks of DNA.*

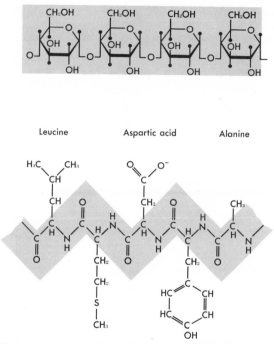

(a)

(b)

FIGURE 3–10   The structure of some biological macromolecules. The backbones are shown in color. (a) The structure of a portion of a glycogen chain composed of glucose subunits. (b) A portion of a polypeptide chain of a protein. The amino acid subunits are, from left to right: leucine, methionine, aspartic acid, tyrosine, and alanine. (c) A portion of the polynucleotide chain of a deoxyribonucleic acid.

acids. The chemical bond that links two amino acids together is the peptide bond. There are 20 important amino acids, each of which has part of its structure identical to that of comparable regions in the other amino acids. Attached to the regular region is a "side group," specific for each amino acid (Figure 3–8). Each amino acid thus has a *specific* region (the side group) and a *nonspecific* region. The nucleic acids, DNA and RNA, are also formed by the union of smaller molecules called nucleotides. The nucleotides of RNA, since they contain the sugar

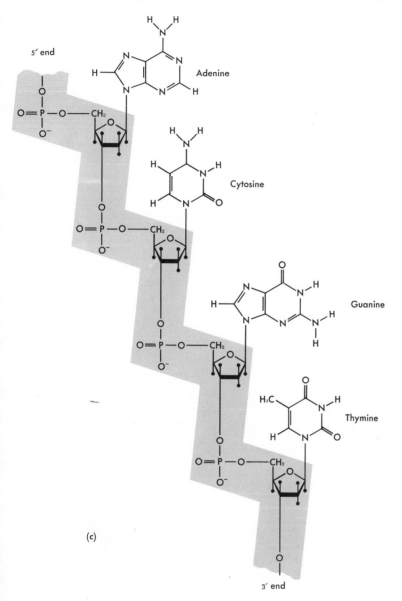

(c)

ribose, are called ribonucleotides, and those of DNA, which contain deoxyribose instead, are called deoxyribonucleotides (Figure 3–9; see Chapter 9 for details). The nucleotides are always linked together through a phosphate group and a hydroxyl group on the sugar component (Table 3–4). Hence these link-ages are called phosphodiester bonds. Each nucleotide, like each amino acid, contains both a specific and a nonspecific region. The phosphate and sugar groups comprise the non-specific portion of a nucleotide, while the purine and pyrimi-dine bases make up the specific portion. DNA and RNA each contain four main bases: two purines and two pyrimidines.

Third, most macromolecules (nucleic acids, proteins, and

FIGURE 3–11   *Hydrolysis of a polypeptide to form amino acids. Here we show a very simple polypeptide containing only three amino acids.*

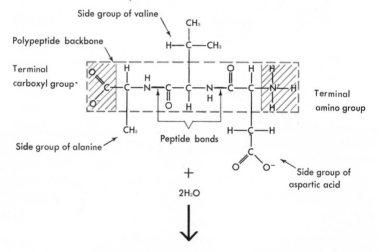

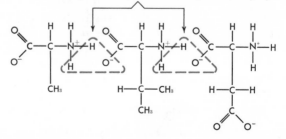

some polysaccharides) are *linear* aggregates in which the subunits are linked together by a chemical bond between atoms in the nonspecific regions. Their linear configuration follows from the fact that most subunits possess only two atoms that form bonds with other subunits. Thus a large fraction of most macromolecules consists of a repeating series of identical chemical groups (the *backbone*, Figure 3–10).

A feature common to all these biological polymers is that the individual subunits in the polymer chain contain two hydrogen atoms and one oxygen atom less than the simple monomers from which they are synthesized. Synthesis thus involves the release of water. When the polymers are degraded to yield smaller molecules, one H_2O molecule is incorporated by each peptide bond broken (Figure 3–11).

Degradative reactions in which H_2O uptake is required are known as hydrolytic reactions. There are many types of hydrolytic reactions, since numerous small molecules can be broken down to still smaller products by the addition of water. Under normal cell conditions, hydrolysis of any of the important polymers or small molecules is very rare. Hydrolysis is, however, speeded up by the presence of specific enzymes. For example, the enzymes pepsin and trypsin specifically catalyze the hydrolytic breakdown of proteins.

DISTINCTION BETWEEN REGULAR AND IRREGULAR POLYMERS

Table 3–4 also reveals an important difference between the polysaccharides, like glycogen, and the proteins and nucleic acids. Polysaccharides are usually constructed by *regular* (or semiregular) aggregation of one or two different kinds of monosaccharide building blocks. In contrast, proteins contain 20 different amino acids, and nucleic acids contain 4 different nucleotides. Moreover, in the nucleic acids and proteins, the order of subunits is highly *irregular* and varies greatly from one specific molecule to another. Polysaccharide synthesis from monosaccharides generally involves only the making of the same backbone bond; the synthesis of nucleic acids and proteins demands in addition a highly efficient mechanism for choosing and ordering the correct subunits.

METABOLIC PATHWAYS

We can see directly that all the molecules in a cell arise from cellular transformation of food molecules if we allow the bacterium E. coli to grow in a simple, well-defined medium containing the sugar glucose (Table 3–1). Under these conditions glucose is the only organic source of carbon. In effect, all the carbon atoms of the E. coli molecules (a few are derived from CO_2) must result from chemical transformations by which glucose molecules are either broken down to smaller fragments or added to each other to form large molecules like the nucleotides or glycogen. The exact way in which all these transformations (collectively known as intermediary metabolism) occur is enormously complex, and most biochemists concern themselves with studying (or even knowing about!) only a small fraction of the total interactions.

Fortunately, some basic simplicity to the general pattern of metabolism is now beginning to emerge. Figure 3–12 shows some of the more important types of chemical events that occur after glucose is taken into an E. coli cell. Much of this information comes from experiments in which E. coli is fed molecules specifically labeled with radioactive isotopes. For example, if we expose E. coli for several seconds (a pulse) to C^{14}-labeled glucose, the radioactive atoms can be detected almost immediately in molecules chemically similar to glucose, such as glucose-6-phosphate. Only later do the labeled atoms find their way into the various amino acids and nucleotides. The amount of time before radioactivity appears in the various compounds corresponds roughly to the number of biochemical reactions separating glucose from the various metabolites.

Figure 3–12 shows that various key intermediates in glucose degradation often have several possible fates. They may be completely degraded via the Embden-Meyerhof pathway, the Krebs cycle, and the respiratory chain, to yield CO_2 and H_2O.

During this process, ADP is converted to ATP. Alternatively, various intermediates may be used to initiate a series of successive chemical reactions that end with the synthesis of vital molecules, such as the amino acids or the nucleotides. For example, dihydroxyacetone-$\circled{P}$ is used as a precursor for the lipid constituent glycerol, whereas 3-phosphoglyceric acid is the beginning metabolite in a series of reactions that leads to the amino acids serine, glycine, and cysteine.

Connected groups of biosynthetic (degradative) reactions are referred to as *metabolic pathways*. Once a molecule has started on a pathway it often has no choice but to undergo a series of successive transformations. All pathways, however, are not necessarily linear. Some may be branched. Intermediates at branch points are transformed into one of two or more possible compounds. Those intermediates that are subject to several alternative fates are very important in cellular metabolism. Prominent among them are glucose-6-$\circled{P}$, pyruvate, α-ketoglutarate, and oxaloacetate; each serves as a starting point for several important pathways. Perhaps the most important such compound is acetyl-CoA, which is not only the main precursor of lipids, but also contains the acetate residue consumed by the citric acid cycle.

The metabolic fates of the majority of molecules are, however, much more limited. An average molecule can be either broken down to compound x or used as an intermediate in the biosynthesis of compound y; correspondingly, each such metabolite is able to combine specifically with only two different enzymes.

DEGRADATION PATHWAYS DISTINCT FROM BIOSYNTHETIC PATHWAYS

When *E. coli* is growing upon glucose as its sole carbon source, all its amino acids must be synthesized from metabolites derived from glucose. Thus there exists a distinct biosynthetic pathway for each of the 20 amino acids (Figure 3–12). *E. coli* can also grow, however, in the absence of a sugar, using any of the 20 amino acids as a *sole* carbon source. This means that there

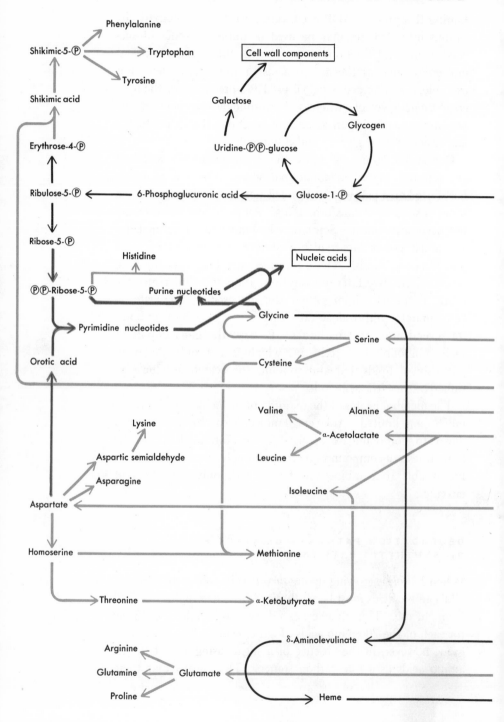

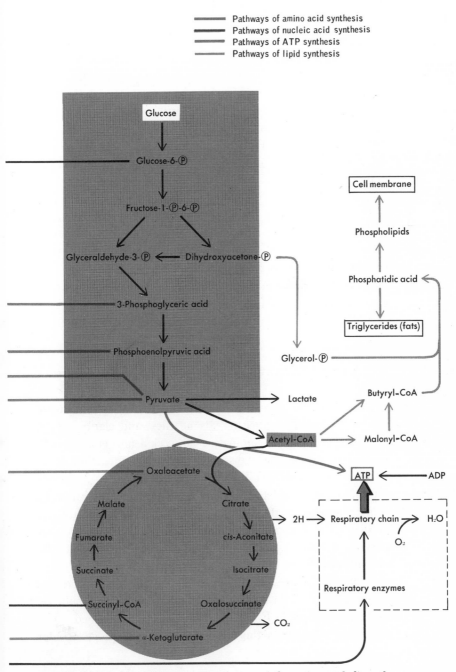

FIGURE 3–12 *Schematic view of some of the main metabolic pathways in* E. coli.

must also exist 20 pathways of amino acid degradation, by which the carbon and nitrogen atoms of the amino acids are usefully freed to form key metabolite compounds such as α-ketoglutarate and acetyl-CoA. These compounds can then be used in the synthesis of other amino acids. Degradative pathways also exist for various lipids, the purine and pyrimidine nucleotides, many pentose and hexose sugars, etc. Most of the degradative pathways are quite specific, and thus a very large number (perhaps 200 to 300) of different degradative intermediates may be found in E. coli. The number must be even larger in many other bacteria, particularly the Pseudomonads, since they degrade a larger, more varied collection of organic molecules than E. coli.

The generalization is beginning to emerge that degradative pathways are usually quite different from pathways of biosynthesis. This observation is not surprising. As we shall see in Chapter 5, most biosynthetic reactions require energy, and often involve the breakdown of ATP, whereas degradative reactions, by their very function, must eventually generate ATP, in addition to supplying carbon and nitrogen skeletons.

THE SIGNIFICANCE OF A FINITE AMOUNT OF DNA

It is easy for the sophisticated pure chemist to look at Figure 3–12 with initial skepticism. Its neatness and clarity cannot obscure the fact that seemingly each week a new enzyme with its corresponding newly discovered metabolic reaction is reported. The question arises whether Figure 3–12, by its simplification, completely misses the point of metabolism in E. coli. This would certainly be the case if there were not just one or two ways of degrading glucose, but 50 to 100 ways, and likewise if there were 20 different pathways leading to the biosynthesis of each of the nucleotides, amino acids, etc.

However, there exists a simple way to refute the heretical thought that only an insignificant fraction of the metabolic reactions that occur in E. coli have to date been described. The argument is based on the fact, which we shall prove in later chapters, that the sequence of nucleotides in DNA carries the genetic information that orders (codes) the sequence of amino acids in proteins. It is now clear that successive groups of three nucleotide pairs code for each amino acid. Thus the average-size protein, containing about 500 amino acids, requires a code of 1500 nucleotide pairs. Since each nucleotide pair has a $MW = 660$, DNA units of $MW = (660)(1500) \cong 10^6$ are needed for each protein. Thus the number of different proteins within a cell can be no greater than the amount of haploid $DNA/10^6$.

This figure can be used further to estimate the number of different types of small molecules a cell can possess. The majority of kinds of proteins in a cell are enzymes, each of which catalyzes a specific metabolic reaction. The approximate number of types of small molecules can be estimated if we know, on the average, how many specific enzymes are needed for the metabolism of the average small molecule. At present it seems a good guess that the number lies between one and two.

ONE–FIFTH TO ONE–THIRD OF THE CHEMICAL REACTIONS IN E. COLI ARE KNOWN

Our best estimate for the haploid amount of DNA in *E. coli* is $2.5 \times 10^9 \pm 0.5 \times 10^9$. This figure corresponds to 2000 to 3000 average size protein molecules, and suggests that the number of different small molecules will be somewhat under 2000. Most pleasingly we find by looking at Table 3–3 that our best guess of the number of different small metabolites involved in already known metabolic pathways is between 600 and 800. This means that we already know at least 1/5, and maybe more than 1/3 of all the metabolic reactions that will ever be described in *E. coli*. The conclusion is most satisfying, for it strongly suggests that within the next 10 to 20 years we shall approach a state in which it will be possible to describe essentially all the metabolic reactions involved in the life of an *E. coli* cell.

Therefore even a cautious chemist, when properly informed, need not look at a bacterial cell as a hopelessly complex object. Instead he might easily adopt an almost joyous enthusiasm, for it is clear that he, unlike his nineteenth-century equivalent, at last possesses the tools to describe completely the essential features of life.

SUMMARY

At the chemical level even the smallest cells are fantastically complicated. Most scientists interested in the essential chemical features of cell growth and division now concentrate on bacteria, since bacterial cells are about 500 times smaller than the average cell of a higher plant or animal. The most commonly employed bacterium, Escherichia coli, weighs about 2×10^{-12} gram (10^{12} daltons), of which about 75 per cent is water. The number of different types of molecules within an E. coli cell probably lies between 3000 and 6000. Approximately half are "small" molecules and the remainder, macromolecules. The large number of different macromolecules means that we shall not know in the near (or conceivably, even in the distant) future the exact 3-D structures of all the molecules in even the smallest cell.

We do, however, know some rules about cell chemistry that make it possible to understand the growth of a cell without knowing the exact molecular structure of all its constituents. We know, for example, that all cellular macromolecules are polymeric molecules built up from much smaller monomers. Proteins are polymers containing amino acids as their monomers; the polymeric nucleic acids are built by the linking of nucleotides. Further simplicity comes from the fact that most polymers, including all the proteins and nucleic acids, are essentially linear molecules.

Another simplifying rule concerns the complexity of intermediary metabolism. Generally compounds cannot be directly transformed into a large number of other compounds. Instead each compound comprises a step in a series of reactions (pathway) leading either to the degradation of a food molecule or to the biosynthesis of a necessary cellular molecule such as amino acid or a fatty acid. Cellular metabolism is the sum total of a large number of such pathways (on metabolic maps) connected in such a way that products of degradative pathways can be used to initiate specific biosynthetic pathways.

The complexity of the metabolic map of an organism is related to the amount of genetic information (DNA) in the organism. The amount of DNA in a cell places an upper limit on the number of different enzymes the cell can produce. E. coli possess sufficient DNA to code for the amino acid sequence in almost 2000 to 3000 different proteins. Some 600 different small molecules have now been detected in E. coli. This indicates that those metabolic reactions which we know of in E. coli account for one-fifth to one-third of its total metabolism.

REFERENCES

Sistrom, W., *Microbial Life*, Holt, New York, 1962. A brief paperback introduction to the biology and chemistry of microbes.

Stanier, R. Y., M. Doudoroff, and E. A. Adelberg, *The Microbial World*, 2nd ed., Prentice-Hall, Englewood Cliffs, N.J., 1963. A superb treatment of microbiology that can be read by any beginning college student.

Loewy, A., and P. Siekevitz, *Cell Structure and Function*, Holt, New York, 1962. Essentials of the physiology of the cell, often with emphasis on the problems of multicellular organization.

Gunsalus, I. C., and R. Y. Stanier, *The Bacteria: A Treatise on Structure and Function* (5 vols.), Academic, New York, 1960–1964. A series of reviews and articles on essentially everything interesting about bacteria.

THE

IMPORTANCE

OF WEAK

CHEMICAL

INTERACTIONS

UNTIL NOW WE HAVE FOCUSED OUR attention on the existence of discrete organic molecules and, following classical organic chemistry, have emphasized the covalent bonds which hold them together. It takes little insight, however, to realize that this type of analysis is inadequate for describing a cell, and that we must also concern ourselves with the exact shape of molecules and with the several factors which bind them together in an organized fashion. The distribution of molecules in cells is not random, and we must ask ourselves what chemical laws determine this distribution. Clearly, covalent bonding cannot be involved; by definition, atoms united by covalent bonds belong to the same molecule.

The arrangement of distinct molecules in cells is controlled instead by chemical bonds much weaker than covalent bonds. Atoms united by covalent bonds are capable of weak interactions with nearby atoms. These interactions, sometimes called "secondary bonds," occur not only between atoms in different molecules, but also between atoms in the same molecule. Weak bonds are important not just in deciding which molecules lie next to each other, but also in giving shape to flexible molecules such as the polypeptides and polynucleotides. It is, therefore, useful to have a feeling for the nature of weak chemical interactions and to understand how their "weak" character makes them indispensable to cellular existence. The most important include van der Waals bonds, hydrogen bonds, and ionic bonds.

DEFINITION AND SOME CHARACTERISTICS OF CHEMICAL BONDS

A chemical bond is an attractive force that holds atoms together. Aggregates of finite size are called molecules. Originally, it was thought that only covalent bonds hold atoms together in molecules, but now, as we shall show later in this chapter, weaker attractive forces are known to be important in holding together many macromolecules. For example, the four polypeptide chains of hemoglobin are held together by the combined action of several weak bonds. It is thus now customary also to call weak positive interactions chemical bonds, even though they are not strong enough, when present singly, to effectively bind two atoms together.

Chemical bonds are characterized in several ways. A most obvious characteristic of a bond is its strength. Strong bonds almost never fall apart at physiological temperatures. This is why atoms united by covalent bonds always belong to the same molecule. Weak bonds are easily broken, and when they exist singly, they exist fleetingly. Only when present in ordered groups do weak bonds exist for a long time. The strength of a bond is correlated with its length, so that two atoms connected by a strong bond are always closer together than the same two atoms held together by a weak bond. For example, two hydrogen atoms bound covalently to form a hydrogen molecule (H:H) are 0.074 A apart, whereas the same two atoms, when held together by the van der Waals forces instead, are held 1.2 A apart.

Another important bond characteristic is the maximum number of bonds that a given atom can make. The number of covalent bonds an atom forms is called its valence. Oxygen, for example, has a valence of two: It can never form more than two covalent bonds. There is more variability in the case of van der Waals bonds, where the limiting factor is purely steric: The

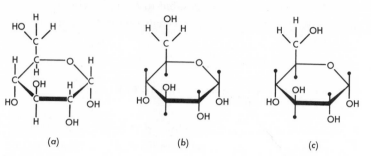

(a)   (b)   (c)

FIGURE 4-1   Rotation about the C_5–C_6 bond in glucose. This carbon-carbon bond is a single bond, and so any of the three configurations (a), (b), (c) may occur.

FIGURE 4-2   The planar shape of the peptide bond. Shown is a portion of an extended polypeptide chain. Almost no rotation is possible about the peptide bond because of its partial double-bond character:

All the atoms in the grey must lie in the same plane. Rotation is possible, however, around the remaining two bonds, which make up the polypeptide configurations. (Redrawn from L. Pauling, The Nature of the Chemical Bond, 3rd ed., Cornell Univ. Press, Ithaca, N.Y., 1960, p. 498, with permission.)

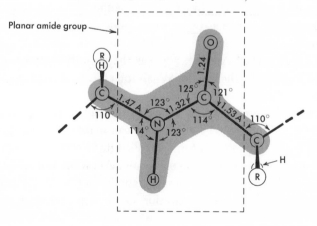

number of possible bonds is limited only by the number of atoms that can simultaneously touch each other. The formation of hydrogen bonds is subject to more restrictions. A covalently bonded hydrogen atom usually participates in only one hydrogen bond, whereas an oxygen atom seldom participates in more than two hydrogen bonds.

The angle between two bonds originating from a single atom is called the bond angle. The angle between two specific covalent bonds is always approximately the same. For example, when a carbon atom has four single bonds, they are directed tetrahedrally (bond angle = 109°). In contrast, the angles between weak bonds are much more variable.

Bonds differ also in the freedom of rotation they allow. Single covalent bonds permit free rotation of bound atoms (Figure 4–1), whereas double and triple bonds are quite rigid. For example, the carbonyl (C=O) and imino (N—H) groups bound together by the rigid peptide bond must lie in the same plane (Figure 4–2), because of the partial double-bond character of the peptide bond. Much weaker, ionic bonds show completely opposite behavior; they impose no restrictions on the relative orientations of bonded atoms.

CHEMICAL BONDS ARE EXPLAINABLE IN QUANTUM—MECHANICAL TERMS

The nature of the forces, strong as well as weak, that give rise to chemical bonds remained a mystery to chemists until the quantum theory of the atom (quantum mechanics) was developed in the 1920s. Then, for the first time, the various empirical laws about how chemical bonds are formed were put on a firm theoretical basis. It was realized that all chemical bonds, weak as well as strong, were based on electrostatic forces. Quantum-mechanical explanations were provided not only for covalent bonding by the sharing of electrons, but also for the formation of weaker bonds.

CHEMICAL–BOND FORMATION INVOLVES
A CHANGE IN THE FORM OF ENERGY

The spontaneous formation of a bond between two atoms always involves the release of some of the internal energy of the unbonded atoms and its conversion to another energy form. The stronger the bond, the greater the amount of energy which is released upon its formation. The bonding reaction between two atoms A and B is thus described by

$$A + B \rightarrow AB + \text{energy} \tag{4-1}$$

where AB represents the bonded aggregate. The rate of the reaction is proportional to the frequency of collision between A and B. The unit most commonly used to measure energy is the calorie, the amount of energy required to raise the temperature of 1 gram of water from 14.5°C to 15.5°C. Since thousands of calories are usually involved in the breaking of a mole of chemical bonds, most chemical-energy changes in chemical reactions are expressed in kilocalories per mole.

Atoms joined by chemical bonds, however, do not forever remain together. There also exist forces which break chemical bonds. By far the most important of these forces arises from heat energy. Collisions with fast-moving molecules or atoms can break chemical bonds. During a collision, some of the kinetic energy of a moving molecule is given up as it pushes apart two bonded atoms. The faster a molecule is moving (the higher the temperature), the greater the probability that, upon collision, it will break a bond. Hence, as the temperature of a collection of molecules is increased, the stability of their bonds decreases. The breaking of a bond is thus always indicated by the formula

$$AB + \text{energy} \rightarrow A + B \tag{4-2}$$

The amount of energy that must be added to break a bond is exactly equal to the amount which was released upon its formation. This equivalence follows from the first law of thermodynamics, which states that energy (except as it is interconvertible with mass) can be neither made nor destroyed.

EQUILIBRIUM BETWEEN BOND MAKING AND BREAKING

Every bond is thus a result of the combined actions of bond-making (arising from electrostatic interactions) and bond-breaking forces. When an equilibrium is reached in a closed system, the number of bonds forming per unit time will equal the number breaking. Then the proportion of bonded atoms is described by the following mass action formula:

$$K_{eq} = \frac{\text{conc}^{AB}}{\text{conc}^A \times \text{conc}^B} \tag{4-3}$$

where K_{eq} is the equilibrium constant, and conc^A, conc^B, and conc^{AB} are the concentrations of A, B, and AB in moles per liter, respectively. Whether we start with only free A and B, with only the molecule AB, or with a combination of AB and free A and B, at equilibrium the proportions of A, B, and AB will reach the concentration given by K_{eq}.

THE CONCEPT OF FREE ENERGY

There is always a change in the form of energy as the proportion of bonded atoms moves toward the equilibrium concentration. Biologically, the most useful way to express this energy change is through the physical chemists' concept of *free energy, G*.* Here we shall not give a rigorous description of free energy nor show how it differs from the other forms of energy. For this, the reader must refer to a chemistry text which discusses the second law of thermodynamics. We must suffice by saying that *free energy is energy that has the ability to do work.*

The second law of thermodynamics tells us that a decrease of free energy (ΔG is negative) always occurs in spontaneous reactions. When equilibrium is reached, there is no further change in the amount of free energy ($\Delta G = 0$). The equilib-

---

* It was the custom in the United States until recently to refer to free energy by the symbol F. Now, however, most new texts have adopted the international symbol G, which honors the great nineteenth-century physicist Gibbs.

rium state for a closed collection of atoms is thus that state that contains the least amount of free energy.

The free energy lost as equilibrium is approached is either transformed into heat or used to increase the amount of entropy. Here, we shall not attempt to define entropy (again this task must be left to a chemistry text), except to say that the amount of entropy is a measure of the amount of disorder. The greater the disorder, the greater the amount of entropy. The existence of entropy means that many spontaneous chemical reactions do not proceed with an evolution of heat. For example, in the dissolving of NaCl in water, heat is absorbed. There is, nonetheless, a net decrease in free energy because of the increase of disorder of the Na^+ and Cl^- ions as they move from a solid to a liquid phase.

K_{eq} IS EXPONENTIALLY RELATED TO ΔG

It is obvious that the stronger the bond, and hence the greater the change in free energy (ΔG) which accompanies its formation, the greater the proportion of atoms that must exist in the bonded form. This common-sense idea is quantitatively expressed by the physical-chemical formula

$$\triangle G = -RT \ln K_{eq} \quad \text{or} \quad K_{eq} = e^{-\Delta G/RT} \tag{4-4}$$

where R is the universal gas constant, T the absolute temperature, $e = 2.718$, ln the logarithm of K to the base e, and K_{eq} the equilibrium constant.

TABLE 4-1   *The numerical relationship between the equilibrium constant and ΔG at 25°C*

K_{eq}	ΔG, kcal/mole
0.001	4.089
0.01	2.726
0.1	1.363
1.0	0
10.0	−1.363
100.0	−2.726
1000.0	−4.089

Insertion of the appropriate values of R ($= 1.987$ cal/deg/mole) and T ($= 298$ at $25°C$) tells us (Table 4–1) that ΔG values as low as 2 kcal/mole can drive a bond-forming reaction to virtual completion if all reactants are present at molar concentrations.

COVALENT BONDS ARE VERY STRONG

The ΔG values accompanying the formation of covalent bonds from free atoms such as hydrogen or oxygen are very large and negative in sign, usually -50 to -110 kcal/mole. Application of Eq. (4–4) tells us that K_{eq} of the bonding reaction will be correspondingly large, and so the concentration of hydrogen or oxygen atoms existing unbound will be very small. For example, a ΔG value of -100 kcal/mole tells us that, if we start with 1 mole/liter of the reacting atoms, only one in 10^{40} atoms will remain unbound when equilibrium is reached.

WEAK BONDS HAVE ENERGIES BETWEEN 1 AND 7 KCAL/MOLE

The main types of weak bonds important in biological systems are the van der Waals bonds, hydrogen bonds, and ionic bonds. Sometimes, as we shall soon point out, the distinction between a hydrogen bond and an ionic bond is arbitrary. The weakest bonds are the van der Waals bonds. These have energies (1 to 2 kcal/mole) that are only slightly greater than the kinetic energy of heat motion. The energies of hydrogen and ionic bonds range between 3 and 7 kcal/mole.

In liquid solutions, almost all molecules are forming a number of weak bonds to nearby atoms. All molecules are able to form van der Waals bonds; hydrogen and ionic bonds can also form between molecules (ions) which have a net charge or in which the charge is unequally distributed. Some molecules thus have the capacity to form several types of weak bonds. Energetic considerations, however, tell us that molecules always have a greater tendency to form the stronger bond.

WEAK BONDS CONSTANTLY MADE AND BROKEN AT PHYSIOLOGICAL TEMPERATURES

The energy of the strongest weak bond is only about ten times larger than the average energy of kinetic motion (heat) at 25°C (0.6 kcal/mole). Since there is a significant spread in the energies of kinetic motion, many molecules with sufficient kinetic energy to break the strongest weak bond always exist at physiological temperatures.

ENZYMES NOT INVOLVED IN MAKING (BREAKING) OF WEAK BONDS

The average lifetime of a single weak bond is only a fraction of a second. Cells thus do not need a special mechanism to speed up the rate at which weak bonds are made and broken. Correspondingly, enzymes never participate in reactions of weak bonds.

DISTINCTION BETWEEN POLAR AND NONPOLAR MOLECULES

All forms of weak interactions are based upon attractions between electric charges. The separation of electric charges can be permanent or temporary, depending upon the atoms involved. For example, the oxygen molecule (O:O) has a symmetric distribution of electrons between its two oxygen atoms, and so each of its two atoms is uncharged. In contrast, there is a nonuniform distribution of charge in water (H:O:H), where the bond electrons are unevenly shared (Figure 4–3). They are held more strongly by the oxygen atom, which thus carries a considerable negative charge, whereas the two hydrogen atoms together have an equal amount of positive charge. The center of the positive charge is on one side of the center of the negative charge. A combination of separated positive and negative charges is called an electric dipole moment. Unequal electron sharing reflects dissimilar affinities of the bonding atoms for electrons. Atoms which have a tendency to gain electrons are called electronegative atoms. Electropositive atoms have a tendency to give up electrons.

Molecules such as H_2O, which contain a dipole moment, are called *polar molecules*. *Nonpolar molecules* are those with no effective dipole moments. In CH_4 (methane), for example, the carbon and hydrogen atoms have similar affinities for their shared electron pairs, and so neither the carbon nor the hydrogen atom is noticeably charged.

The distribution of charge in a molecule can also be affected by the presence of nearby molecules, particularly if the affected molecule is polar. This effect may cause a nonpolar molecule to acquire a slight polar character. If the second molecule is not polar, its presence will still alter the nonpolar molecule, establishing a fluctuating charge distribution. Such induced effects, however, give rise to a much smaller separation of charge than is found in polar molecules, thus resulting in smaller interaction energies and, correspondingly, weaker chemical bonds.

FIGURE 4–3 *The structure of a water molecule.*

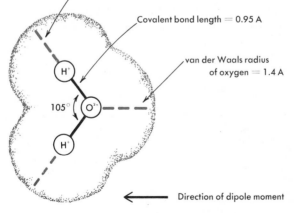

van der Waals radius of hydrogen = 1.2 A

Covalent bond length = 0.95 A

van der Waals radius
of oxygen = 1.4 A

105°

H⁺

H⁺

O²⁻

Direction of dipole moment

VAN DER WAALS FORCES

Van der Waals bonding arises from a nonspecific attractive force originating when two atoms come close to each other. It is based not upon the existence of permanent charge separations, but rather upon the induced fluctuating charges caused by the nearness of molecules. It therefore operates between all types of molecules, polar as well as nonpolar. It depends heavily upon the distance between the interacting groups, since it is inversely proportional to the sixth power of distance (Figure 4–4).

There also exists a more powerful van der Waals repulsive force, which comes into play at even shorter distances. This repulsion is caused by the overlapping of the outer electron shells of the atoms involved. The van der Waals attractive and repulsive forces balance at a certain distance specific for each type of atom. This distance is the so-called van der Waals radius (Table 4–2 and Figure 4–5). The van der Waals bonding energy between two atoms separated by the sum of their van der Waals radii increases with the size of the respective atoms. For two average atoms it is only about 1 kcal/mole, which is just slightly more than the average thermal energy of molecules at room temperature (0.6 kcal/mole).

This means that van der Waals forces are an effective binding force at physiological temperatures only when several atoms in a given molecule are bound to several atoms in another molecule. Then the energy of interaction is much greater than the

TABLE 4–2   *van der Waals radii of the atoms in biological molecules*

Atom	van der Waals radius, Å
H	1.2
N	1.5
O	1.4
P	1.9
S	1.85
CH_3 group	2.0
Half thickness of aromatic molecule	1.7

dissociating tendency resulting from random thermal movements. In order for several atoms to interact effectively, the molecular fit must be precise, since the distance separating any two interacting atoms must not be much greater than the

FIGURE 4-4   *Diagram illustrating van der Waals attraction and repulsion forces in relation to electron distribution of monoatomic molecules on the inert rare gas argon. (Redrawn from L. Pauling, General Chemistry, 2nd ed., Freeman, San Francisco, 1958, p. 322, with permission.)*

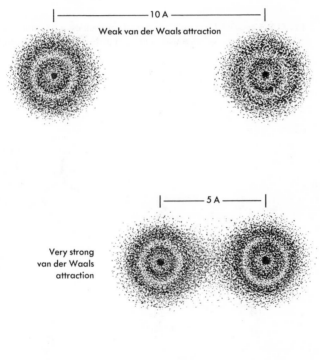

sum of their van der Waals radii (Figure 4–6). The strength of interaction rapidly approaches zero when this distance is only slightly exceeded. Thus, the strongest type of van der Waals contact arises when a molecule contains a cavity exactly complementary in shape to a protruding group of another molecule (Figure 4–7). This is the type of situation thought to exist between an antigen and its specific antibody (see Chapter 15). In this instance, the binding energies sometimes can be as large as 10 kcal/mole, so that antigen-antibody complexes seldom fall apart. Many polar molecules are only seldom af-

FIGURE 4–5   *Drawings of several molecules with atoms shown as spheres with radii equal to their van der Waals radii.*

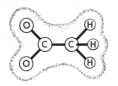

Acetate

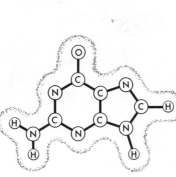

Glycine

Guanine

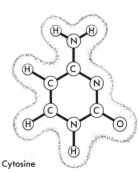

Cytosine

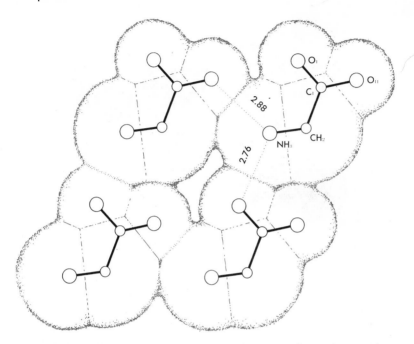

FIGURE 4-6 The arrangement of molecules in a layer of a crystal
formed by the amino acid glycine. The packing of the
molecules is determined by the van der Waals radii of
the groups, except for the N–H····O contacts, which
are shortened by the formation of hydrogen bonds.
(Redrawn from L. Pauling, *The Nature of the Chemical
Bond*, 3rd ed., Cornell Univ. Press, Ithaca, N.Y., 1960,
p. 262, with permission.)

fected by van der Waals interactions, since such molecules can
acquire a lower energy state (lose more free energy) by forming
other types of bonds.

HYDROGEN BONDS

A hydrogen bond arises between a covalently bound hydrogen
atom with some positive charge and a negatively charged,
covalently bound acceptor atom (Figure 4-8). For example,
the hydrogen atoms of the imino group (N—H) are attracted
by the negatively charged keto oxygen atoms (C=O). Some-

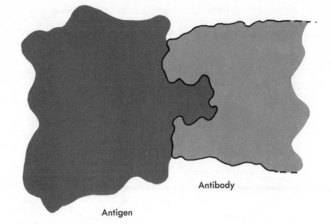

Antibody

Antigen

FIGURE 4-7   Schematic drawing showing the complementary relation between the surface configurations of an antigen and an antibody.

times the hydrogen-bonded atoms belong to groups with a unit of charge (e.g., NH_3^+ or COO^-). In other cases, both the donor hydrogen atoms and the negative acceptor atoms have less than a unit of charge.

The biologically most important hydrogen bonds involve hydrogen atoms covalently bound to oxygen (O—H) or nitrogen atoms (N—H). Likewise, the negative acceptor atoms are usually nitrogen or oxygen. Table 4-3 lists some of the most important hydrogen bonds. Bond energies range between 3 and 7 kcal/mole, the stronger bonds involving the greater charge differences between donor and acceptor atoms. Hydrogen bonds are thus weaker than covalent bonds, yet considerably

TABLE 4-3   Approximate bond lengths of biologically important hydrogen bonds

Bond	Approximate bond length, A
O–H — — — O	$2.70 \pm .10$
O–H — — — O⁻	$2.63 \pm .10$
O–H — — — N	$2.88 \pm .13$
N–H — — — O	$3.04 \pm .13$
N⁺H — — — O	$2.93 \pm .10$
N–H — — — N	$3.10 \pm .13$

stronger than van der Waals bonds. A hydrogen bond, therefore, will hold two atoms closer together than the sum of their
van der Waals radii, but not so close together as a covalent bond
would hold them.

Hydrogen bonds, unlike van der Waals bonds, are highly

FIGURE 4–8 *Examples of cellular hydrogen bonds.*

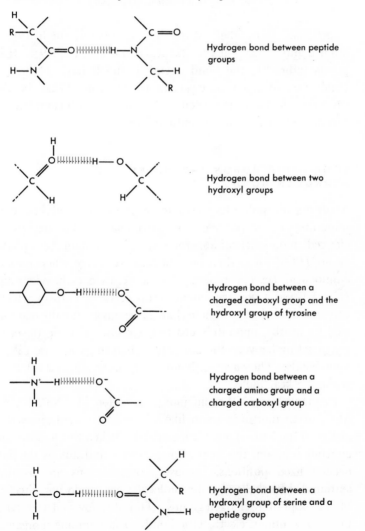

Hydrogen bond between peptide groups

Hydrogen bond between two hydroxyl groups

Hydrogen bond between a charged carboxyl group and the hydroxyl group of tyrosine

Hydrogen bond between a charged amino group and a charged carboxyl group

Hydrogen bond between a hydroxyl group of serine and a peptide group

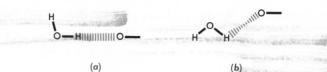

(a)   (b)

FIGURE 4-9   *Directional properties of hydrogen bonds. In (a) the*
vector along the covalent O—H bond points directly
at the acceptor oxygen, thereby forming a strong bond.
In (b) the vector points away from the oxygen atom,
resulting in a much weaker bond.

directional. In optimally strong hydrogen bonds, the hydrogen
atom points directly at the acceptor atom (Figure 4-9). If it
points indirectly, the bond energy is much less. Hydrogen
bonds are also much more specific than van der Waals bonds,
since they demand the existence of molecules with complementary donor hydrogen and acceptor groups.

SOME IONIC BONDS ARE, IN EFFECT, HYDROGEN BONDS

Many organic molecules possess ionic groups that contain one or
more units of net positive or negative charge. The negatively
charged mononucleotides, for example, contain phosphate
groups (PO_3^{3-}) with three units of negative charge, whereas each
amino acid (except proline) has a negative carboxyl group
(COO^-) and a positive amino group (NH_3^+), both of which
carry a unit of charge. These charged groups are usually neutralized by nearby, oppositely charged, groups. The electrostatic
forces acting between the oppositely charged groups are called
ionic bonds. Their average bond energy in an aqueous solution
is about 5 kcal/mole.

In many cases, either an inorganic cation like Na^+, K^+, or
Mg^{2+}, or an inorganic anion like Cl^- or SO_4^{2-}, neutralizes the
charge of the ionized organic molecules. When this happens in
aqueous solution, the neutralizing cations and anions do not
occupy fixed positions, because inorganic ions are usually
surrounded by shells of water molecules and so do not directly
bind to oppositely charged groups. Thus it is now believed that,
in water solutions, electrostatic bonds to surrounding inorganic

cations or anions are not of primary importance in determining the molecular shapes of organic molecules.

On the other hand, highly directional bonds result if the oppositely charged groups can form hydrogen bonds to each other. For example, both the COO^- and NH_3^+ groups are often held together by strong hydrogen bonds. Since these hydrogen bonds are stronger than those that involve groups with less than a unit of charge, they are correspondingly shorter. A strong hydrogen bond can also form between a group with a unit charge and a group having less than a unit charge. For example, a hydrogen atom belonging to an amino group ($—NH_2$) bonds strongly to an oxygen atom of a carboxyl group (COO^-).

WEAK INTERACTIONS DEMAND COMPLEMENTARY MOLECULAR SURFACES

Weak binding forces are effective only when the interacting surfaces are close. This proximity is possible only when the molecular surfaces have complementary structures, so that a protruding group (or positive charge) on one surface is matched by a cavity (or negative charge) on another; i.e., the interacting molecules must have a lock-and-key relationship. In cells this requirement often means that some molecules hardly ever bond to other molecules of the same kind, because such molecules do not have the properties of symmetry necessary for self-interaction. For example, some (polar) molecules contain donor hydrogen atoms and no suitable acceptor atoms, whereas others can accept hydrogen bonds but have no hydrogen atoms to donate. On the other hand, many molecules do exist with the symmetry to permit strong self-interaction in cells, water being the most important example.

H_2O MOLECULES FORM HYDROGEN BONDS

Under physiological conditions, water molecules rarely ionize to form H^+ and OH^- ions. Instead, they exist as polar $H—O—H$ molecules. Both the hydrogen and oxygen atoms form strong hydrogen bonds. In each H_2O molecule, the oxygen atom can bind to two external hydrogen atoms, whereas each hydrogen atom can bind to one adjacent oxygen atom. These bonds are directed tetrahedrally (Figure 4–10), so that, in its solid and liquid forms, each water molecule tends to have four nearest neighbors, one in each of the four directions of a tetrahedron. In ice the bonds to these neighbors are very rigid and the arrangement

FIGURE 4–10   Schematic diagram of a lattice formed by H_2O molecules. The energy gained by forming specific hydrogen bonds (||||||) between H_2O molecules favors the arrangement of the molecules in adjacent tetrahedrons. Oxygen atoms are indicated by large circles, and hydrogen atoms by small circles. Although the rigidity of the arrangement depends upon the temperature of the molecules, the pictured structure is, nevertheless, predominant in water as well as in ice. (Redrawn from L. Pauling, The Nature of the Chemical Bond, 3rd ed., Cornell Univ. Press, Ithaca, N.Y., 1960, p. 465, with permission.)

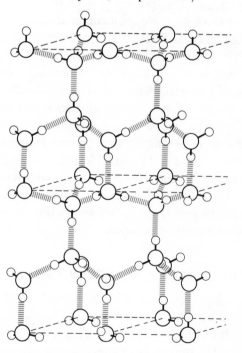

of molecules fixed. Above the melting temperature (0°C) the energy of thermal motion is sufficient to break the hydrogen bonds and to allow the water molecules to change their nearest neighbors continually. Even in the liquid form, however, at a given instant most water molecules are bound by four strong hydrogen bonds.

WEAK BONDS BETWEEN MOLECULES IN AQUEOUS SOLUTIONS

The average energy of a secondary bond, though small compared to that of a covalent bond, is nonetheless strong enough compared to heat energy to ensure that most molecules in aqueous solution will form secondary bonds to other molecules. The proportion of bonded to nonbonded arrangements is given by Eq. (4-4), corrected to take into account the high concentration of molecules in a liquid. It tells us that interaction energies as low as 2 to 3 kcal/mole are sufficient at physiological temperatures to force most molecules to form the maximum number of good secondary bonds.

The specific structure of a solution at a given instant is markedly influenced by which solute molecules are present, not only because molecules have specific shapes, but also because molecules differ in which types of secondary bonds they can form. These differences mean that a molecule will tend to move until it is next to a molecule with which it can form the strongest possible secondary bond.

Solutions of course are not static. Because of the disruptive influence of heat, the specific configuration of a solution is constantly changing from one arrangement to another of approximately the same energy content. Equally important in biological systems is the fact that metabolism is continually transforming one molecule into another and so automatically changing the nature of the secondary bonds that can be formed. The solution structure of cells is thus constantly disrupted not only by heat motion, but also by the metabolic transformations of the cell's solute molecules.

ORGANIC MOLECULES THAT TEND TO FORM HYDROGEN BONDS ARE WATER SOLUBLE

The energy of hydrogen bonds per atomic group is much stronger than that of van der Waals contacts. Thus those molecules that can form hydrogen bonds will form them in preference to van der Waals contacts. For example, if we try to mix water with a compound which cannot form hydrogen bonds, such as benzene, the water and benzene molecules rapidly separate from each other, the water molecules forming hydrogen bonds among themselves, while the benzene molecules attach to each other by van der Waals bonds. Thus it is effectively impossible to insert a non-hydrogen-bonding organic molecule into water.

On the other hand, polar molecules such as glucose and pyruvate, which contain a large number of groups that form excellent hydrogen bonds (e.g., $=O$ or $-OH$), are somewhat soluble in water (hydrophylic as opposed to hydrophobic). This effect occurs because, while the insertion of such groups into a water lattice breaks water-water hydrogen bonds, it results simultaneously in hydrogen bonds between glucose and water. These alternative arrangements, however, are not usually as energetically satisfactory as the water-water arrangements, so that even the most polar molecules ordinarily have only limited solubility.

Thus almost all the molecules which cells are constantly acquiring, either through food intake or biosynthesis, are somewhat insoluble in water. These molecules, by their thermal movements, randomly collide with other molecules until they find complementary molecular surfaces on which to attach and thereby release water molecules for water-water interactions.

THE UNIQUENESS OF MOLECULAR SHAPES; THE CONCEPT OF SELECTIVE STICKINESS

Even though most cellular molecules are built up from only a small number of groups, such as OH, NH_2, and CH_3, great specificity exists as to which molecules tend to lie next to each other. This is because each molecule has unique bonding properties. One very clear demonstration comes from the specificity of stereoisomers. For example, proteins are always constructed from L-amino acids, never from their mirror images, the D-amino acids (Figure 4–11). Though the D- and L-amino acids have identical covalent bonds, their binding properties to asymmetric molecules are often very different. Thus most enzymes are specific for L-amino acids. If an L-amino acid is able to attach to a specific enzyme, the D-amino acid is unable to bind.

The general rule exists that most molecules in cells can make good "weak" bonds with only a small number of other molecules. This is partly because all molecules in biological systems exist in an aqueous environment. The formation of a bond in a cell depends not only upon whether two molecules bind well to each other, but also upon whether the bond will permit their water solvent to form the maximum number of good hydrogen bonds.

FIGURE 4–11   *The two stereoisomers of the amino acid alanine. (Redrawn from L. Pauling, General Chemistry, 2nd ed., Freeman, San Francisco, 1958, p. 598, with permission.)*

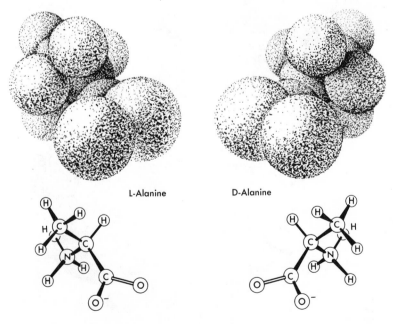

L-Alanine   D-Alanine

The strong tendency of water to exclude nonpolar groups is frequently referred to as *hydrophobic bonding*. Some chemists like to call all the bonds between nonpolar groups *in a water solution* hydrophobic bonds (Figure 4–12). In a sense this term is a confusing misnomer, for the phenomenon that it seeks to emphasize is the absence, not the presence, of bonds. (The bonds that tend to form between the nonpolar groups are due to van der Waals attractive forces.) On the other hand, the term

FIGURE 4–12   *Illustrative examples of van der Waals (hydrophobic) bonds between the nonpolar side groups of amino acids. The hydrogens are not indicated individually. For the sake of clarity, the van der Waals radii are reduced by 20 per cent. The structural formulas adjacent to each space-filling drawing indicate the arrangement of the atoms; (a) phenylalanine-leucine bond; (b) phenylalanine-phenylalanine bond. (Redrawn from H. A. Scheraga, in The Proteins, H. Neurath (ed.), 2nd ed., Vol. I, Academic Press, New York, 1963, p. 527, with permission.)*

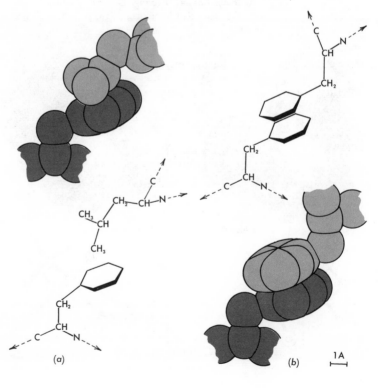

(a)   (b)   1A

hydrophobic bond is often useful, since it emphasizes the fact that nonpolar groups will try to arrange themselves so that they are not in contact with water molecules.

Consider, for example, the energy difference between the binding in water of the amino acids alanine and glycine to a third molecule which has a surface complementary to alanine. Alanine differs from glycine by the presence of one methyl group in the former. When alanine is bound to the third molecule, the van der Waals contacts around the methyl group yield 1 kcal/mole of energy, which is not released when glycine is bound instead. This small energy difference alone would give [using Eq. (4–4)] only a factor of 6 between the binding of alanine and glycine. This calculation does not take into consideration, however, the fact that water is trying to exclude alanine much more than glycine. The presence of alanine's CH_3 group upsets the water lattice much more seriously than does the hydrogen atom side group of glycine. At present it is still difficult to predict how large a correction factor must be introduced for this disruption of the water lattice by the hydrophobic side groups. A current guess is that the water tends to exclude alanine, thrusting it toward a third molecule with a hydrophobic force 2 to 3 kcal/mole larger than the force excluding glycine.

We thus arrive at the important conclusion that the energetic difference between the binding of even the most similar molecules to a third molecule (when the difference involves a nonpolar group) is at least 2 to 3 kcal/mole greater in the aqueous interior of cells than under nonaqueous conditions. Frequently, the energetic difference is 3 to 4 kcal/mole, since the molecules involved often contain polar groups which can form hydrogen bonds.

THE ADVANTAGE OF ΔG'S BETWEEN 2 AND 5 KCAL/MOLE

We have seen that the energy of just one secondary bond (2 to 5 kcal/mole) is often sufficient to ensure that a molecule preferentially binds to a selected group of molecules. Equally important, these energy differences are not so large that rigid lattice arrangements develop within a cell—the interior of a cell never crystallizes as it would if the energy of secondary bonds were several times greater. Larger energy differences would mean that the secondary bonds break only seldom, resulting in low diffusion rates incompatible with cellular existence.

WEAK BONDS ATTACH ENZYMES TO SUBSTRATES

Secondary forces are necessarily the basis by which enzymes and their substrates initially combine with each other. Enzymes do not indiscriminantly bind all molecules but, in general, have noticeable affinity only for their own substrates.

Since enzymes catalyze both directions of a chemical reaction, they must have specific affinities for both sets of reacting molecules. In some special cases it is possible to calculate an equilibrium constant for the binding of an enzyme and one of its substrates, which consequently enables us [Eq. (4–4)] to calculate the ΔG upon binding. This calculation in turn hints at which types of bonds may be involved. ΔG values ranging between 5 and 10 kcal/mole suggest that from one to several good secondary bonds are the basis of specific enzyme-substrate interactions. Also worth noting is that the ΔG of binding is never exceptionally high; thus enzyme-substrate complexes can be both made and broken apart rapidly as a result of random thermal movement. This fact explains why enzymes can function so quickly, sometimes as often as 10^6 times per second. If enzymes were bound to their substrates by more powerful bonds, they would act much more slowly.

MOST MOLECULAR SHAPES DETERMINED BY WEAK BONDS

The shapes of numerous molecules are automatically given by the distribution of covalent bonds. This inflexibility occurs when groups are attached by covalent bonds about which free rotation is impossible. Rotation is only possible when atoms are attached by single bonds. (For example, the methyl groups of ethane, $H_3C—CH_3$, rotate about the carbon-carbon bond.) When more than one electron pair is involved in a bond, rotation does not occur; in fact, the atoms involved must lie in the same plane. Thus the aromatic purine and pyrimidine rings are planar molecules 3.4 A thick. There is no uncertainty about the shape of any aromatic molecules. They are almost always flat, independent of their surrounding environment.

On the contrary, for molecules containing single bonds, the possibility of rotation around the bond suggests that a covalently bonded molecule exists in a large variety of shapes. This theoretical possibility, however, is seldom in fact realized, because the various possible 3-D configurations differ in the number of good weak bonds which can be formed. Generally, there is one configuration that has significantly less free energy than any of the other geometric arrangements.

Two classes of secondary bonds may be important in determining 3-D shapes. One class is internal, forming between atoms connected by a chain of covalent bonds. Internal bonds often cause a linear molecule to bend back upon itself, allowing contacts between atoms separated by a large number of covalent bonds. In such molecules the final shape is usually compact (globular). The other class of bonds is external, forming between atoms not connected by covalent bonds. In cases in which the optimal 3-D configuration is achieved by forming external bonds, molecules most often have extended (fibrous) configurations.

It is no simple matter to guess the correct shape of a large molecule from its covalent-bond structure; although one configuration for a protein or a nucleic acid may be energetically much more suitable than any other, we cannot yet derive it from our knowledge of bond energies. There are two reasons for this difficulty. One is purely logistical. The number of possible configurations of a nucleic acid or even a small protein molecule is immense. Given present techniques for building molecular models, a single person (or even a small group of people) cannot rapidly calculate the sum of the energies of the weak bonds for each possible configuration; years would be required. Future work using electronic computers, however, should simplify some of this task. The second reason for our present inability to derive protein and nucleic acid structures is that our knowledge about the nature of weak bonds is still very incomplete; in many cases, we are not sure about either the exact bond

energies or of the possible angles they form to each other.
Today, protein and nucleic acid shapes can be revealed only
by x-ray diffraction analysis. Fortunately these experimental
structure determinations are beginning to reveal some general
rules that tell us which weak chemical interactions are most
important in governing the molecular shapes of large molecules.
In particular, these rules emphasize the vital importance of
interactions of the macromolecules with water, by far the most
common molecule in all cells.

POLYMERIC MOLECULES ARE SOMETIMES HELICAL

Earlier we emphasized that polymeric molecules, like proteins
and nucleic acids, have regular linear backbones in which
specific groups (e.g., —CO—NH—) repeat over and over along
the molecule.

Often these regular groups are arranged in helical configurations held together by secondary bonds. The helix is a natural
conformation for regular linear polymers, since it places each
monomer group in an identical orientation within the molecule
(Figure 4–13). Each monomer thereby forms the same group of
secondary bonds as every other monomer. On the contrary,
when a regular linear polymer has a nonhelical arrangement,
different monomers must form different secondary bonds.
Clearly, an unstable state occurs if any one set of secondary
bonds is much stronger than any of the other arrangements.
Thus, helical symmetry does not evolve from the particular
shape of the monomer, but is instead the natural consequence
of the existence of a unique monomer arrangement which is
significantly more stable than all other arrangements.

It is important to remember that most biopolymers are not
regular polymers containing identical monomers. Instead they
often have irregular side groups attached to a regular backbone.
When this happens, as it does in both nucleic acids and
proteins, we need not necessarily expect a helical structure:
A 3-D arrangement that is energetically very satisfactory for the
backbone groups often produces very unsatisfactory bonding of
the side groups. The 3-D structure of many irregular polymers
is thus a compromise between the tendency of regular backbones

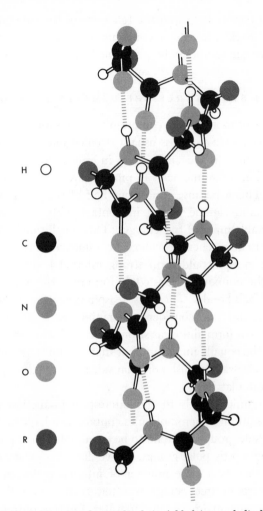

H ○

C ●

N ●

O ●

R ●

FIGURE 4–13 A polypeptide chain folded into a helical configuration called the α-helix. All the backbone atoms have
identical orientations within the molecule. It may
be looked at as a spiral staircase in which the steps are
formed by amino acids. There is an amino acid every
1.5 A along the helical axis. The distance along the
axis required for one turn is 5.4 A, giving 3.6 amino
acids per turn. The helix is held together by hydrogen bonds between the carbonyl group of one
residue and the imino group of the fourth residue
down along the chain. (Redrawn from L. Pauling,
The Nature of the Chemical Bond, 3rd ed., Cornell
Univ. Press, Ithaca, N.Y., 1960, p. 500, with permission.)

to form a regular helix and the tendency of the side groups to twist the backbone into a configuration that maximizes the strength of the secondary bonds formed by the side groups.

PROTEIN STRUCTURES ARE USUALLY IRREGULAR

In the case of proteins, the compromise between the side groups and the backbone groups is usually decided in favor of the side groups. Thus, as we shall show in much greater detail in Chapter 6, most amino acids in proteins are not part of regular helices. This is because almost one half of the side groups are nonpolar and can be placed in contact with water only by a considerable input of free energy. This conclusion was at first a surprise to many chemists, who were influenced by the fact that backbone groups could form strong internal hydrogen bonds, whereas the nonpolar groups could form only the much weaker van der Waals bonds. Their past reasoning was faulty, however, because it did not consider either the fact that the polar backbone can form almost as strong external hydrogen bonds to water, or the equally important fact that a significant amount of energy is necessary to push nonpolar side groups into a hydrogen-bonded water lattice.

This argument leads to the interesting prediction that in aqueous solutions macromolecules containing a large number of nonpolar side groups will tend to be more stable than molecules containing mostly polar groups. If we disrupt a polar molecule held together by a large number of internal hydrogen bonds, the decrease in free energy is often small, since the polar groups can then hydrogen bond to water. On the contrary, when we disrupt molecules having many nonpolar groups, there is usually a much greater loss in free energy, because the disruption necessarily inserts nonpolar groups into water.

DNA CAN FORM A REGULAR HELIX

At first glance, DNA looks even more unlikely to form a regular helix than does an irregular polypeptide chain. DNA not only has an irregular sequence of side groups, but in addition, all its side groups are hydrophobic. Both the purines (adenine and guanine) and the pyrimidines (thymine and cytosine), even though they contain polar C=O and NH$_2$ groups, are quite insoluble in water because their flat sides are completely hydrophobic.

Nonetheless, DNA molecules usually have regular helical configurations. This is because most DNA molecules contain two polynucleotide strands that have complementary structures (see Chapter 9 for more details). Both internal and external secondary bonds stabilize the structure. The two strands are held together by hydrogen bonds between pairs of complementary purines and pyrimidines (Figure 4–14). Adenine (amino) is always hydrogen bonded to thymine (keto), whereas guanine (keto) is hydrogen bonded to cytosine (amino). In addition, virtually all the surface atoms in the sugar and phosphate groups form bonds to water molecules.

The purine-pyrimidine base pairs are found in the center of the DNA molecule. This arrangement allows their flat surfaces to stack on top of each other and so limits their contact with water. This stacking arrangement would be much less satisfactory if only one chain were present. A single chain could not have a regular backbone because its pyrimidines are smaller than the purines, and so the angle of helical rotation would have to vary with the sequence of bases. The presence of complementary base pairs in double-helical DNA makes a regular structure possible, since each base pair is of the same size.

DNA MOLECULES ARE STABLE AT PHYSIOLOGICAL TEMPERATURES

The double-helical DNA molecule is very stable at physiological temperatures, for two reasons. First, disruption of the double helix breaks the regular hydrogen bonds and brings the hydrophobic purines and pyrimidines into contact with water. Second, individual DNA molecules have a *very large number of weak bonds,* arranged so that most of them cannot break without the simultaneous breaking of many others. Even though thermal motion is constantly breaking apart the terminal purine-pyrimidine pairs at the ends of each molecule, the two chains do not usually fall apart, because the hydrogen bonds in the

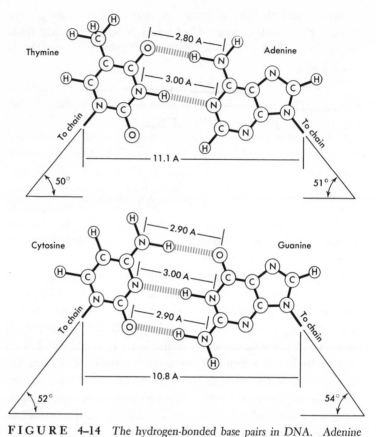

FIGURE 4-14   *The hydrogen-bonded base pairs in DNA. Adenine is always attached to thymine by two hydrogen bonds, whereas guanine always bonds to cytosine by three hydrogen bonds. The obligatory pairing of the smaller pyrimidine with the larger purine allows the two sugar-phosphate backbones to have identical helical configurations. All the hydrogen bonds in both base pairs are strong, since each hydrogen atom points directly at its acceptor atom (nitrogen or oxygen).*

middle are still intact (Figure 4-15). Once a break occurs, the most likely next event is the reforming of the same hydrogen bonds to restore the original molecular configuration. Sometimes, of course, the first breakage is followed by a second one,

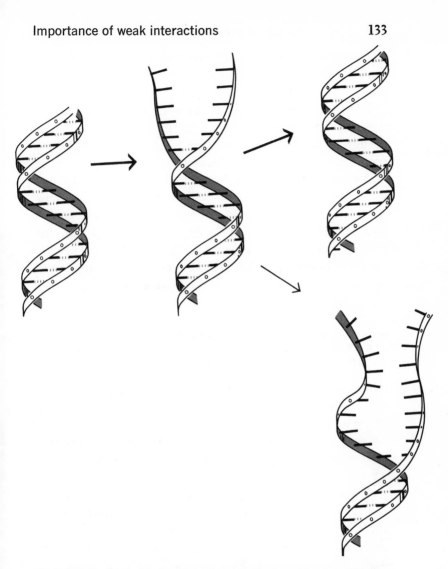

FIGURE 4-15   The breaking of terminal hydrogen bonds in DNA by random thermal motion.   Because the internal hydrogen bonds continue to hold the two chains together, the immediate reforming of the broken bonds is highly probable.   Also shown is the very rare alternative: the breaking of further hydrogen bonds, and the consequent disentangling of the chains.

and so forth. Such multiple breaks, however, are quite rare, so that double helices held together by more than ten nucleotide pairs are very stable at room temperature.

The same principle also governs the stability of most protein molecules. Stable protein shapes are never due to the presence of just one or two weak bonds, but must always represent the cooperative result of a number of weak bonds.

Ordered collections of hydrogen bonds become less and less stable as their temperature is raised above physiological temperatures. At physiologically abnormally high temperatures, the simultaneous breakage of several weak bonds is more frequent. After a significant number have broken, a molecule usually loses its original form (the process of denaturation) and assumes an inactive (denatured) configuration.

MOST MEDIUM SIZE AND ALMOST ALL LARGE PROTEIN MOLECULES ARE AGGREGATES OF SMALLER POLYPEPTIDE CHAINS

Earlier we pointed out how the realization that macromolecules are all polymers constructed from small regular monomers, such as the amino acids, greatly simplified the problem of solving macromolecule structure. It has recently become clear that most of the very large proteins are regular aggregates of much smaller polypeptide chains, containing up to 400 amino acids apiece. For example, the protein ferritin, which functions in mammals to store iron atoms, has a molecular weight of about 480,000. It contains, however, not just one long polypeptide chain of 4000 amino acids, but instead 20 identical smaller polypeptide chains of about 200 amino acids each. Similarly, the protein component of tobacco mosaic virus was originally thought to have the horrendous molecular weight of 36,000,000. Most fortunately, it was subsequently discovered (see Chapter 12) that each TMV protein contains 2150 identical smaller protein molecules, each containing 158 amino acids. Even much smaller protein molecules are frequently constructed from a number of polypeptide chains. Hemoglobin, which has a molecular weight of only 64,500, contains four polypeptide chains, 2 α chains, and 2 β chains, each of which has a molecular weight of about 16,000.

In all three examples, as with most other protein aggregates, the smaller units are held together by secondary bonds. This fact is known because they can be dispersed by the addition of reagents (e.g., urea), which tend to break secondary bonds but not covalent bonds. But weak bonds are not the only force holding macromolecular units together. In some cases, for example, the protein insulin, disulfide bonds (S—S) between cysteine residues are also a binding force.

SUBUNITS ARE ECONOMICAL

Both the construction of polymers from monomers and the use of polymeric molecules themselves as subunits to build still larger molecules reflect a general building principle applicable to all complex structures, nonliving as well as living. This principle states that it is much easier to reduce the impact of construction mistakes if we can discard them before they are incorporated into the final product. For example, let us consider two alternative ways of constructing a molecule with 1,000,000 atoms. In scheme (a) we build the structure atom by atom; in scheme (b) we first build 1000 smaller units, each with 1000 atoms, and subsequently put the subunits together into the 1,000,000-atom product. Now consider that our building process randomly makes mistakes, inserting the wrong atom with a frequency of 10^{-5}. Let us assume that each mistake results in a nonfunctional product.

Under scheme (a), each molecule will contain, on the average, 10 wrong atoms, and so almost no good products will be synthesized. Under scheme (b), however, mistakes will occur in only 1 per cent of the subunits. If there is a device to reject the bad subunits, then good products can be easily made and the cell will hardly be bothered by the presence of the 1 per cent of nonfunctional subunits. This concept is the basis of the assembly line in which complicated industrial products such as radios and automobiles are constructed. At each stage of assembly there are devices to throw away bad subunits. In industrial assembly lines, mistakes were initially removed by human hands; now automation often replaces manual control. In cells, mistakes are sometimes controlled by the specificity of enzymes: if a monomeric subunit is wrongly put together, it usually will not be recognized by the polymer-making specific enzyme, and hence not incorporated into a macromolecule. In other cases, faulty substances are rejected because they are unable spontaneously to become part of stable molecular aggregates.

THE PRINCIPLE OF SELF–ASSEMBLY

ΔG values of 1 to 5 kcal/mole mean not only that single weak bonds will be spontaneously made, but also that structures held together by several weak bonds will be spontaneously formed. For example, an unstable, unfolded polypeptide chain tends to assume a large number of random configurations as a result of thermal movements. Most of these conformations are thermodynamically unstable. Inevitably, however, thermal movements bring together groups that can form good weak bonds. These groups tend to stay together, because more free energy is lost when they form than can be regained by their breakage. Thus, by a random series of movements, the polypeptide chain gradually assumes a configuration in which most of, if not all, the atoms have fixed positions within the molecule.

Aggregation of separate molecules also occurs spontaneously. The protein hemoglobin furnishes a clear example (Figure 4–16). It can be broken apart by the addition of reagents such as urea, which break secondary bonds to yield half molecules of $MW = 32,000$. If, however, the urea is removed, the half molecules quickly aggregate to form functional hemoglobin molecules. The surface structure of the half molecules is very specific, for they bind only to each other and not with any other cellular molecules.

This same general principle of self-assembly operates to build even larger and more complicated structures, like the cell membrane and the cell wall. Both are mosaic surfaces containing large numbers of various molecules, some large, like proteins, and others much smaller, like lipids. At present, practically nothing is known about the precise arrangement of the molecules in these very large, complicated structures. Nonetheless, there is every reason to believe that the constituent molecules form stable contacts only with other molecules in the cell membrane (or wall). This situation is easy to visualize in the case of lipids, which are extremely insoluble in water because of their long, nonpolar hydrocarbon chains. Newly synthesized lipids have a stronger tendency to attach to other lipids in the cell membrane or cell wall by van der Waals forces than to enter some other more polar area, such as the aqueous (polar) interior of the cell.

FIGURE 4–16   Formation of an active hemoglobin molecule from two half molecules. Each hemoglobin molecule contains two α and two β chains. When placed in urea (a reagent which destabilizes weak bonds), the native molecule falls apart to two halves, containing two α and two β chains, respectively. Upon removal of the urea, the halves reassociate to form the complete molecule.

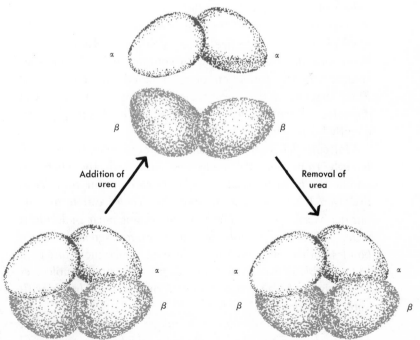

Addition of
urea

Removal of
urea

SUMMARY

Many important chemical events in cells do not involve the making or breaking of covalent bonds. The cellular location of most molecules depends on the existence of "weak" (secondary) attractive or repulsive forces. In addition, weak bonds are important in determining the shape of many molecules, especially very large ones. The most important of these "weak" forces are: hydrogen bonding, van der Waals interactions, and ionic bonds. Even though these forces are relatively weak, they are still large enough to ensure that the right molecules (groups) interact with each other. For example, the surface of an enzyme is uniquely shaped to allow specific attraction of its substrates.

The formation of all chemical bonds, weak interactions as well as strong covalent bonds, proceeds according to the laws of thermodynamics. A bond tends to form when the result would be a release of free energy (ΔG negative). In order for the bond to be broken, this same amount of free energy must be supplied. Because the formation of covalent bonds between atoms usually involves a very large negative ΔG, covalently bound atoms almost never separate spontaneously. In contrast, the ΔG values accompanying the formation of weak bonds are only several times larger than the average thermal energy of molecules at physiological temperatures. Single weak bonds are thus frequently being made and broken in living cells.

Molecules having polar (charged) groups interact quite differently from nonpolar molecules (in which the charge is symmetrically distributed). Polar molecules can form good hydrogen bonds, whereas nonpolar molecules can form only van der Waals bonds. The most important polar molecule is water. Each water molecule can form four good hydrogen bonds to other water molecules. Although polar molecules tend to be soluble in water (to various degrees), nonpolar molecules are insoluble, because they cannot form hydrogen bonds with water molecules.

Every distinct molecule has a unique molecular shape that restricts the number of molecules with which it can form good secondary bonds. Strong secondary interactions demand both a complementary (lock-and-key) relationship between the two bonding surfaces, and the involvement of many atoms. Although molecules bound together by only one or two secondary bonds frequently fall apart, a collection of these weak bonds can result in a stable aggregate. The fact that double-helical DNA never falls apart spontaneously demonstrates the extreme stability possible in such an aggregate. The formation of such aggregates can proceed spontaneously, with the correct bonds forming in a step-by-step fashion (the principle of self-assembly).

The shape of polymeric molecules is determined by secondary bonds. All biological polymers contain single bonds about which free rotation is possible. They do not, however, exist in a variety of shapes as might be expected, because the formation of one of the possible configurations generally involves a maximum decrease in free energy. This energetically preferred configuration thus is formed exclusively. Some polymeric molecules have regular helical backbones held in shape by sets of regular internal secondary bonds between backbone groups. Regular helical structures cannot be formed, however, if they place the specific side groups in positions in which they cannot form favorable weak bonds. This situation occurs in many proteins where an irregular distribution of nonpolar side groups forces the backbone into a highly irregular conformation, permitting the nonpolar groups to form van der Waals bonds with each other. Irregularly distributed side groups do not always lead, however, to nonhelical molecules. In the DNA molecule, for example, the specific pairing of purines with pyrimidines in a double-stranded helix allows the nonpolar aromatic groups to stack on top of each other in the center of the molecule.

REFERENCES

Lehninger, A. L., *Energy of the Living Cell: Molecular Basis of Energy Transformations in the Cell*, Benjamin, New York, 1965. A concise description of the laws of thermodynamics written for the beginning biology student appears in the first several chapters.

Blum, H. F., *Time's Arrow and Evolution*, Princeton University Press, Princeton, N.J., 1951. Chapter 3 provides an exceptionally clear introduction to the thermodynamics applicable to biological systems.

Klotz, I. M., *Some Principles of Energetics in Biochemical Reactions*, Academic, New York, 1957. A somewhat advanced discussion of thermodynamics as it relates to biochemical reactions.

Pauling, L., *The Nature of the Chemical Bond*, 3rd ed., Cornell University Press, Ithaca, N.Y., 1960. One of the great classics of all chemical literature; a treatment of structural chemistry with considerable emphasis on the hydrogen bond.

Haggis, G. H., D. Michie, A. R. Muir, K. B. Roberts, and P. M. B. Walker, *Introduction to Molecular Biology*, Wiley, New York, 1964. A college-level text emphasizing the relation between the structure and function of macromolecules.

5

COUPLED

REACTIONS

AND GROUP

TRANSFERS

IN THE PREVIOUS CHAPTER WE LOOKED at the formation of weak bonds from the thermodynamic viewpoint. Each time a potential weak bond was considered, the question was posed, "Does its formation involve a gain or a loss of free energy?", because only when ΔG is negative does the thermodynamic equilibrium favor a reaction. This same approach holds with equal validity for covalent bonds. The fact that enzymes are usually involved in the making or breaking of a covalent bond does not in any sense alter the requirement of a negative ΔG.

On superficial examination, however, many of the important covalent bonds in cells appear to be formed in violation of the laws of thermodynamics, particularly those bonds joining small molecules together to form large polymeric molecules. The formation of such bonds involves an increase in free energy. Originally this fact suggested to some people that cells had the unique property of working somehow in violation of thermodynamics, and that this property was, in fact, the real "secret of life."

Now, however, it is clear that these biosynthetic processes do not violate thermodynamics but, instead, that they are based upon different reactions from those originally postulated. Nucleic acids, for example, do not form by the condensation of nucleoside phosphates; glycogen is not formed directly from glucose residues; proteins are not formed by the union of amino acids. Instead, the monomeric precursors, using energy present in ATP, are first converted to high-energy "activated" precursors, which then spontaneously (with the help of specific enzymes) unite to form larger molecules. In this chapter we shall illustrate these ideas by concentrating on the thermodynamics of peptide (protein) and phosphodiester (nucleic acid) bonds. First, however, we must briefly look at some general thermodynamic properties of covalent bonds.

FOOD MOLECULES ARE THERMODYNAMICALLY UNSTABLE

There is great variation in the amount of free energy possessed by specific molecules. This is a consequence of the fact that all covalent bonds do not have the same bond energy. As an example, the covalent bond between oxygen and hydrogen is considerably stronger than the bonds between hydrogen and hydrogen or oxygen and oxygen. The formation of an O—H bond at the expense of O—O or H—H will thus release energy. Energetic considerations tell us that a sufficiently concentrated mixture of oxygen and hydrogen will be transformed into water. A molecule thus possesses a larger amount of free energy if linked together by weak covalent bonds than if it is linked together by strong bonds. This idea seems almost paradoxical at first glance, since it means that the stronger the bond the less energy it can give off. But the notion automatically makes sense when we realize that an atom that has formed a very strong bond has already lost a large amount of free energy in this process. Therefore, the best food molecules (molecules which donate energy) are those molecules that contain weak covalent bonds and are, thereby, thermodynamically unstable.

For example, glucose is an excellent food molecule, since there is a great decrease in free energy when it is oxidized by O_2 to yield CO_2 and H_2O. On the contrary, CO_2 is not a food molecule in animals, since, in the absence of the energy donor ATP, it cannot spontaneously be transformed to more complex organic molecules even with the help of specific enzymes. CO_2

can be used as a primary source of carbon in plants only because the energy supplied by light quanta during photosynthesis results in the formation of ATP.

DISTINCTION BETWEEN DIRECTION AND RATE OF A REACTION

The chemical reactions by which molecules are transformed into other molecules which contain less free energy do not occur at significant rates at physiological temperatures in the absence of a catalyst. This is because even a "weak covalent bond" is, in reality, very strong and is only rarely broken by thermal motion within a cell. In order for a covalent bond to be broken in the absence of a catalyst, energy must be supplied to push apart the bonded atoms. When the atoms are partially apart, they can recombine with new partners to form stronger bonds. In the process of recombination, the energy released is the sum of the free energy supplied to break the old bond plus the difference in free energy between the old and the new bond (Figure 5–1).

The energy that must be supplied to break the old covalent

FIGURE 5–1   *The energy of activation of a chemical reaction* (A–B) + (C–D) → (A–D) + (C–B).

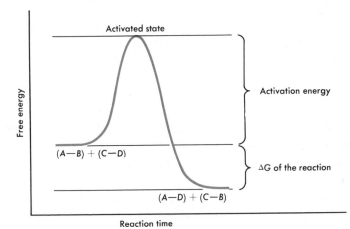

bond in a molecular transformation is called the *activation energy*. The activation energy is usually less than the energy of the original bond because molecular rearrangements, generally do not involve the production of completely free atoms. Instead, a collision between the two reacting molecules is required, followed by the temporary formation of a molecular complex (the *activated state*). In the activated state, the close proximity of the two molecules labilizes each other's bonds, so that less energy is needed to break a bond than when the bond is present in a free molecule.

Most reactions of covalent bonds in cells are, therefore, described by

$$A\text{-}B + C\text{-}D \rightarrow A\text{-}D + C\text{-}B - \Delta G \tag{5-1}$$

The mass action expression for such reaction is

$$K_{eq} = \frac{conc^{A-D} \times conc^{C-B}}{conc^{A-B} \times conc^{C-D}} \tag{5-2}$$

where $conc^{A-B}$, $conc^{C-D}$, etc., are the concentrations of the several reactants in moles per liter. Here also, the value of K_{eq} is related to ΔG by Eq. (4-4).

Since energies of activation are generally between 20 and 30 kcal/mole, activated states practically never occur at physiological temperatures. High activation energies should thus be considered barriers preventing spontaneous rearrangements of cellular covalent bonds.

These barriers are enormously important. Life would be impossible if they did not exist, for all atoms would be in the state of least possible energy. There would be no way to temporarily store energy for future work. On the other hand, life would also be impossible if means were not found to selectively lower the activation energies of certain specific reactions. This also must happen if cell growth is to occur at a rate sufficiently fast so as not to be seriously impeded by random destructive forces, such as ionizing or ultraviolet radiation.

ENZYMES LOWER ACTIVATION ENERGIES

Enzymes are absolutely necessary for life because they lower activation energies. The function of enzymes is to speed up the rate of the chemical reactions requisite to cellular existence by lowering the activation energies of molecular rearrangements to values that can be supplied by the heat of motion. When a specific enzyme is present, there is no longer an effective barrier preventing the rapid formation of the reactants possessing the lowest amounts of free energy. Enzymes never affect the nature of an equilibrium: They merely speed up the rate at which it is reached. Thus, if the thermodynamic equilibrium is unfavorable for the formation of a molecule, the presence of an enzyme can in no way bring about its accumulation.

The need for enzymes to catalyze essentially every cellular molecular rearrangement means that knowledge of the free energy of various molecules cannot by itself tell us whether an energetically feasible rearrangement will, in fact, occur. The rate of the reactions must always be considered. Only if a cell possesses a suitable enzyme will the corresponding reaction be important.

A METABOLIC PATHWAY IS CHARACTERIZED BY A DECREASE IN FREE ENERGY

Thermodynamics tells us that all biochemical pathways must be characterized by a decrease in free energy. This is obviously the case for degradative pathways, in which thermodynamically unstable food molecules are converted to more stable compounds, such as CO_2 and H_2O, with the evolution of heat. All degradative pathways have two primary purposes: (1) to produce the small organic fragments necessary as building blocks for larger organic molecules, and (2) to conserve a significant fraction of the free energy of the original food molecule in a form that can do work, by coupling some of the steps in degradative pathways with the simultaneous formation of molecules that can store free energy (high-energy molecules).

Not all the free energy of a food molecule is converted into the free energy of high-energy molecules. If this were the case, a degradative pathway would not be characterized by a decrease in free energy. No driving force would exist to favor the breakdown of food molecules. Instead, we find that all degradative pathways are characterized by a conversion of at least one-half the free energy of the food molecule into heat or entropy. For example, it is now believed that, in cells, approximately 40 per cent of the free energy of glucose is used to make new high-energy compounds, the remainder being dissipated into heat energy and entropy.

HIGH–ENERGY BONDS HYDROLYZE WITH LARGE NEGATIVE ΔG'S

A high-energy molecule contains a bond(s) whose breakdown by water (hydrolysis) is accompanied by a large decrease in free energy (5 kcal/mole or more). The specific bonds whose hydrolysis yields these large negative ΔG's are called high-energy bonds. Both these terms are, in a real sense, misleading, since it is not the bond energy but the free energy of hydrolysis that is high. Nonetheless, the term high-energy bond is generally employed, and, for convenience, we shall continue this usage by marking high-energy bonds with the symbol ~.

The energy of hydrolysis of the average high-energy bond (7 kcal/mole) is very much smaller than the amount of energy that would be released if a glucose molecule were to be completely degraded in one step (688 kcal/mole). A one-step breakdown of glucose would be inefficient in making high-energy bonds. This is undoubtedly the reason why biological glucose degradation requires so many steps. In this way, the amount of energy released per degradative step is of the same order of magnitude as the free energy of hydrolysis of a high-energy bond.

The most important high-energy compound is ATP. It is formed from inorganic phosphate ℗ and ADP, using energy obtained either from degradative reactions (some of which are shown in Chapters 2 and 3) or from the sun (photosynthesis). There are, however, many other important high-energy compounds. Some are directly formed during degradative reactions;

others are formed using some of the free energy of ATP. Table 5–1 lists the most important types of high-energy bonds. All involve either phosphate or sulfur atoms. The high-energy pyrophosphate bonds of ATP arise from the union of phosphate

T A B L E 5–1 *Important classes of high-energy bonds*

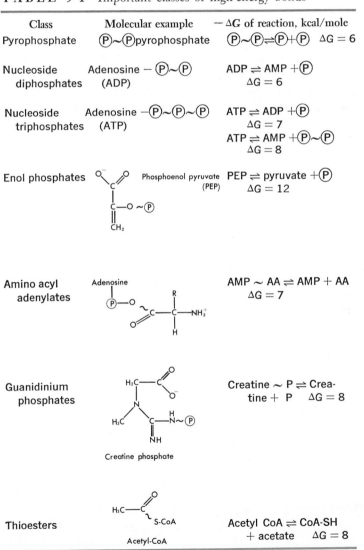

Class	Molecular example	$-\Delta G$ of reaction, kcal/mole
Pyrophosphate	Ⓟ~Ⓟpyrophosphate	Ⓟ~Ⓟ⇌Ⓟ+Ⓟ ΔG = 6
Nucleoside diphosphates	Adenosine − Ⓟ~Ⓟ (ADP)	ADP ⇌ AMP +Ⓟ ΔG = 6
Nucleoside triphosphates	Adenosine −Ⓟ~Ⓟ~Ⓟ (ATP)	ATP ⇌ ADP +Ⓟ ΔG = 7 ATP ⇌ AMP +Ⓟ~Ⓟ ΔG = 8
Enol phosphates	Phosphoenol pyruvate (PEP)	PEP ⇌ pyruvate +Ⓟ ΔG = 12
Amino acyl adenylates	Adenosine	AMP ~ AA ⇌ AMP + AA ΔG = 7
Guanidinium phosphates	Creatine phosphate	Creatine ~ P ⇌ Creatine + P ΔG = 8
Thioesters	Acetyl-CoA	Acetyl CoA ⇌ CoA-SH + acetate ΔG = 8

groups. The pyrophosphate linkage (Ⓟ~Ⓟ) is not, however, the only kind of high-energy phosphate bond: The attachment of a phosphate group to the oxygen atom of a carboxyl group creates a high-energy acyl bond. It is now clear that high-energy bonds involving sulfur atoms play almost as important a role in energy metabolism as those involving phosphorus. The most important molecule containing a high-energy sulfur bond is acetyl-CoA. This bond is the main source of energy for fatty acid biosynthesis.

The wide range of ΔG values of high-energy bonds (Table 5–1) means that calling a bond "high-energy" is sometimes arbitrary. The usual criterion is whether its hydrolysis can be coupled with another reaction to effect an important biosynthesis. For example, the negative ΔG accompanying the hydrolysis of glucose-6-Ⓟ is 3 to 4 kcal/mole. This ΔG is not sufficient for efficient synthesis of peptide bonds, for example, so this phosphate ester bond is not included among high-energy bonds.

HIGH–ENERGY BONDS NECESSARY FOR BIOSYNTHETIC REACTIONS

Often the construction of a large molecule from smaller building blocks requires the input of free energy. Yet a biosynthetic pathway, like a degradative pathway, would not exist if it were not characterized by a net decrease in free energy. This means that many biosynthetic pathways demand the existence of an external source of free energy. These free-energy sources are the "high-energy compounds." The making of many biosynthetic bonds is coupled with the breakdown of a high-energy bond, so that the net change of free energy is always negative. High-energy bonds in cells, therefore, generally have a very short life. Almost as soon as they are formed during a degradative reaction, they are enzymatically broken down to yield the energy needed to drive another reaction to completion.

Not all the steps in a biosynthetic pathway require the breakdown of a high-energy bond. Often only one or two steps involve such a bond. Sometimes this is because the ΔG, even in the absence of an externally added high-energy bond, favors the biosynthetic direction. In other cases, ΔG is effectively zero, or in some cases may even be slightly positive. These small positive ΔG's, however, are not significant so long as they are followed by a reaction characterized by the hydrolysis of a high-energy bond. Instead, it is the *sum* of all the free-energy changes in a pathway that is significant. It does not really matter that the K_{eq} of a specific biosynthetic step is slightly (80:20) in favor of degradation, if the K_{eq} of the succeeding step is 100:1 in favor of the forward biosynthetic direction.

Likewise, not all the steps in a degradative pathway generate high-energy bonds. For example, only two steps in the lengthy glycolytic (Embden-Meyerhof) breakdown of glucose generate ATP. Moreover, there are many degradative pathways that have one or more steps requiring the breakdown of a high-energy bond. The glycolytic breakdown of glucose is again an example. It uses up two molecules of ATP for every four that it generates. Here, of course, as in every energy-yielding degradative process, more high-energy bonds must be made than consumed.

PEPTIDE BONDS HYDROLYZE SPONTANEOUSLY

The formation of a dipeptide and a water molecule from two amino acids requires a ΔG of 1 to 4 kcal/mole, depending upon which amino acids are being bound. This ΔG value decreases progressively if amino acids are added to longer polypeptide chains; for an infinitely long chain the ΔG is reduced to ~ 0.5 kcal/mole. This decrease reflects the fact that the free, charged NH_3^+ and COO^- groups at the chain ends favor the hydrolysis (breakdown accompanied by the uptake of a water molecule) of nearby peptide bonds.

These positive ΔG values by themselves tell us that polypeptide chains cannot form from free amino acids. In addition, we must take into account the fact that water molecules have a much, much higher concentration (generally > 100) than any other cellular molecules. All equilibrium reactions in which water participates are thus strongly pushed in the direction that consumes water molecules. This is easily seen in the definition of equilibrium constants. For example, the reaction forming a dipeptide,

amino acid(a) + amino acid(b) → dipeptide(a-b) + H_2O (5–3)

has the following equilibrium constant:

$$K_{eq} = \frac{\text{conc } (a) \times \text{conc } (b)}{\text{conc } (a\text{-}b) \times \text{conc } (H_2O)}$$ (5–4)

where concentrations are given in moles/liter. Thus, for a given K_{eq} value (related to ΔG by the formula $\Delta G = -RT \ln K$) a much greater concentration of H_2O means a correspondingly smaller concentration of the dipeptide. The relative concentrations are, therefore, very important. In fact, a simple calculation shows that hydrolysis may often proceed spontaneously even when the ΔG for the nonhydrolytic reaction is -3 kcal/mole.

Thus, in theory, proteins are unstable and, given sufficient time, will spontaneously degrade to free amino acids. On the other hand, in the absence of specific enzymes, these spontaneous rates are too slow to have a significant effect on cellular metabolism. That is, once a protein is made, it remains stable unless its degradation is catalyzed by a specific enzyme.

COUPLING OF NEGATIVE WITH POSITIVE ΔG

Free energy must be added to amino acids before they can be united to form proteins. How this could happen became clear with the discovery of the fundamental role of ATP as an energy donor. ATP contains three phosphate groups attached to an adenosine molecule (adenosine—O—Ⓟ~Ⓟ~Ⓟ). When one or two of the terminal ~Ⓟ groups are broken off by hydrolysis, there is a significant decrease of free energy.

adenosine − O − Ⓟ ~ Ⓟ ~ Ⓟ + H_2O →
(ATP)
　　　adenosine − O − Ⓟ ~ Ⓟ + Ⓟ   ($\Delta G = -7$ kcal/mole)   (5–5)
　　　(ADP)

adenosine — O — (P) ～(P) ～(P) + H₂O →
(ATP)
    adenosine — O — (P) + (P) ～(P)   ($\Delta G = -8$ kcal/mole)   (5-6)
    (AMP)

adenosine — O — (P) ～(P) + H₂O →
(ADP)
    adenosine — O — (P) + (P)   ($\Delta G = -6$ kcal/mole)   (5-7)
    (AMP)

All these breakdown reactions have negative ΔG values considerably greater in absolute value (numerical value without regard to sign) than the positive ΔG values accompanying the formation of polymeric molecules from their monomeric building blocks. The essential trick underlying those biosynthetic reactions, which by themselves have a positive ΔG, is that they are coupled with breakdown reactions characterized by negative ΔG of greater absolute value. Thus, during protein synthesis, the formation of each peptide bond ($\Delta G = +0.5$ kcal/mole) is coupled with the breakdown of ATP to AMP and pyrophosphate, which has a ΔG of -8 kcal/mole. This results in a net ΔG of -7.5 kcal/mole, more than sufficient to ensure that the equilibrium favors protein synthesis rather than breakdown.

ACTIVATION THROUGH GROUP TRANSFER

When ATP is hydrolyzed to ADP and (P), most of the free energy is liberated as heat. Since heat energy cannot be used to make covalent bonds, a coupled reaction cannot be the result of two completely separate reactions, one with a positive, the other with a negative, ΔG. Instead, a coupled reaction is achieved by two or more successive reactions. These are always *group-transfer* reactions: reactions not involving oxidations or reductions, in which molecules exchange functional groups. The enzymes that catalyze these reactions are called transferases.

A-X + B-Y → A-B + X-Y   (5-8)

In this example, groups X and Y are exchanged with components A and B. Group-transfer reactions are arbitrarily defined to exclude H_2O as a participant. When H_2O is involved,

A-B + H-OH → A-OH + BH   (5-9)

the reaction is called a hydrolysis, and the enzymes involved, hydrolases.

The group-transfer reactions which interest us here are those involving groups attached by high-energy bonds (high-energy groups). When a high-energy group is transferred to an appropriate acceptor molecule, it becomes attached to the acceptor by a high-energy bond. Group transfer thus allows the transfer of high-energy bonds from one molecule to another. For example, Eqs. (5–10) and (5–11) show how energy present in ATP is transferred to form GTP, one of the precursors used in RNA synthesis:

adenosine — (P)~(P)~(P)+ guanosine — (P)→
　(ATP)　　　　　　　　　　　(GMP)

　　　　　adenosine — (P)~(P)+ guanosine — (P)~(P)　　(5–10)
　　　　　　(ADP)　　　　　　　　　(GDP)

adenosine — (P)~(P)~(P)+ guanosine — (P)~(P)→
　(ATP)　　　　　　　　　　　(GDP)

　　　　　adenosine — (P)~(P)+ guanosine — (P)~(P)~(P)　　(5–11)
　　　　　　(ADP)　　　　　　　　　(GTP)

The high-energy (P)~(P) group on GTP allows it to unite spontaneously with another molecule. GTP is thus an example of what is called an *activated molecule*; correspondingly, the process of transferring a high-energy group is called *group activation*.

ATP VERSATILITY IN GROUP TRANSFER

In Chapter 2 we emphasized the key role of ATP synthesis in the controlled trapping of the energy of food molecules. In both oxidative and photosynthetic phosphorylations, energy is used to synthesize ATP from ADP and P:

adenosine — (P)~(P)+(P)+ energy → adenosine — (P)~(P)~(P)　　(5–12)

Since ATP is, thus, the original biological recipient of high-energy groups, it must be the starting point of a variety of reactions in which high-energy groups are transferred to low-energy molecules to give them the potential to react spontaneously. ATP's central role utilizes the fact that it contains two high-energy bonds whose splitting releases specific groups. This is shown in Figure 5–2, which shows three important groups arising from ATP: (1) Ⓟ~Ⓟ, a pyrophosphate group, (2) ~AMP, an adenosyl monophosphate group, and (3) ~Ⓟ, a phosphate group. It is important to notice that these high-energy groups retain their high-energy quality only when transferred to an appropriate acceptor molecule. For example, although the transfer of a ~Ⓟ group to a COO⁻ group yields a high-energy COO~Ⓟ acyl-phosphate group, the transfer of the same group to a sugar hydroxyl group (—C—OH), as for example in the formation of glucose-6-Ⓟ, gives rise to a low-energy bond (<5 kcal/mole decrease in ΔG upon hydrolysis).

FIGURE 5–2   *Important group transfers involving ATP.*

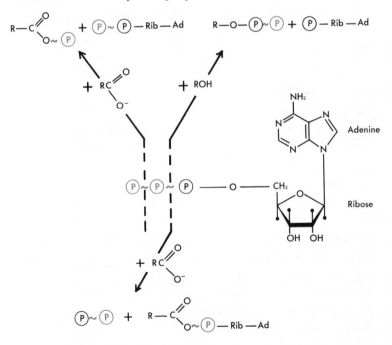

ACTIVATION OF AMINO ACIDS
BY ATTACHMENT OF AMP

The activation of an amino acid is achieved by transfer of an AMP group from ATP to the COO⁻ group of the amino acid:

$$
\begin{array}{c}
\text{H} \quad \text{R} \quad \quad \text{O} \\
| \quad \quad | \quad \quad \quad \diagup \\
\text{H}-\text{N}^+-\text{C}-\text{C} \quad + \text{ adenosine} - \text{(P)} \sim \text{(P)} \sim \text{(P)} \rightarrow \\
| \quad \quad | \quad \quad \quad \diagdown \\
\text{H} \quad \text{H} \quad \quad \text{O}^-
\end{array}
\quad
\begin{array}{c}
\text{H} \quad \text{R} \quad \quad \text{O} \\
| \quad \quad | \quad \quad \quad \diagup \\
\text{H}-\text{N}^+-\text{C}-\text{C} \\
| \quad \quad | \quad \quad \quad \diagdown \\
\text{H} \quad \text{H} \quad \quad \text{O} \sim \text{(P)} = \text{adenosine}
\end{array}
\quad \text{(5–13)}
$$

(R represents the specific side group of the amino acid.) The specific enzymes that catalyze this type of reaction are called amino acid-synthetases. Upon activation, an amino acid is thermodynamically capable of being efficiently used for protein synthesis. Nonetheless, the AA~AMP complexes are not the direct precursors of proteins. Instead, for a reason which we shall explain in Chapter 11, a second group transfer must occur to transfer the amino acid, still activated at its carboxyl group, to the end of an sRNA molecule:

AA ~ AMP + sRNA → AA ~ sRNA + AMP   (5–14)

A peptide bond then forms by the condensation of the AA~ sRNA molecule onto the end of a growing polypeptide chain:

AA ~ sRNA + growing polypeptide chain (of *n* amino acids) →

    sRNA + growing polypeptide chain (of *n* +1 amino acids)   (5–15)

Thus the final step of this "coupled reaction," like that of all other coupled reactions, necessarily involves the removal of the activating group and the conversion of a high-energy bond into one with a lower free energy of hydrolysis. This is the source of the negative ΔG which drives the reaction in the direction of protein synthesis.

NUCLEIC ACID PRECURSORS ACTIVATED BY PRESENCE OF (P)~(P)

Both types of nucleic acid, DNA and RNA, are built up of mononucleotide monomers (nucleoside (P)). Mononucleotides, however, are thermodynamically even less likely to combine than amino acids. This is because the phosphodiester bonds which link the former together release considerable free energy upon hydrolysis (−6 kcal/mole). This means that nucleic acids will spontaneously hydrolyze, at a slow rate, to mononucleotides. Thus it is even more important that activated precursors be used in their synthesis than in that of proteins.

Recently it has been found that the immediate precursors for both DNA and RNA are the nucleoside-5'-triphosphates. For DNA these are dATP, dGTP, dCTP, and dTTP (d stands for deoxy); for RNA the precursors are ATP, GTP, CTP, and UTP. ATP thus not only serves as the main source of high-energy groups in group-transfer reactions, but in addition is itself a direct precursor for RNA. The other three RNA precursors all arise by group-transfer reactions like those described in Eqs. (6–10) and (6–11). The deoxytriphosphates are formed in basically the same way: After the deoxymononucleotides have been synthesized, they are transformed to the triphosphate form by group transfer from ATP:

deoxynucleoside− (P)+ ATP → deoxynucleoside− (P)~(P)+ ADP   (5–16)

deoxynucleoside− (P)~(P)+ ATP → deoxynucleoside− (P)~(P)~(P)+ ADP
                                                                    (5–17)

These triphosphates can then unite to form polynucleotides held together by phosphodiester bonds. In this process (a group-transfer reaction), a pyrophosphate bond is broken and a pyrophosphate group released:

deoxynucleoside− (P)~(P)~(P)+ growing polynucleotide chain (of n nucleotides)

   → (P)~(P)+ growing polynucleotide chain (n +1 nucleotides)   (5–18)

This reaction, unlike that which forms peptide bonds, does not have a negative ΔG. In fact, the ΔG is slightly positive (~0.5

kcal/mole). This immediately poses the question, since poly-nucleotides obviously form: What is the source of the necessary free energy?

VALUE OF Ⓟ~Ⓟ RELEASE IN NUCLEIC ACID SYNTHESIS

The needed free energy arises from the splitting of the high-energy pyrophosphate group which is formed simultaneously with the high-energy phosphodiester bond. All cells contain a powerful enzyme, pyrophosphatase, which breaks down pyro-phosphate molecules almost as soon as they are formed:

$$Ⓟ~Ⓟ \rightarrow 2\,Ⓟ \quad (\Delta G = -7 \text{ kcal/mole}) \tag{5–19}$$

The large negative ΔG means that the reaction is effectively irreversible: This means that once Ⓟ~Ⓟ is broken down it never reforms.

The union of the nucleoside monophosphate group [Eq. (5–16)], coupled with the splitting of the pyrophosphate groups [Eq. (5–19)], has an equilibrium constant determined by the combined ΔG values of the two reactions: (0.5 kcal/mole) + (−7 kcal/mole). The resulting value ($\Delta G = -6.5$ kcal/mole) tells us that nucleic acids almost never break down to reform their nucleoside triphosphate precursors.

Here we see a powerful example of the fact that often it is the free-energy change accompanying a *group of reactions* that determines whether a reaction in the group will take place. Reactions with small, positive ΔG values, which by themselves would never take place, are often part of important metabolic pathways in which they are followed by reactions with large negative ΔG's. At all times we must remember that a single reaction (or even a single pathway) never occurs in isolation, but rather that the nature of the equilibrium is constantly being changed through the addition and through the removal of me-tabolites.

℗~℗ SPLITS CHARACTERIZE MOST BIOSYNTHETIC REACTIONS

The synthesis of nucleic acids is not the only reaction where direction is determined by the release and splitting of ℗~℗. In fact, the generalization is emerging that essentially all biosynthetic reactions are characterized by one or more steps that release pyrophosphate groups. Consider, for example, the activation of an amino acid by the attachment of AMP. By itself, the transfer of a high-energy bond from ATP to the AA~AMP complex has a slightly positive ΔG. Therefore, it is the release and splitting of ATP's terminal pyrophosphate group that provides the negative ΔG that are necessary to drive the reaction.

The great utility of the pyrophosphate split is neatly demonstrated by considering the problems that would arise if a cell attempted to synthesize nucleic acid from nucleoside diphosphates rather than triphosphates. Phosphate, rather than pyrophosphate, would be liberated as the backbone phosphodiester linkages were made. The phosphodiester linkages, however, are not stable in the presence of significant quantities of phosphate, since they are formed without a significant release of free energy. Thus, the biosynthetic reaction would be easily reversible; as soon as phosphate began to accumulate, the reaction would begin to move in the direction of nucleic acid breakdown (mass action law). Moreover, it is not possible for a cell to remove the phosphate groups as soon as they are generated (thus preventing this reverse reaction), since all cells need a significant internal level of phosphate in order to grow. Thus the use of nucleoside triphosphates as precursors of nucleic acids is not a matter of chance.

This same type of argument tells us why ATP, and not ADP, is the key donor of high-energy groups in all cells. At first this preference seemed arbitrary to biochemists. Now, however, we see that many reactions using ADP as an energy donor would occur equally well in both directions.

SUMMARY

The biosynthesis of many molecules appears, at a superficial glance, to violate the thermodynamic law that spontaneous reactions always involve a decrease in free energy (ΔG is negative). For example, the formation of proteins from amino acids has a positive ΔG. This paradox is removed when we realize that the biosynthetic reactions do not proceed as initially postulated. Proteins, for example, are not formed from free amino acids. Instead, the precursors are first enzymatically converted to high-energy activated molecules, which, in the presence of a specific enzyme, spontaneously unite to form the desired biosynthetic product.

Many biosynthetic processes are thus the result of "coupled" reactions, the first of which supplies the energy that allows the spontaneous occurrence of the second reaction. The primary energy source in cells is ATP. It is formed from ADP and inorganic phosphate, either during degradative reactions (e.g., fermentation or respiration) or during photosynthesis. ATP contains several (high-energy) bonds whose hydrolysis has a large negative ΔG. Groups linked by high-energy bonds are called high-energy groups. High-energy groups can be transferred to other molecules by group-transfer reactions, thereby creating new high-energy compounds. These derivative high-energy molecules are then the immediate precursors for many biosynthetic steps.

Amino acids are activated by the addition of an AMP group, originating from ATP, to form an AA $\sim$ AMP molecule. The energy of the high-energy bond in the AA $\sim$ AMP molecule is similar to that of a high-energy bond of ATP. Nonetheless, the group-transfer reaction proceeds to completion because the high-energy ⓟ$\sim$ⓟ molecule, created when the AA$\sim$AMP molecule is formed, is broken down by the enzyme pyrophosphatase to low-energy groups. Thus, the reverse reaction, ⓟ$\sim$ⓟ + AA $\sim$ AMP $\rightarrow$ ATP + AA, cannot occur.

The general rule exists that ⓟ$\sim$ⓟ is released in almost all biosynthetic reactions. Almost as soon as it is made, it is enzymatically broken down to 2ⓟ, thereby making impossible a *reversal of the biosynthetic reaction. The great utility of the* Ⓟ~Ⓟ *split provides an explanation for why ATP, not ADP, is the primary energy donor. ADP cannot transfer a high-energy group and, at the same time, produce* Ⓟ~Ⓟ *groups as a by-product.*

REFERENCES

Lehninger, A. L., *Energy of the Living Cell: Molecular Basis of Energy Transformations in the Cell*, Benjamin, New York, 1965. This book contains an expanded description of high-energy bonds and their use in biosynthetic reactions.

Karlson, P., *Introduction to Modern Biochemistry*, Academic, New York, 1963. A medium-sized introduction to biochemistry with emphasis on intermediary metabolism.

Fruton, J. S., and S. Simmonds, *General Biochemistry*, 2nd ed., Wiley, New York, 1958. A very thorough description of biochemistry up to 1958.

White, A., P. Handler, and E. L. Smith, *Principles of Biochemistry*, 3rd ed., McGraw-Hill, New York, 1964. An admirable survey of cell biochemistry, strongest in its emphasis on intermediary metabolism.

Krebs, H. A., and H. L. Kornberg, "A Survey of the Energy Transformation in Living Material," *Ergeb. Physiol. Biol. Chem. Exptl. Pharmakol.,* **49,** 212 (1957). This comprehensive review is one of the few classics in biochemistry. Though many of its facts have been modified by subsequent research, it can still be used with great profit.

Kornberg, A., "On the Metabolic Significance of Phosphorolytic and Pyrophosphorolytic Reactions," in M. Kasha and B. Pullman (eds.), *Horizons in Biochemistry*, pp. 251–264, Academic, New York, 1962. In this short article are found some detailed arguments about the importance of the release of pyrophosphate.

6

THE CONCEPT

OF TEMPLATE

SURFACES

BY NOW OUR CHEMIST KNOWS THAT there are several "key secrets of life" upon which the ability of a cell to grow and divide depends. First, there must exist a highly organized surface membrane capable of maintaining, through selective permeability, a high concentration of internal molecules. Second, enzymes that catalyze the movement of the atoms from food molecules into new cellular building blocks must exist. Third, useful energy must be derived from food molecules or the sun to ensure that the thermodynamic equilibria favor biosynthetic rather than degradative reactions.

All these properties depend intimately upon the existence of proteins. Only these very large molecules with their 20 different building blocks possess sufficient specificity to build selectively permeable membranes or to catalyze highly specific chemical transformations. We must thus add to the list of key secrets of life the ability to synthesize the physiologically correct amounts of specific proteins. This requirement at first might seem to fall under the more general prerequisite of enzyme-catalyzed biosynthesis. But as we shall soon learn, the synthesis of a protein does not proceed according to rules governing the synthesis of small molecules. This point becomes clear when we look at the way enzymes are used to construct increasingly larger molecules.

160

SYNTHESIS OF SMALL MOLECULES

Let us first look at how the amino acid serine is normally put together in *E. coli* cells growing upon glucose as their sole energy and carbon source. Figure 6–1 illustrates how serine is formed in three steps from 3-phosphoglyceric acid, a key metabolite in the normal degradation of glucose (Figure 2–6). Serine can be further broken down in several more steps (whose exact chemistry has yet to be worked out) to give the simplest amino acid glycine. Each of these steps requires a specific enzyme with a characteristic surface capable of combining only with its correct substrate. Each of the other 18 amino acids is synthesized according to the same principle. In every case a metabolite derived from glucose serves as the starting point for a series of specific enzymatically mediated reactions leading finally to an amino acid. Likewise, the purine and pyrimidine nucleotides, the building blocks from which the nucleic acids DNA and RNA are constructed, are synthesized by a series of consecutive reactions starting with smaller molecular units whose carbon atoms are derived from glucose molecules.

Some of the reactions leading to the synthesis of the pyrimidine nucleotide, uridine-5'-phosphate, are seen in Figure 6–2. The synthesis of the larger purine nucleotides requires more steps, since more covalent bonds must be built. Again, however, the same basic principles govern: (1) each reaction requires a different specific enzyme and (2) the sum of the reactions results in a release of free energy.

This energy release (usually as heat) means that the thermodynamic equilibrium favors the generation of the biosynthetic reaction products necessary for cell growth. It is often accomplished by having one of the substrates react with the energy-rich molecule ATP to form an activated substrate in which a phosphate ($\sim$ⓟ), pyrophosphate ($\sim$ⓟ$\sim$ⓟ), or adenylic acid ($\sim$AMP) group is attached to an atom involved in the formation of the desired biosynthetic bond. A typical ATP-driven synthesis is the transformation of ribose-5-ⓟ into 5-phosphoribosylamine (PRA) (Figure 6–3). This transformation, one of the initial steps in purine nucleotide formation, occurs in two enzymatic steps. In the first, ribose-5-$\textcircled{P}$ and ATP combine to form ADP and 5-phosphoribosylpyrophosphate (PRPP). The second step involves the reaction of PRPP with glutamine to yield PRA, $\textcircled{P}\sim\textcircled{P}$, and glutamic acid. The equilibrium of the

FIGURE 6–1 *Serine biosynthesis.*

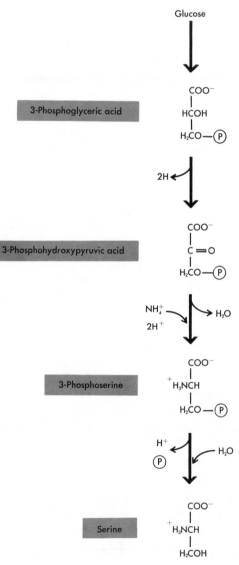

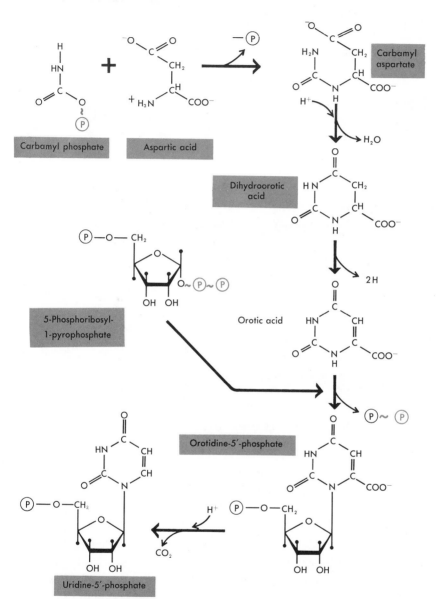

FIGURE 6-2 *The biosynthesis of uridine-5-phosphate.*

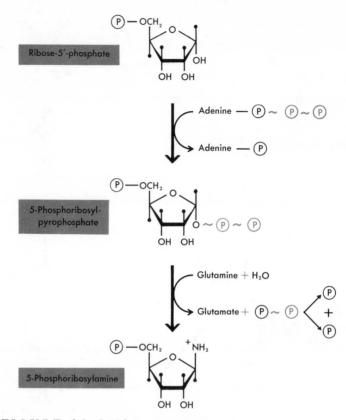

FIGURE 6–3 *Initial steps in purine formation.*

first reaction favors PRPP synthesis because there is more energy in an ATP-pyrophosphate bond than in the phosphate ester (C—O—Ⓟ) bond attaching Ⓟ~Ⓟ to ribose-5-Ⓟ. Likewise, the second equilibrium favors PRA formation because the Ⓟ~Ⓟ product is broken down by pyrophosphatase to 2Ⓟ.

Both biosynthetic steps are thus accompanied by the release of energy as heat. In contrast there is little energy difference between the initial C—O bond of ribose-5-Ⓟ and the final C—N linkage. Hence, activation by an energy donor is a necessary prerequisite for this biosynthetic step. Activation is not, however, an obligatory feature of all biosyntheses. Sometimes the relevant covalent bonds in a necessary cell constituent have significantly less free energy than the bonds in the metabolites from which they are derived.

SYNTHESIS OF A LARGE "SMALL MOLECULE"

The construction of chlorophyll (Figure 6–4) is a good example. Here is a molecule (MW = 892) whose total laboratory synthesis has just been recently achieved, and which still looks very complex even to a first-rate organic chemist. It contains the complicated porphyrin ring, to which is attached a long unbranched alcohol (phytol). As yet, only the broad outlines of its biosynthesis are known. The porphyrin and phytol components are most likely synthesized separately and later joined together. Most of what is now known about its synthesis con-

FIGURE 6–4   *The structure of chlorophyll.*

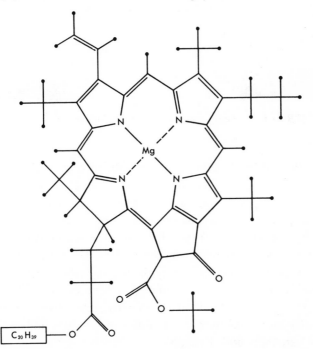

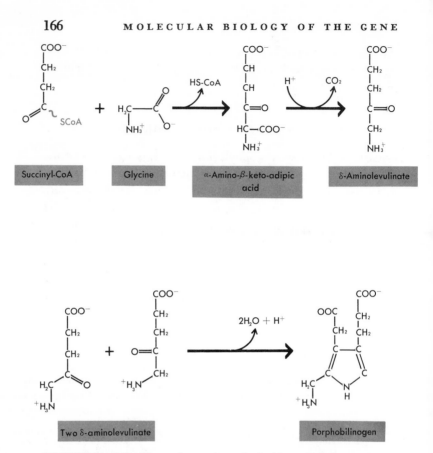

FIGURE 6–5   *The pathway of porphyrin biosynthesis.*

cerns the putting together of the porphyrin ring (Figure 6–5). Here a very large number of different enzymes are used to re-arrange the C, N, O and H atoms found initially in the much smaller glycine and succinyl~CoA precursors. No new qualitative features thus appear to distinguish the synthesis of molecules with chlorophyll-like complexity from the construction of small organic molecules. In both cases specific enzymes and favorable thermodynamic equilibria are necessary. There is only the quantitative difference that the biosynthesis of large complex molecules needs more different enzymes and usually more externally added energy.

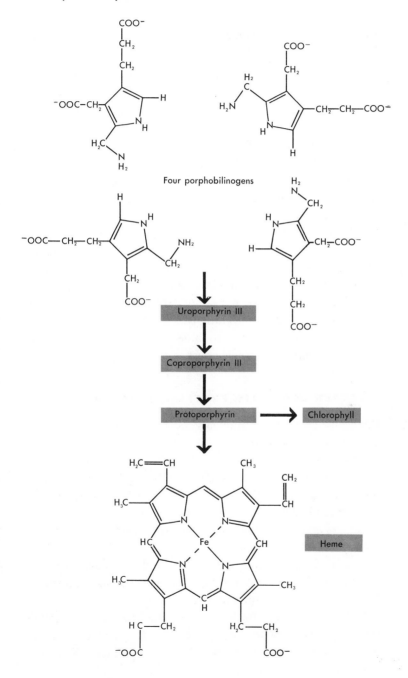

Four porphobilinogens

SYNTHESIS OF A REGULAR, VERY LARGE POLYMERIC MOLECULE

Glycogen is a macromolecule whose molecular weight is often above a million. Nonetheless, only four different enzymes are necessary to derive glycogen from glucose, because glycogen is a polymeric molecule built up by the repetitive linking together of glucose units. Figure 6–6 shows the specific chemical steps by which glucose is activated at its number 1 carbon atom and then polymerized. Only one enzyme is required for the final polymerization because each polymerization step makes the same type of chemical bond. Almost all the linkages are glucosidic bonds (C—O—C) between carbon atoms numbers 1 and 4. Much less commonly, another enzyme catalyzes the formation of 1–6 glucosidic bonds. As a result glycogen is often branched.

We thus see that the number of enzymes necessary to synthesize a molecule is related not necessarily to its size, but rather to its chemical complexity. Thus glycogen, which is an easy molecule for the organic chemist to understand, also poses no fundamental problems to the biochemist.

A DEEPER LOOK INTO PROTEIN STRUCTURE

Before we go into the problems involved in protein synthesis, we must first look more closely into protein structure. Proteins are immensely complex macromolecules since they are polymers built up from 20 different building blocks (the amino acids). Thus the organic chemist must determine both how the amino acids are linked together and what their order is within a given linear polypeptide chain. Likewise, the biochemist wishes to know both how the backbone linkages are connected and what trick is used to order the amino acids during synthesis. In both types of work, the questions involving sequence have proved to be the more difficult questions to answer.

It was, in fact, not until 1953 that the first complete amino acid sequence became known. The protein studied was the hormone insulin, a relatively small protein containing 51 amino

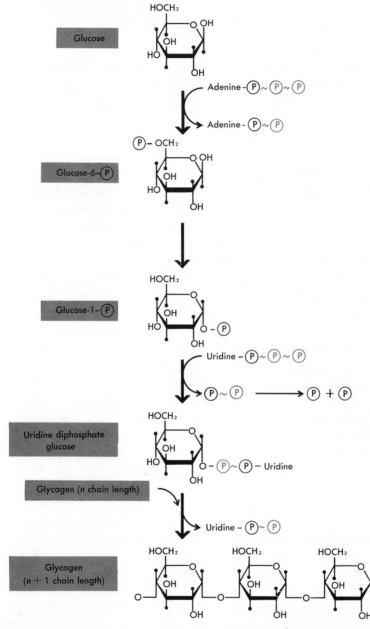

FIGURE 6-6 *The biosynthesis of glycogen from glucose.*

acids (Figure 6–7). More recently, the sequences of a number of additional proteins have been solved. The largest, containing 246 amino acids, is the enzyme chymotrypsinogen, which catalyzes the hydrolysis of peptide bonds. The determination of its sequence (Figure 6–8) required almost 15 man years of work by several talented chemists. Now, new experimental techniques make sequence determinations easier. Nonetheless, even today at least several years' hard work is usually required to solve the structure of a relatively small protein.

Aside from the question of sequence, there is also the problem of how polypeptide chains assume their final 3-D configurations. The correct functioning of almost all proteins depends not only upon possession of the correct amino acid sequence but also upon their exact arrangement in space. As we pointed out in Chapter 4, however, the polypeptide backbone is not completely rigid, for many of its atoms can freely rotate and assume different relative locations. Nonetheless, the tendency to form optimal weak bonds favors a unique conformation for a given protein. Very good indirect evidence indicates that in a given environmental situation all protein molecules with identical sequences have the same "native" 3-D form. Very recently this belief has received direct support from the complete 3-D structural determination of the oxygen-carrying protein myoglobin. In Figure 6–9 is shown its structure as revealed by x-ray diffraction analysis. Though the molecule is immensely complex, detailed inspection shows an important, simplifying structural

FIGURE 6–7   *The amino acid sequence of beef insulin.*

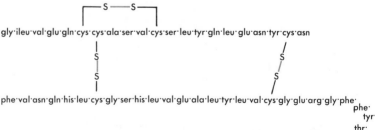

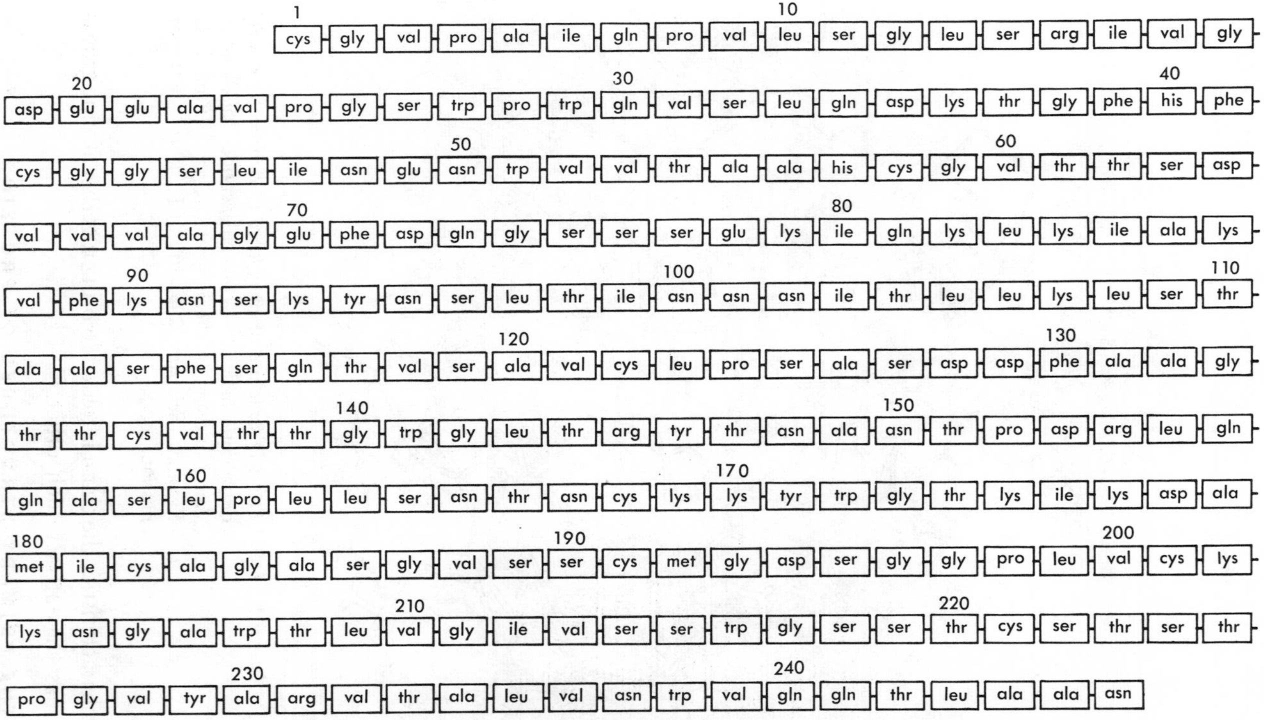

FIGURE 6-8 The amino sequence of the protein chymotrypsinogen.

171

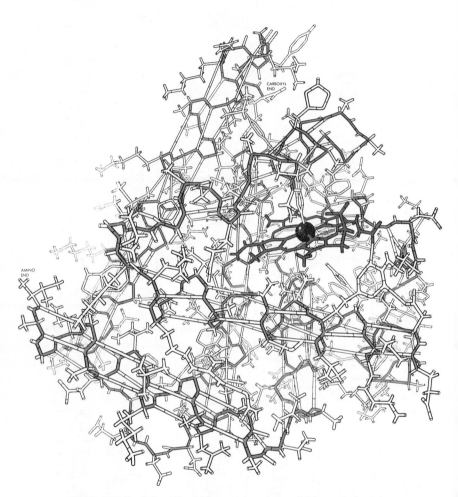

FIGURE 6–9 *The 3-D structure of myoglobin as derived from x-ray diffraction analysis. The polypeptide backbone is shown in color, the heme group in gray. [From J. C. Kendrew, Sci. Am.* **205**, *100–101 (1961), with permission.]*

characteristic: the chain is folded to bring together atomic groupings that attract each other.

THE PRIMARY STRUCTURES OF PROTEINS

Myoglobin, which has 153 amino acids, is one example of the many proteins that contain only one polypeptide chain. Many other proteins have two or more chains. For example, there are four polypeptide chains in the hemoglobin molecule, which has a MW of 64,500. The number of chains and the sequence of residues within them constitute the *primary structure of proteins*. When several polypeptide chains are present in the same molecule, they are often held together by secondary forces. In other cases, disulfide bonds (S—S) between cysteine side groups keep them together; they are what hold together the two chains of the insulin molecule (Figure 6–7). Disulfide bonds are important also in helping a single chain to maintain a rigid shape. In chymotrypsinogen there are 5 disulfide bridges, each linking specific cysteine residues (Figure 6–10).

In addition, a number of proteins have attached to them nonprotein (prosthetic) groups that play a vital role in their functional activity. They are often metal-organic compounds.

FIGURE 6–10   *The arrangement of S–S bonds in chymotrypsinogen. Intact chymotrypsinogen molecules are enzymatically inactive. They become active by enzymatic splitting of the peptide bond between amino acids 15 and 16. The active split-product is called chymotrypsin. The 3-D arrangement of chymotrypsinogen is now being studied actively through x-ray diffraction analysis, and it is hoped that a complete solution will be available within several years. Now there is indirect evidence that the histidine residues of positions 40 and 57 and the serine residue of position 195 are involved in the catalytic action of chymotrypsin. If so, the chain must be folded to bring these amino acids near each other.*

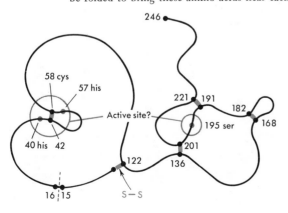

Both myoglobin and hemoglobin contain the prosthetic group heme, a metal-organic compound closely related to the porphyrin component of chlorophyll. Heme combines with O_2 and gives to hemoglobin and myoglobin the ability to bind O_2.

A characteristic feature of prosthetic groups is that they possess very little functional activity unless they are attached to a polypeptide partner. Heme by itself, for example, combines with O_2 in an effectively irreversible fashion. Only when heme is attached to either myoglobin or hemoglobin does it possess the quality of reversibly binding oxygen. Then it can release bound oxygen when it is needed under conditions of oxygen scarcity.

SECONDARY STRUCTURES OF PROTEINS MAY BE SHEETS OR HELICES

The term *protein secondary structure* refers to the regular configurations of the polypeptide backbone. One class of these regular arrangements contains hydrogen bonds between groups on different polypeptide chains. These configurations, collectively called β structures, use fully extended polypeptide chains

FIGURE 6–11   An example of extended polypeptide chains held together in sheets by hydrogen bonds (β configuration). (Redrawn from L. Pauling, The Nature of the Chemical Bond, 3rd ed., Cornell Univ. Press, Ithaca, N.Y., p. 501, with permission.)

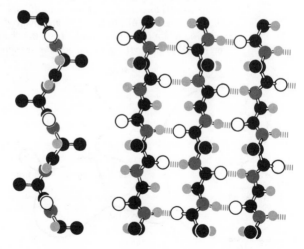

to form sheet-like structures held together by N—H · · · O=C hydrogen bonds (Figure 6–11). β structures are favored by the presence of large numbers of glycine and alanine residues. In nature they occur chiefly in silk proteins.

The most important regular arrangement of the polypeptide chain, however, is brought about by hydrogen bonding between groups on the same chain. This bonding results in the twisting of the polypeptide backbone to form a helix. The most important polypeptide helix is the α-helix, which we have shown in Chapter 4 (Figure 4–13) to illustrate helical symmetry. X-ray diffraction analysis tells us that large sections of the polypeptide backbone of myoglobin are folded into α-helices. There is much suggestive evidence for helices in a large variety of proteins.

TERTIARY STRUCTURES OF PROTEINS ARE EXCEEDINGLY IRREGULAR

The *tertiary structure* of a protein is its 3-D form. It is, in many cases, very irregular. Practically no proteins exist in the form of a simple helix: Instead, many proteins contain both helical and nonhelical regions. Some, in fact, seem to have almost no helical regions. There are a number of stereochemical reasons why the α-helix or another regular arrangement is not found more extensively in spite of almost perfectly regular hydrogen bonding in the backbone. One reason is that the amino acid proline does not contain an amino group, and so where it occurs the regular hydrogen bonding must be interrupted. Another reason is the formation of disulfide (S—S) bridges between cysteine residues. When these cysteine residues are on the same polypeptide chain, the helix is necessarily distorted.

Perhaps, however, the most important reason for irregularity in protein structures arises from the diverse chemical nature of the amino acid side groups. Each of these side groups will tend to make the energetically most favorable secondary interactions with other atomic groups. As an example, the free hydroxyl group on tyrosine will tend to assume a position where it can form a hydrogen bond. The considerable energy of the bond would be lost if, for example, it were next to a hydrophobic isoleucine side group.

Furthermore, the side groups of several amino acids, like valine and leucine, are very insoluble in water, whereas others, like those of glutamic acid or lysine, are highly water soluble. It thus makes chemical sense that the water-insoluble side groups are found stacked next to each other in the interior of myoglobin, and the external surface contains groups that mix easily with water. The 3-dimensional configuration represents the energetically most favorable arrangement of the polypeptide chain. Each specific sequence of amino acids takes up the particular "native" arrangement that makes possible a maximum number of favorable atomic contacts between it and its normal environment. This view is strongly supported by very striking experiments in which high temperature or some other unnatural condition breaks down the native 3-D form (denaturation) to give randomly oriented, biologically inactive polypeptide chains. When the denatured chains are carefully returned to their normal environment, some of them can then reassume their native conformation (renaturation) with full biological activity.

S–S BONDS FORM SPONTANEOUSLY BETWEEN CORRECT PARTNERS

In many cases, renaturation of a disordered protein to an active form involves not only the formation of the thermodynamically favorable weak bonds, but also the making of specific disulfide (S—S) bridges. This was first shown by experiments with the enzyme ribonuclease, a protein constructed from one polypeptide chain of 124 amino acids, crosslinked by four specific S—S bonds. The native, active configuration of the enzyme can be destroyed by reducing the S—S groups to sulfhydryl (SH) groups in the presence of the denaturing agent 8 M urea and the reducing agent mercaptoethanol (Figure 6–12). When the urea is removed, the SH bonds are reoxidized in air to yield S—S bonds identical to those found in the original molecule. A given SH group reassociates, not randomly with any of the other seven SH groups in the molecule, but rather with a specific SH group brought into close contact with it by the folding of the polypeptide chain. Thus S—S bridges are not a primary reason for the peculiar folding of the chain. They might be better viewed as a device for increasing the stability of an already stable configuration. The presence or absence of S—S bonds does not affect the argument that the final structure of a protein is determined by the amino acid sequence.

FIGURE 6–12   *Schematic illustration of the fate of S–S bonds during protein denaturation and renaturation. When the denaturing agents are removed, most of the polypeptide chains resume the native configuration with the original S–S bonds. Only a few polypeptide chains fold up in an inactive form characterized by a different set of S–S bonds than those found in the native molecules.*

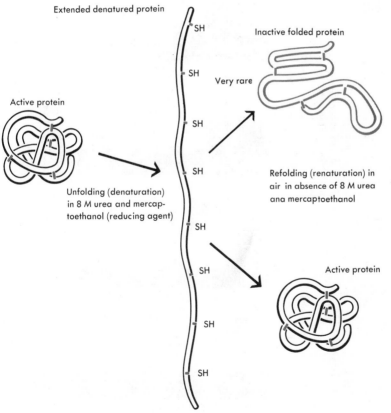

Extended denatured protein

SH

SH

SH

SH

SH

SH

SH

SH

Active protein

Unfolding (denaturation) in 8 M urea and mercaptoethanol (reducing agent)

Inactive folded protein

Very rare

Refolding (renaturation) in air in absence of 8 M urea and mercaptoethanol

Active protein

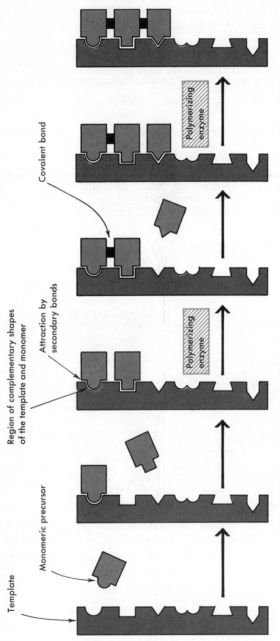

Template

Monomeric precursor

Region of complementary shapes
of the template and monomer

Attraction by
secondary bonds

Covalent bond

Polymerizing
enzyme

Polymerizing
enzyme

FIGURE 6-13   *Diagrammatic view of the formation of a specific polymeric molecule upon a template surface.*

178

ENZYMES CANNOT BE USED TO ORDER
AMINO ACIDS IN PROTEINS

We have seen that the sequence of amino acids in the poly-peptide chains largely determines the 3-D structure of a protein. Now we come back to the ordering dilemma with the realization that it is the heart of the matter of protein synthesis. In comparison, the problem of how the connecting links form is minor, for this connective process involves the synthesis of only one type of covalent bond (the peptide bond), a fact that hints a need of only one enzyme or, at most, several enzymes.

On the other hand, the ordering itself cannot be accomplished by recourse to enzymes specific for each amino acid in a protein for the following reason. Such a device would require as many ordering enzymes as there are amino acids in the protein; but since all known enzymes are themselves proteins, still additional ordering enzymes would be necessary to synthesize the enzymes, and so on. This is clearly a paradox, unless we assume a fantastically interrelated series of syntheses in which a given protein can alternatively have many different enzymatic specificities. With such an assumption it might be just possible (and then with great difficulty) to visualize a workable cell. It does not seem likely, however, that most proteins really do have more than one task. All our knowledge, in fact, points toward the opposite general conclusion of one protein, one function.

It is, therefore, necessary to throw out the idea of ordering proteins with enzymes and to predict instead the existence of a specific surface, *the template* (Figure 6–13), that attracts the amino acids (or their activated derivatives) and lines them up in the correct order. Then a specific enzyme common to all protein synthesis could make the peptide bonds. It is, furthermore, necessary to assume that the templates must also have the capacity of serving either directly or indirectly as templates for themselves (self-duplication). That is, in some way their specific surfaces must be exactly copied to give new templates. Again we cannot invoke the help of specific enzymes, for this immediately leads us back to the "enzyme cannot make enzyme" paradox.

TEMPLATE INTERACTIONS ARE BASED
ON RELATIVELY WEAK BONDS

The existence of proteins thus simultaneously demands the co-existence of highly specific template molecules. Moreover, the templates themselves must be macromolecules, at least as large as their polypeptide products. This is clear when we examine the rules that govern the selective binding of small molecules to their templates. We first see that the binding is not done by using strong covalent bonds. Instead the attraction is based on relatively weak bonds that can form without enzymes. These are (1) ionic bonds, (2) hydrogen bonds in which an electro-positive hydrogen atom is attracted to electronegative atoms, such as oxygen or nitrogen, and (3) van der Waals forces.

Since all these forces operate only over very short distances (< 5 A), templates can order small molecules only when they are in close contact on the atomic level. Thus, it is to be expected that the specific (attracting) regions of the template will be in the same size range as the amino acid side groups in the protein product.

ATTRACTION OF OPPOSITES
VERSUS SELF—ATTRACTION

Here we pose the obvious question: Can a polypeptide chain serve as a template for its own synthesis? If it could, it would make possible a great reduction in the chemical prerequisites for life. Then the problems of protein synthesis and template replication would be the same, and the additional biochemical complexity required to maintain a special class of template mole-cules would be unnecessary. This conceptual possibility finds no support, however, from close inspection of the amino acid side groups. There is no chemical reason why, for example, the occurrence of valine on a template should preferentially attract the specific side group of another valine molecule. In fact, none of the amino acid side groups have specific affinities for them-selves. Instead it is much easier to imagine molecules with opposite or complementary features attracting each other.

Negative charges obviously attract positive groups, and hydrogen atoms can form hydrogen bonds only to electronegative atoms. Similarly, molecules can specifically attract by van der Waals forces only when they possess complementary shapes, to allow a cavity in one molecule to be filled with a protruding group of another molecule.

A formal way remains, however, to save the possibility of protein templates. We might imagine the existence of 20 different specific molecules that we could call connectors. Each would possess two identical surfaces complementary in charge and/or shape to a given amino acid. The intervention of these connector molecules would then make possible the lining up of amino acids in a sequence identical to that of the template polypeptide chain. No evidence exists for such molecules, however. Instead, as we shall shortly show, a specific template class (the nucleic acids) does in fact exist.

A CHEMICAL ARGUMENT AGAINST THE EXISTENCE OF PROTEIN TEMPLATES

The failure of proteins ever to evolve a template role may originate in the composition of the amino acid side groups. The argument can be made that no template whose specificity depends upon the side groups of closely related amino acids, like valine or alanine, could ever be copied with the accuracy demanded for efficient cellular existence. This follows from the fact that some amino acids are chemically similar. For example, valine and isoleucine differ only by the presence of an additional methyl group in isoleucine. Likewise, glycine and alanine also differ by only one methyl group. This close chemical similarity immediately poses the question whether any copying process can be sufficiently accurate to distinguish between such closely related molecules. Our answer depends in part upon what we mean by "sufficiently accurate." A good speculative guess is that each amino acid in an hereditary molecule would have to be copied with an accuracy of not more than one error in 10^8. On the other hand, a semirigorous chemical argument can be made that no chemical reaction could distinguish between molecules differing by only one methyl group with an accuracy of better than one in 10^6. Moreover, when we look at the accuracy of protein synthesis itself, we observe that some amino acids can be inserted into polypeptide chains with no greater than a 99.9 per cent accuracy. Thus proteins do not have the "smell" of an hereditary molecule.

SUMMARY

The frequent occurrence of most chemical reactions within cells depends both on the presence of specific enzymes and on the availability of an external energy supply (the sun or food molecules) to make energy-rich molecules like ATP. There is a different enzyme for almost every specific reaction involved in the synthesis of a small molecule. This rule holds even when the "small molecule" is as large as chlorophyll. The problem arises, however, whether the same general scheme can hold for the biosynthesis of the enzymes themselves. Are a number of specific enzymes used to synthesize each enzyme involved in the metabolism of small molecules? This number would need to be very large, since all enzymes are proteins, themselves very large molecules, constructed by the linear linking together in a definite order of the 20 amino acids. The average protein contains about 300 to 500 amino acids, and so an equivalent number of enzymes would be necessary if enzymes are used to specify amino acid sequences.

This is clearly an unworkable scheme, and the ordering of amino acids in proteins is instead accomplished by template molecules. The templates for protein are also macromolecules. They have surfaces that specifically attract and thereby line up the amino acids in the correct sequence. There is a specific template for each specific protein. No enzymes are involved in the attraction of the amino acid residues to the templates. Attraction is accomplished by weak secondary forces. Specific regions of the template specifically attract one of the 20 different amino acid residues.

When a cell grows and divides, the number of protein template molecules must also double. Templates must in some way *also be templates for their own highly exact synthesis. The templates are not protein molecules; there are chemical arguments why proteins should not be highly accurate templates. Instead, all cells contain a special class of molecules specifically devoted to being templates for protein synthesis.*

REFERENCES

Kornberg, A. "Pathways of Enzymatic Synthesis of Nucleotides and Polynucleotides," in W. D. McElroy and B. Glass (eds.), *The Chemical Basis of Heredity*, Johns Hopkins, Baltimore, 1957, pp. 579–608. An excellent survey of the biosynthesis of the purine and pyrimidine nucleotides.

Anfinsen, C. B., *The Molecular Basis of Evolution*, Wiley, New York, 1960. Now available in paperback. Though somewhat out of date, some of its description of protein chemistry is quite lucid.

Haurowitz, F., *The Chemistry and Function of Proteins*, 2nd. ed., Academic, New York, 1963. A textbook at the college level on protein structure.

Perutz, M. F., *Proteins and Nucleic Acids: Structure and Function*, Elsevier, Amsterdam, 1962. A superb description of the structures of the proteins and nucleic acids, followed by a description of how the nucleic acids are involved in protein synthesis.

Perutz, M. F., "The Hemoglobin Molecule," *Sci. Am.*, November, 1964, pp. 64–76. Relates what is currently known about the architecture of the hemoglobin molecule, in the presence or absence of oxygen.

Neurath, H., "Protein-Digesting Enzymes," *Sci. Am.*, December, 1964, pp. 68–79. An informative description of the structure of several proteolytic enzymes together with speculations on their mode of action.

Neurath, H. (ed.), *The Proteins*, 2nd ed., Academic, New York, Vol. 1, 1963, Vol. 2, 1965. A collection of advanced articles about various aspects of protein chemistry.

Muller, H. J., "The Gene," *Proc. Roy. Soc. (London)*, **B134**, 1–37 (1947). A lecture given in 1945 in which a distinguished geneticist traces the history of the gene concept and speculates about how it might function as a template.

7

THE ARRANGEMENT OF GENES ON CHROMOSOMES

OUR CHEMICAL INTUITION TELLS US that proteins are unlikely to serve as the templates necessary to order amino acid sequences in proteins. Instead, we must look for a class of molecules capable of both the protein template function and self-replication. Here the direction of our search is completely dictated by the results of modern genetics. This flourishing science has shown in amazing detail how the chromosomes are responsible for the perpetuation of heredity: it is by means of genes, located on the chromosomes, that daughter cells come to resemble parental cells. The major task of the geneticists has been to show how this resemblance occurs.

Parallel to their work in mapping the location of genes, geneticists began to ask the fundamental question of how the genes chemically controlled specific cellular processes. Usually, however, the mutations they studied were not easily analyzed. In the 1920s and the 1930s, as even today, virtually nothing was known of the biochemical basis of development.

Fortunately, however, the mutations affecting color in flowers and eyes were open to a chemical approach. For example, mutations in many genes change the color of the eyes of *Drosophila*. Here biochemical analysis was possible because it was known that eye color is directly related to the presence of definite colored molecules called pigments. It could thus be

184

asked how a gene difference could convert the color of fruit fly eyes from red to white. The obvious and correct answer is that no pigment is found in the eyes of flies thus altered. This in turn hints that an enzyme necessary for its synthesis is absent, a suggestion soon extended to the general hypothesis that genes directly control the synthesis of all proteins, whether or not they are enzymes.

As this way of thinking became generally accepted (about 1946), geneticists began to deal with the deeper problem of how a gene dictates which particular protein is present. Little progress could be made until protein chemists showed unambiguously (in the early 1950s) that proteins were linear collections of the 20 amino acids. It was then a simple matter for the more theoretically inclined geneticists to hypothesize that the chromosomes carry the genetic information that orders amino acid sequences, and to predict that the study of the structure of genes might lead to the elucidation of the molecular basis of the templates that order amino acid sequences. This was, in fact, what did happen. But before we can examine the problem more deeply, some genetic concepts must first be explained.

MUCH REMAINS TO BE LEARNED ABOUT THE MOLECULAR ASPECTS OF CHROMOSOME STRUCTURE

Even today, our knowledge of the molecular structure of chromosomes is very incomplete. This is especially true for the more complex chromosomes of higher plants and animals. In bacteria and viruses there is evidence (which we shall later relate) that the principal chemical component is deoxyribonucleic acid (DNA). The chromosomes of higher organisms, however, also contain a significant fraction (as great as 50 per cent) of protein.

Most of this protein belongs to a class of protein molecules called histones. All histones are basic (have a net positive charge), and it is believed that they neutralize part of the negative charge of the acid DNA molecules. The primary function of histones is still a mystery. Before 1943 many biologists believed that they carried genetic information, but their complete absence in many, if not all, bacteria now argues against the assignment of a fundamental genetic role. Instead there is a growing belief that they have essentially inhibitory functions. When a gene in higher plants and animals is not functioning, it tends to be combined with histones.

Up to now, electron microscopy has provided no useful insight into the structure of chromosomes of higher organisms. This failure is in striking contrast with the success of electron microscopy in examining very thin sections of muscle and nerve fibers. The failure arises from the *irregular* shape not only of the highly extended chromosomes found during interphase, but even of the more contracted metaphase chromosomes. At the molecular level the various muscle proteins are nicely lined up in parallel array. In contrast, the path of a chromosome through a cell is excessively irregular: When a thin section is observed, it has so far been impossible even to follow the contour, much less to observe details of molecular structure. Thus purely morphological examination has given us no useful information about the chromosomal arrangement of genes; instead genetic crosses are the only way of attacking this problem. Fortunately, as we shall soon see, the powers of resolution of this method are indeed very great.

THE GENETIC CROSS

A variety of devices exist in nature that bring together genetic material from different organisms (the genetic cross) for the purpose of achieving genetic recombination. These devices, collectively known as *sexual processes*, greatly speed up the rate of evolution, since they bring collections of favorable mutations into one cell much faster than successive cycles of favorable mutations could by themselves. Here, however, we are not at all concerned with the evolutionary advantages of the various sexual processes. Our interest in them arises instead from the variety of tools that their existence has provided for finding the location of genes along chromosomes.

The essential trick of locating genes through genetic crosses involves the determination of whether the genes donated by a given parent remain together when haploid segregants are produced. When genes are located on different chromosomes they will assort randomly, and there will be a 50–50 chance that they will be found together in a given haploid segregant. When, on the contrary, they are located on the same chromosome, they will tend to segregate together, unless they have been separated by crossing over.

Crossing over occurs at the stage of meiosis where two homologous chromosomes specifically attract each other to form pairs. The mechanism of this attraction (*pairing*) remains a great mystery. It is clearly a very specific process, since it occurs only between chromosomes containing the same genes. Following the formation of pairs, both chromosomes occasionally break at the same point and rejoin crossways. This allows the formation of recombinant chromosomes containing some genes derived from the paternal chromosome and some from the maternal one. Crossing over greatly increases the amount of genetic recombination and, except in highly specialized cases, is universally observed. The frequency of crossing over, however, varies greatly with the particular species involved. On the average, one to several crossovers occur every time chromosomes pair.

All our early knowledge of gene locations came from the study of gene segregation after conventional meiotic divisions. The organisms studied were those in which there is a regular fusion of the male and the female cells to produce diploid cells half of whose chromosomes are derived from the male parent and half from the female. When meiosis occurs, the diploid chromosome number is regularly reduced to the haploid number. Crossing over always takes place after each of the parental chromosomes has split to form two chromatids held together by a single centromere. Two chromatids are involved in each crossover event, so that each crossover produces two recombinant chromatids and leaves the two parental chromosomes intact (Figure 7–1). (This does not mean that half the chromatids produced during meiosis have the parental genotype. Each chromatid in a pair has an equal chance of crossing

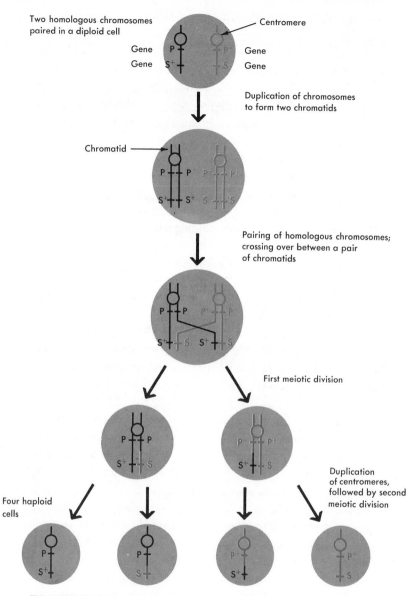

FIGURE 7–1   Crossing over between homologous chromatids during meiosis.

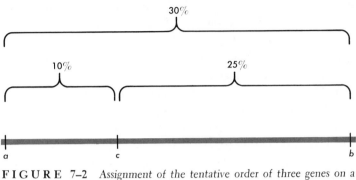

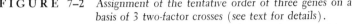

FIGURE 7-2 *Assignment of the tentative order of three genes on a basis of 3 two-factor crosses (see text for details).*

over, so that, even though a particular chromatid is not involved in a given crossover, it may still participate in another.)

CHROMOSOME MAPPING

The existence of crossing over provides a means of locating genes along chromosomes. Crossing over occurs randomly through-out the length of many chromosomes, so that the farther apart two genes are, the greater the probability that a break will occur between them to cause genetic recombination. The way in which the frequencies of the various recombinant classes are used to locate genes is straightforward. It is especially easy when the progeny are haploid, and the question of dominance versus recessiveness is irrelevant. Consider the segregation pattern of three genes all located on the same chromosome of a haploid organism. The arrangement of the genes can be determined by means of three crosses, in each of which two genes are followed (two-factor crosses). A cross X between a^+b^+ and ab yields four progeny types: the two parental genotypes (a^+b^+ and ab) and two recombinant genotypes (a^+b and ab^+). The cross Y between a^+c^+ and ac similarly, gives the two parental combinations as well as the a^+c and ac^+ recombinants, whereas the cross Z between b^+c^+ and bc produces the parental types, and the recombinants b^+c and cb^+. Each cross will produce a specific ratio of parental to recombinant progeny. Consider, for example, the result that cross X gives 30 per cent recombinants, cross Y, 10 per cent, and cross Z, 25 per cent. This hints that genes a and c are closer together than a and b or b and c, and that the genetic distances between a and b and b and c are more similar. The gene arrangement which best fits this data is acb (Figure 7–2).

The correctness of gene orders suggested by crosses of two gene factors can usually be unambiguously confirmed by three-factor crosses. When the three genes used in the above example are followed in the cross $a^+b^+c^+ \times abc$, six recombinant genotypes are found (Figure 7–3). They fall into three groups of reciprocal pairs. The rarest of these groups arises from a double crossover. By looking for the least frequent class, it is often possible instantly to confirm (or deny) a postulated arrangement. The results in Figure 7–3 immediately confirm the order hinted by the two-factor crosses. Only if the order is acb does the fact that the rare recombinants are a^+cb^+ and ac^+b make sense.

FIGURE 7–3   *The use of three-factor crosses to assign gene order. The least frequent pair of reciprocal recombinants must arise from a double crossover. The percentages listed for the various classes are the theoretical values expected for an infinitely large sample. When finite numbers of progeny are recorded, the exact values will be subject to random statistical fluctuations.*

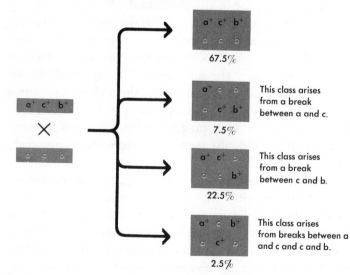

The existence of multiple crossovers means that the amount of recombination (ab) between the outside markers a and b is usually less than the sum of the recombination frequencies (ac and cb) between a and c and c and b. To obtain a more accurate approximation of the distance between the outside markers, we calculate the probability (ac × cb) that, when a crossover occurs between c and b, an ac crossover also occurs, and vice versa (cb × ac). This probability subtracted from the sum of the frequencies expresses more accurately the amount of recombination. This gives the simple formula

$$ab = ac + cb - 2(ac)(cb)$$

It is applicable in all cases where the occurrence of one cross-over does not affect the probability of another crossover. Unfortunately, accurate mapping is often disturbed by *interference* phenomena, which can either increase or decrease the probability of correlated crossovers.

The results of a very large number of such crosses have led to an important genetic conclusion: All the genes on a chromosome can be located on a line. The gene arrangement is strictly linear, and never branched. Thus chromosomes are linear, not only in shape, but also in gene arrangement. The arrangement of genes on a particular chromosome is called a *genetic map*, and the locating of genes on a chromosome is often referred to as mapping a gene. Figure 7–4 shows the genetic map of one of the chromosomes of *Drosophila*. Distances between genes on a map are usually measured in map units, which are related to the frequency of recombination between the genes: Thus if the frequency of recombination between two genes is found to be 5 per cent, the genes are said to be separated by five map units. Because of the occurrence of double crossovers, the assignment of map units can be considered accurate only if recombination between closely spaced genes is followed.

Even when two genes are at the far ends of a very long chromosome, they will show not less than 50 per cent linkage (assort together at least 50 per cent of the time), because of multiple crossovers. Genes will be separated if 1,3,5,7 . . .

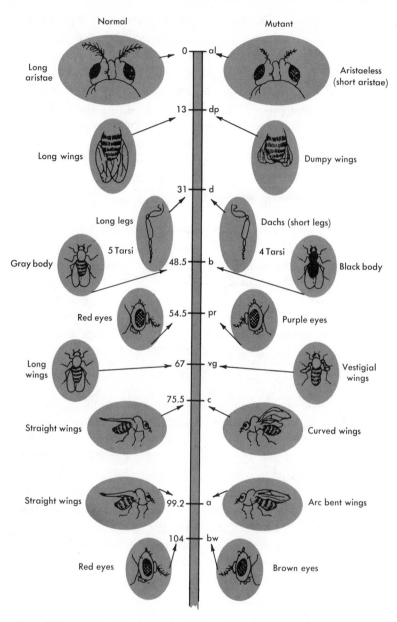

FIGURE 7-4 A portion of the genetic map of Drosophila melanogaster (chromosome 2).

crossovers occur between them; they will end up together if 2,4,6,8 . . . occur between them. Thus in the beginning of the genetic analysis of an organism, it is practically impossible to determine immediately whether two genes are on different chromosomes or are at the opposite ends of one long chromosome. After a large number of genes have been mapped, we often find that two genes thought to be on different chromosomes are, in fact, on the same one. For example, the genes of the phage T4 were thought for many years to lie on three separate chromosomes, until further mapping, using newly discovered genes, revealed that they all lie on a single chromosome.

It is important to remember that a genetic map derived from recombinant frequencies gives only the relative physical distances between mutable sites. It would give the actual physical distances only if the probability of crossing over were the same throughout the length of a chromosome. Thus, just as soon as geneticists made maps, they sought methods that could relate mutational sites to true physical locations. Now a number of tricks, some too complicated to be explained here, tell us that often, *but not always*, genetic maps are a good reflection of the actual chromosome structure. One of these tricks will be described in a subsequent section, in which we discuss the genetic map of E. coli.

IMPORTANCE OF WORK WITH MICROORGANISMS

Most of our initial ideas about genes arose from work with large, multicellular plants and animals. Now, however, unless there is an economic or social need for information about a particular species (e.g., the corn plant, man), microorganisms are much more preferable for study. Several important advantages favor work with microorganisms. First they are usually haploid, so that the ease of genetic analysis does not depend upon whether a mutation is dominant or recessive. Since most mutations are recessive, they cannot be detected when the normal wild-type gene is also present. In work with diploids, several generations of genetic crosses must often be carried out to detect the presence of a particular mutant gene; in a haploid organism the mutant gene can express itself almost immediately. Second, microorganisms multiply very rapidly. There is enormous advantage to working with an organism, such as a bacterium, which has a new cell generation every 20 minutes, rather than with a plant like corn, where at best only two generations per year can be studied, even in tropical environments.

Fifty years ago, *Drosophila*, with its average life cycle of 14 days, looked very attractive. Today it cannot be conveniently used to answer the fundamental questions being asked at the molecular level about what genes are and how they act.

Now the most exciting materials for genetic study are yeasts, molds, bacteria, and viruses, particularly the bacterial viruses, or phages. Genetic work with these effectively began some 25 years ago. Until then their small size was considered an enormous disadvantage. Microorganisms do not have easily recognized morphological features, such as red eyes, and so it was very difficult to know when they contained mutations. Until 1945, it was generally believed that some did not have chromosomes and some biologists even suspected they might not have genes.

THE VALUE OF MUTAGENS

Most mutant genes studied by the early Mendelian geneticists arose spontaneously. Now there is increasing use of mutations specifically induced by external agents, such as ionizing radiation, ultraviolet light, and certain specific chemicals. These agents, collectively called mutagens, greatly increase the rate at which geneticists can isolate mutant genes. For many years the various forms of radiation were the most powerful mutagens known. Now chemical mutagens are more often used, because they produce a much higher fraction of mutated genes. Treatment of bacteria with the highly reactive compound nitrosoguanidine can produce viable mutations in almost 1 per cent of the bacterial genes.

Mutagens act quite indiscriminately. No presently known

mutagen increases the probability of mutating a given gene without also increasing the probability of mutating all other genes. Until recently, the mechanisms of mutagenesis were completely unclear. Now, as we shall point out in Chapter 9, the realization that DNA is the primary genetic material allows the development of precise hypotheses about how several chemical mutagens act.

BACTERIAL MUTATIONS: THE USE OF GROWTH FACTORS

The essential breakthrough in the use of bacteria as genetic material came in 1944 with the realization that mutations could be obtained affecting the ability of bacteria to synthesize essential metabolites. For example, E. coli ordinarily grows well with only glucose as a carbon source. But as a result of specific mutations, there now exist mutant E. coli strains that will grow only when their normal medium is supplemented with a specific metabolite (growth factor). These types of mutation had been described just a few years earlier (1941) in the haploid lower plant Neurospora (a mold). Such mutations are very easy to work with: To test for their presence one need merely grow a suspected mutant both in the presence and in the absence of a metabolite, for example, the amino acid arginine (Figure 7–5). If a mutation inhibiting arginine biosynthesis has occurred, the bacteria will grow only in the presence of arginine. The use of this approach quickly led (with the help of mutagens) to the isolation of a large number of different gene mutations affecting the synthesis of specific molecules.

Another important type of mutation involves the resistance of bacteria to poisonous compounds such as antibiotics. For example, most E. coli cells are rapidly killed by small amounts of streptomycin. Very rarely, however, there occur mutations (Strep^R), which make the cells resistant to certain amounts of the drug. Mutations also can occur to make cells resistant to the growth of viruses. One of the most useful mutations in E. coli strain B confers resistance to the phage T1; these mutant cells are designated B/1. Correspondingly, E. coli strain B

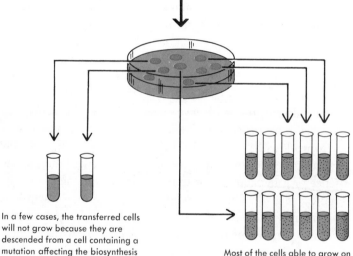

Treatment of *E. coli* cells
with a mutagen—nitrosoguanidine

The treated cells are placed on a Petri dish filled with a rich nutrient solid agar
medium containing the 20 amino acids, the various purines and pyrimidines, all
known vitamins, etc. Many of the treated cells fail to multiply because they are
killed by the mutagen. The remaining survivors multiply to form distinct colonies
on the solid agar surface.

In a few cases, the transferred cells
will not grow because they are
descended from a cell containing a
mutation affecting the biosynthesis
of a compound present in the rich
medium. The identity of the needed
growth factor can be found quickly
by selective addition of the various
compounds present in the rich medium.

Most of the cells able to grow on
the rich medium can grow also
when transferred to a minimal
medium containing only glucose
and inorganic salts.

FIGURE 7–5　*The isolation of mutant E. coli cells with specific*
growth factor requirements.

cells resistant to phages T2 and T4 are called B/2 and B/4,
respectively. Still other mutations affect the ability of *E. coli*
cells to grow upon sugars such as lactose, galactose, or maltose;
a specific mutation can cause the loss of the ability of *E. coli* to
use one of these sugars as a sole carbon source.

The isolation of growth factor, antibiotic resistance, and phage resistance mutations were quickly followed by experiments demonstrating existence of genetic recombination (hence a sexual process) in E. coli (Figure 7–6). Twofold use was made of these mutant genes. First, they were used as conventional genetic markers, their segregation patterns revealing the chromosomal arrangement of genes. Second, they provided a method

FIGURE 7–6 *The use of growth factor requirements to demonstrate sexuality in* E. coli.

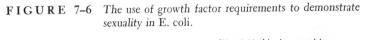

(thr⁻) Threonine requiring   (Met⁻) Methionine requiring
(leu⁻) Leucine requiring   (bio⁻) Biotin requiring
(T1ˢ) Sensitive to phage T1   (T1ᴿ) Resistant to phage T1
(lac⁻) Unable to grow on lactose   (lac⁺) Able to grow on lactose

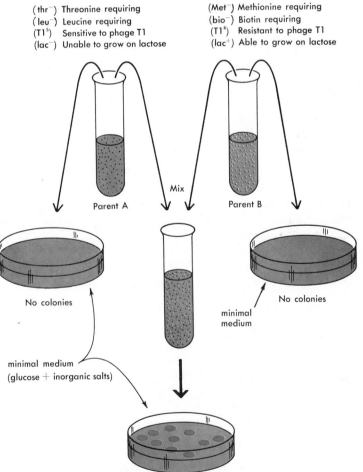

Parent A   Mix   Parent B

No colonies   No colonies

minimal medium

minimal medium
(glucose + inorganic salts)

A very small fraction of the cells are met⁺, bio⁺, thr⁺, leu⁺. They arise by genetic recombination shown by examination of the lac and T1 markers. In addition to the parental lac⁻T1ˢ and lac⁺T1ᴿ genotypes, there are found lac⁻T1ᴿ and lac⁺T1ˢ cells.

of detecting a genetic recombination process occurring in only a very small fraction of the population at a given time. In E. coli, for example, simple morphological examination of bacterial cells gave no clues that cell fusion and genetic recombination existed: To detect recombination it was necessary to devise an experiment in which only the recombinant cells would be able to multiply. This was done by using parental strains with specific growth requirements such that they could not multiply in minimal media.

In these experiments, two strains of bacteria, each possessing specific growth requirements, were mixed together. Neither strain alone was able to grow in the absence of specific metabolites or growth factors (that is, the amino acids threonine and leucine were required by one strain, the vitamin biotin and the amino acid methionine by the other). After the two strains had been mixed together, a small number of cells were able to grow without any growth factors. This meant that they had somehow acquired good copies of each of their mutant genes. This result strongly suggested that E. coli has a sexual phase that can bring together the chromosomes of two different cells. Crossing over could then place in one chromosome good copies of all its necessary genes. Further genetic analysis confirmed this hypothesis, and within the past 10 years E. coli has become one of the genetically best known of all organisms.

VIRUSES ALSO CONTAIN CHROMOSOMES

Chromosomal control of heredity even extends to viruses. These disease-causing particles, much smaller than bacteria, can enter (infect) cells and multiply to form large numbers of new virus particles. The common cold, influenza, and poliomyelitis are among the many diseases caused by viruses. The relation of viruses to their host cells is very intimate, since they are able to increase in numbers only after they have entered a cell; outside cells they are completely inert. There exist viruses active on most, if not all, plants and animals. Viruses can even multiply in bacteria (bacterial viruses are usually called bacteriophages or phages). The replication of many new virus particles within a single cell usually kills the host cell—hence their disease-causing property.

Our knowledge of the genetics of several bacterial viruses has shown an expansion similar to and simultaneous with the expansion of our knowledge of bacteria. Before 1940, almost no one thought about the genetics of viruses. To most people viruses seemed much too small to be studied unless they caused a disease that we wished to control. They could not be seen in the light microscope, and were generally detected only by their property of killing cells. Several factors changed this outlook. First, it was realized that the bacterial viruses were very easy to experiment with and that the phage-bacterium system was ideally suited to the study of the general problem of how genes multiply and work. Second, it was found that phage mutations were as easy to obtain as mutations in bacteria, if not easier.

Chemically, viruses are extremely heterogeneous both in size and in variety of molecular constituents (Figure 7–7). For many years their biological significance was obscure and the question often asked was, "Are viruses living?" Now we realize that they are small pieces of genetic material, each enclosed within a protective coat, rich in protein, which allows it to be transported from one cell to another. Progeny virus particles resemble their parents because they contain identical chromosomes. We also see that they are no more "alive" than isolated chromosomes; both the chromosomes of cells and those of viruses can duplicate only in the complex environment of a living cell. The study of viruses has been of immense value to the understanding of how cells live: Viruses are almost unique in affording convenient systems for quickly studying the consequences of the sudden introduction of new genetic material into a cell.

VIRUSES DO NOT GROW
BY GRADUAL INCREASE IN SIZE

The life cycle of an average cell involves gradual increase to twice its initial size, followed by a division process (mitosis)

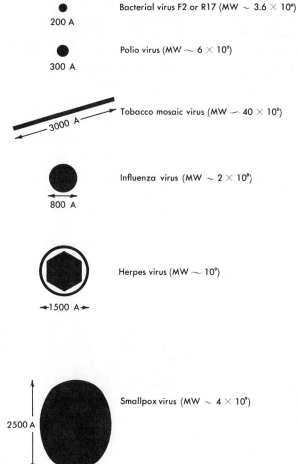

FIGURE 7–7   *Variation in size and shape of a number of viruses.*

producing two identical daughter cells. Viruses, however, do not multiply in this fashion. They are not produced by the fission of a large pre-existing particle—all the virus particles of a given variety have approximately similar (in some cases identical) masses. During viral multiplication there is a temporary disappearance (the eclipse period) of the original parental particle, because the parental particle breaks down upon infection and releases its chromosome from the protective outer shell. Then the free chromosome serves as a template to direct the synthesis of new viral components. This breakdown process is an obligatory feature of viral multiplication, for as long as the chromosome is tightly enclosed within the protein-containing shell, it cannot be a template for the synthesis of either new chromosomes or new shell protein molecules.

VIRUSES ARE PARASITES AT THE GENETIC LEVEL

In most cases, the viral chromosomes (which we shall later show to be always constructed from nucleic acids) and proteins are constructed from the same four main nucleotides and 20 amino acids used in normal cells. All these precursors are usually synthesized by host cell enzymes. Likewise, the energy needed to push the various chemical reactions in the biosynthetic direction usually comes from ATP produced by food molecule degradation controlled by host enzymes.

The parasitism of viruses is thus obligatory. It is impossible to imagine viruses reproducing outside cells, on which they are completely dependent for supply of both the necessary precursors and the ribosomes, the structural machinery for making proteins. The essential aspect of viruses is thus not really their small size, but the fact that they do not possess the capacity to independently construct proteins. Thus for their replication, they must insert their nucleic acid into a functional cell. This fact enables us to distinguish the larger viruses, like smallpox, from very small cellular organisms, like the Rickettsiae. Even though the Rickettsiae are obligatory parasites, they contain both DNA and RNA and grow by increasing in size and splitting into two smaller cells. At no time does their cell membrane break down; moreover, all their protein is synthesized upon their own protein synthesizing machinery.

BACTERIAL VIRUSES (PHAGES) ARE OFTEN EASY TO STUDY

As mentioned before, the most exciting viruses from the viewpoint of the geneticist are the bacterial viruses (phages). Their discovery in 1914 produced great excitement, for it was hoped that they might afford an effective and simple way to combat bacterial diseases. Phages were unfortunately never medically useful, because their bacterial hosts mutate readily to forms resistant to viral growth. Thus almost everyone lost interest in the phage, and almost no one studied how it multiplied until the late 1930s. Then a small group of biologists and physicists, intrigued by the problem of gene replication, began to investigate the reproduction of several phages which multiplied in *E. coli*. They chose to work with phages

FIGURE 7–8   *Some bacterial viruses that have been important in the study of the chemistry of genetics.*

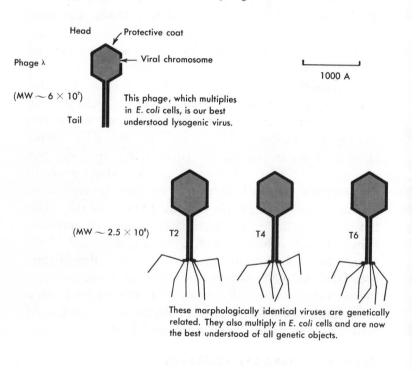

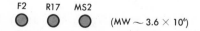

These are the smallest known group of *E. coli* viruses. Even though they have been known only for a few years, they are quickly becoming some of the most intensively studied of all viruses.

rather than with plant or animal viruses because, under laboratory conditions, it is immensely easier to grow bacterial cells than plant or animal cells.

Almost all work with phages has concentrated on several particular phages, arbitrarily given names like T1, T2, P1, F2, or λ (Figure 7–8). The best known are the closely related strains T2, T4, and T6. These similar strains reproduce in essentially the same way. The growth cycle starts when a phage particle collides with a sensitive bacterium and the phage tail specifically attaches to the bacterial wall. An enzyme in the phage tail then breaks down a small portion of the cell wall, creating a small hole through which the viral chromosome enters the cell. The viral chromosome duplicates, and the daughter chromosomes continue to duplicate, to form eventually 100 to 1000 new chromosomes, which become encapsulated with newly synthesized protective coats, to form a large number of new bacteriophage particles. The growth cycle is complete when the bacterial cell wall breaks open (lyses) and releases the progeny particles into the surrounding medium.

PHAGES FORM PLAQUES

The presence of viable phage particles can be quickly demonstrated by adding the virus-containing solution to the surface of a nutrient agar plate, on which bacteria susceptible to this virus are rapidly multiplying. If no virus particles are present, the rapidly dividing bacteria will form a uniform surface layer of bacteria. But if even one virus particle is present, it will attach to a bacterium and multiply to form several hundred new progeny virus particles, which are then suddenly released by dissolution (lysis) of the cell wall, some 15 to 60 minutes after the start of phage infection. Each of these several hundred progeny particles can then attach to a new bacterium and multiply. After several such cycles of attachment, multiplication, and release, all the bacteria in the immediate region of the original virus particle are killed. These regions of killed virus particles appear as circular holes (plaques) in the lawn of healthy bacteria (Figure 7–9).

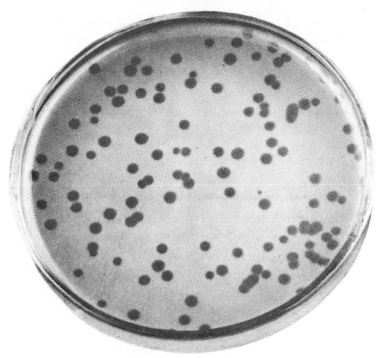

FIGURE 7-9 Photograph of phage T2 plaques on a lawn of E. coli bacteria growing in a Petri plate. (From G. S. Stent, *Molecular Biology of Bacterial Viruses*, Freeman, San Francisco, 1963, p. 41, with permission.)

VIRUS CHROMOSOMES ARE SOMETIMES INSERTED INTO THE CHROMOSOMES OF THEIR HOST CELLS

Some bacterial viruses (e.g., phage λ) do not always multiply upon entering a host cell. Instead their chromosome sometimes becomes inserted into a specific section of a host chromosome. Then the viral chromosome is, for all practical purposes, an integral part of its host chromosome and is duplicated, like the bacterial chromosome, just once every cell generation (Figure 7-10). The virus chromosome when it is integrated into a host chromosome is called the *prophage*; those bacteria containing prophages are called *lysogenic bacteria*; and those types of virus whose chromosomes can become prophages are known as *lysogenic viruses*. In contrast, those viruses (e.g., T2)

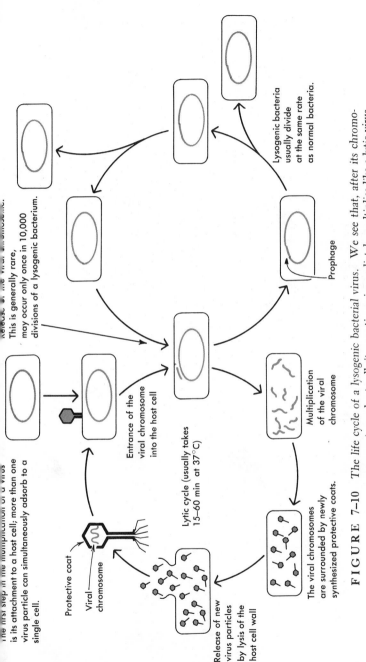

The first step in the multiplication of a virus is its attachment to a host cell; more than one virus particle can simultaneously adsorb to a single cell.

Protective coat

Viral chromosome

Lytic cycle (usually takes 15–60 min at 37°C)

Entrance of the viral chromosome into the host cell

Multiplication of the viral chromosome

The viral chromosomes are surrounded by newly synthesized protective coats.

Release of new virus particles by lysis of the host cell wall

This is generally rare, may occur only once in 10,000 divisions of a lysogenic bacterium.

Lysogenic bacteria usually divide at the same rate as normal bacteria.

Prophage

FIGURE 7-10 *The life cycle of a lysogenic bacterial virus. We see that, after its chromosome enters a host cell, it sometimes immediately multiplies like a lytic virus and at other times becomes transformed into prophage. The lytic phase of its life cycle is identical to the complete life cycle of a lytic (nonlysogenic) virus. Lytic bacterial viruses are so called because their multiplication results in the rupture (lysis) of the bacteria.*

205

that always multiply when they enter a host cell are called *lytic viruses*. It is often difficult to know when a bacterium is lysogenic. We can be sure only when the virus chromosome is released from the host chromosome and the multiplication process which forms new progeny particles commences. Why only certain viruses (lysogenic viruses) form lysogenic associations and what advantage they receive from this association is still an open question.

How the viral chromosome is transformed into prophage was until recently very mysterious. Now there is good genetic evidence that the integration of the viral chromosome is achieved by crossing over between the host chromosome and a *circular form* of the viral chromosome. Prior to integration, the viral chromosome forms a circle and attaches to a specific region of the host chromosome. Both the host chromosome and the viral chromosome then break and rejoin in such a way that the broken ends of the viral chromosomes join to the broken ends

FIGURE 7–11   *Insertion of the chromosome of phage λ into the E. coli chromosome by crossing over.*

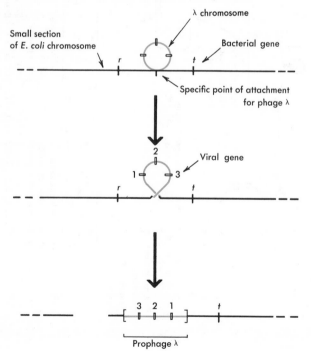

of the bacterial chromosome instead of to each other, thereby inserting the prophage into the host chromosome (Figure 7–11). The prophage detaches from the host chromosome by the reverse process: The two ends of the prophage pair prior to a crossover event which ejects the viral chromosome. The now free viral genome then can begin to multiply as if it were the chromosome of a lytic virus.

BACTERIAL–CHROMOSOME MAPPING BY MATING

Many organisms now of greatest use in revealing what genes are and how they work do not have a conventional meiosis. When sexuality in bacteria was first discovered, it seemed simplest to believe that a conventional cycle of cell fusion followed by meiotic segregation occurred. Now we know, however, that the E. coli cycle has distinctive factors complicating conventional genetic analysis. The complications arise from the nature of the mating process. As in higher organisms, there exist male and female cells. The sexual cycle starts when the male and female cells attach to each other by a narrow bridge (Figure 7–12). A male chromosome then begins to move through the bridge to the female cell. Usually the transfer is incomplete, and only part of the male chromosome enters the female cell before the mating cells separate. Thus only rarely are complete diploid cells formed, partially diploid cells usually occurring instead. Crossing over then occurs between the female parent and the male chromosome (or fragment), followed by a segregation process, which yields haploid progeny cells.

The sex difference between the male and female cells is determined by the presence of a specific genetic factor, called the F(ertility) factor. When it is present in cells (F$^+$) the cells are male, and when it is absent (F$^-$) they are female. The F factor can exist in two alternative states, either as part of the E. coli chromosome or as a very small free chromosome that multiplies once per cell division. In the latter case, the F$^+$ cells are only potentially male, since they cannot transfer their genes to F$^-$ cells; only when the F factor is part of the chromosome can the male cells mate. F$^+$ cells containing integrated

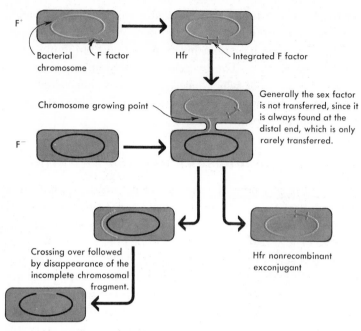

Bacterial   F factor   Hfr   Integrated F factor
chromosome

Chromosome growing point

Generally the sex factor
is not transferred, since it
is always found at the
distal end, which is only
rarely transferred.

F⁻

Crossing over followed
by disappearance of the
incomplete chromosomal
fragment.

Hfr nonrecombinant
exconjugant

F⁻ recombinant cell

FIGURE 7–12   Sexuality in E. coli. Chromosomal transfer from male
to female cells provides a primitive sexuality in E. coli.
When the F agent has become attached to the male
chromosome, the male cell, now Hfr, is competent to
transfer a chromosome to a female cell. When the
Hfr and F⁻ cells join together by a narrow bridge,
the Hfr chromosome breaks and begins to duplicate
at the site where the F factor has been inserted. A
free end of one of the daughter Hfr chromosome
segments then begins to move into the F⁻ cell. At
37°C, the transfer of a complete chromosome requires about 90 minutes. Generally, however, only
part of the Hfr chromosome moves to the F⁻ cell
before the cells separate; crossing over then occurs between the donor genetic material and the F⁻ chromosome. The haploid condition is reestablished by
elimination of the supernumerary genes that have not
become part of complete chromosomes. The recombinant cells can then be screened for the presence
of various Hfr and F⁻ genes, thereby allowing the
construction of a genetic map.

sex factors are called *Hfr* (high frequency of recombination). A variety of different Hfr strains exist, each containing an F factor integrated into a different region of the chromosome. Until recently, there was no good hypothesis about how the F agent becomes part of the host chromosome. Now there are strong hints that the F agent, like the chromosomes of lysogenic phages, has a circular shape and becomes integrated by crossing over.

Both the F factor and the lysogenic phage chromosomes are called *episomes*. An episome is defined as a genetic particle that can exist either free or as a part of a normal cellular chromosome. Now we have good evidence for the existence of episomes only in bacteria; there are hints, however, that they exist in higher plants and animals as well.

At first the fact that only part of the male chromosome enters the female cell made genetic analysis more difficult. Then it was realized that a fixed end of the male chromosome, specific for a given Hfr strain, always enters the female cell first, and that the relative frequency with which male genes are incorporated into the recombinant chromosome is a measure of how close they are to the entering end. Moreover it is possible to break apart the male and female cells artificially by violent agitation (this was first done in a mixing machine called the Waring Blendor); matings can be made and the couples violently agitated at fixed times during the process (the Blendor experiments). If the pairs are disrupted soon after mating, only the genes very close to the forward end will have entered the cell. It is thus possible to obtain the *E. coli* gene positions merely by observing the time intervals at which various male alleles have entered the female cells.

BACTERIAL CHROMOSOMES ARE CIRCULAR

The genetic map obtained through analysis of interrupted matings is the same as that arrived at by analysis of frequencies of various recombinant classes. As in the chromosomal maps of higher organisms, the bacterial genes are arranged on an unbranched line. However, one important distinction exists: The

TABLE 7-1   *Key to the genes of the E. coli chromosome*[a]

Genetic symbols	Mutant character	Enzyme or reaction affected
araD	⎫	L-Ribulose-5-phosphate-4-epimerase
araA	Cannot use the sugar arabinose as a carbon source	L-Arabinose isomerase
araB		L-Ribulokinase
araC	⎭	
argB	⎫	N-Acetylglutamate synthetase
argC		N-Acetyl-γ-glutamokinase
argH		N-Acetylglutamic-γ-semi-aldehyde dehydrogenase
argG	Requires the amino acid arginine for growth	Acetylornithine-d-transaminase
argA		Acetylornithinase
argD		Ornithine transcarbamylase
argE		Argininosuccinic acid synthetase
argF	⎭	Argininosuccinase
aroA, B, C	⎫	Shikimic acid to 3-enolpyruvyl-shikimate-5-phosphate
aroD	Requires several aromatic amino acids and vitamins for growth	Biosynthesis of shikimic acid
azi	Resistant to sodium azide	
bio	Requires the vitamin biotin for growth	
cysA	⎫	
cysB		3-Phosphoadenosine-5-phosphosulfate to sulfide
	Requires the amino acid cysteine for growth	
cysC	⎭	Sulfate to sulfide; 4 known enzymes
dapA	⎫	Dihydrodipicolinic acid synthetase
dapB	Requires the cell wall component diaminopimelic acid	N-Succinyl-diaminopimelic acid deacylase
dap + hom	Requires the amino acid precursor homoserine and the cell-wall component diaminopimelic acid for growth	Aspartic semialdehyde dehydrogenase

T A B L E 7–1 (*continued*)

Genetic symbols	Mutant character	Enzyme or reaction affected
Dsd	Cannot use the amino acid D-serine as a nitrogen source	D-Serine deaminase
fla	Flagella are absent	
galA	Cannot use the sugar	Galactokinase
galB	galactose as a carbon source	Galactose-1-phosphate uridyl transferase
galD	Constitutive synthesis of galactose operon pro-	Uridine-diphosphogalactose-4-epimerase
galC	teins (see Chapter 14)	Defective operator (see Chapter 11)
gua	Requires the amino acid guanine for growth	
H	The H antigen is present	
his	Requires the amino acid histidine for growth	10 known enzymes[b]
ile	Requires the amino acid isoleucine for growth	Threonine deaminase
ilvA		α-Hydroxy-β-keto acid rectoisomerase
ilvB	Requires the amino acids isoleucine and valine for growth	α,β-dihydroxyisovaleric dehydrase[b]
ilvC		Transaminase B
ind (indole)	Cannot grow on tryptophan as a carbon source	Tryptophanase
λ	Chromosomal location where prophage λ is normally inserted	
lac Y	Unable to concentrate β-galactosides	Galactoside permease
lac Z	Cannot use the sugar lactose as a carbon source	β-Galactosidase
lac O	Constitutive synthesis of lactose operon proteins (see Chapter 14)	Defective operator
leu	Requires the amino acid leucine for growth	3 known enzymes[b]
lon (long form)	Filament formation and radiation sensitivity are affected	

(*continued*)

TABLE 7–1 (*continued*)

Genetic symbols	Mutant character	Enzyme or reaction affected
lys	Requires the amino acid lysine for growth	Diaminopimelic acid de-carboxylase
lys + met	Requires the amino acids lysine and methionine for growth	
λ rec, malA	Resistant to phage λ and cannot use the sugar maltose	Phage λ receptor, and maltose permease
malB	Cannot use the sugar maltose as a carbon source	Amylomaltase(?)
metA	⎫	Synthesis of succinic ester of homoserine[b]
metB	⎪ Requires the amino acid methionine for growth Requires either the amino acid methionine or cobalamine for growth	Succinic ester of homo-serine + cysteine to cystathionine
metF	⎬	5,10-Methylene tetra-hydrofolate reductase
metE	⎭	
mtl	Cannot use the sugar mannitol as a carbon source	Mannitol dehydro-genase(?)
muc	Forms mucoid colonies	Regulation of capsular polysaccharide syn-thesis
O	The O antigen is present	
pan	Requires the vitamin pantothenic acid for growth	
phe A, B	Requires the amino acid phenylalanine for growth	
pho	Cannot use phosphate esters	Alkaline phosphatase
pil	Has filaments (pili) at-tached to the cell wall	
proA proB proC	Requires the amino acid proline for growth	

T A B L E 7–1 (*continued*)

Genetic symbols	Mutant character	Enzyme or reaction affected
purA		Adenylosuccinate synthetase
purB	Requires certain purines for growth	Adenylosuccinase
purC, E		5-Aminoimidazole ribotide (AIR) to 5-aminoimidazole-4-(N-succino carboximide) ribotide
purD		Biosynthesis of AIR
pyrA	Requires the pyrimidine uracil and the amino acid arginine for growth	Carbamate kinase
pyrB		Aspartate transcarbamylase
pyrC		Dihydroorotase
pyrD	Requires the pyrimidine uracil for growth	Dihydroorotic acid dehydrogenase
pyrE		Orotidylic acid pyrophosphorylase
pyrF		Orotidylic acid decarboxylase
R arg	Constitutive synthesis of arginine (see Chapter 14)	Repressor for enzymes involved in arginine synthesis
R gal	Constitutive production of galactose	Repressor for enzymes involved in galactose production
Rl pho, R2 pho	Constitutive synthesis of phosphatase	Alkaline phosphatase repressor
R try	Constitutive synthesis of tryptophan	Repressor for enzymes involved in tryptophan synthesis
RC (RNA control)	Uncontrolled synthesis of RNA	
rha	Cannot use the sugar rhamnose as a carbon source	
serA	Requires the amino acid serine for growth	3-Phosphoglycerate dehydrogenase
serB		Phosphoserine phosphatase

(*continued*)

214   MOLECULAR BIOLOGY OF THE GENE

TABLE 7–1 (*continued*)

Genetic symbols	Mutant character	Enzyme or reaction affected
str	Resistant to or dependent on streptomycin	
suc	Requires succinic acid	
T1, T5 rec	Resistant to phages T1 and T5 (mutants called B/1,5)	T1, T5 receptor sites absent
T1 rec	Resistant to phage T1 (mutants called B/1)	T1 receptor site absent
T6, colK rec	Resistant to phage T6 and colicine K	T6 and colicine receptor sites absent
T4 rec	Resistant to phage T4 (mutants called B/4)	T4 receptor site absent
thi	Requires the vitamin thiamine for growth	
thr	Requires the amino acid threonine for growth	
thy	Requires the pyrimidine thymine for growth	Thymidylate synthetase
tryA		Tryptophan synthetase, A protein
tryB		Tryptophan synthetase, B protein
tryC	Requires the amino acid tryptophan for growth	Indole-3-glycerolphosphate synthetase
tryE		Anthranilic acid to anthranilic-deoxyribulotide
tryD		3-Enolpyruvylshikimate-5-phosphate to anthranilic acid
tyr	Requires the amino acid tyrosine for growth	
uvrA	Resistant to ultraviolet radiation	Ultraviolet-induced lesions in DNA are reactivated
xyl	Cannot use the sugar xylose as a carbon source	

ᵃ Each known gene or gene cluster is listed by its symbol and with the character caused by a mutation in the gene or gene cluster. The enzyme affected or reaction prevented is listed where known.

ᵇ Denotes enzymes controlled by the homologous gene loci of *Salmonella typhimurium*.

genetic map of E. *coli* is a circle (Figure 7–13); the male chromosome must break at a certain point before a free end can move into a female cell. If the point of breakage were not always the same point, we would not observe that in a given bacterial strain some genes tend to be transferred before others. The place where the break occurs, however, is not the same in all strains. This is because the break always occurs at the point where the F factor is integrated. There is one Hfr strain, for example, in which some of the genes connected for the synthesis of threonine and leucine are transferred soon after mating, whereas in another, a gene involved in methionine synthesis is among the first to enter the female cell. The existence of many strains, with various breakage points, has been very important in assigning gene locations. If only one entering point existed, it would be nearly impossible to assign even a rough order to those genes that would always enter last, since they enter the female cell only rarely.

We are still not sure what force drives the male chromosome into the female cell. There are hints that the transfer may be connected to the process of chromosome duplication; that is, the male chromosome does not merely break and one end begin to be transferred. Instead it looks as if the breakage initiates a cycle of chromosome replication, and that as the Hfr chromosome splits to form two chromosomes, one of the progeny chromosomes moves into the female cell. Chromosome transfer may thus accompany the synthesis of a new chromosome or chromosome segment.

The biological significance of circular genetic maps is surrounded with mystery. Circular maps also exist for viral chromosomes, and so the E. *coli* form should not be viewed as a strange exception. We shall return to a discussion of circles when we look at the precise chemistry of the chromosome.

PHAGES OCCASIONALLY CARRY BACTERIAL GENES

Not only can bacterial genes be transferred in mating, but they can also be passively carried from one bacterium to another by phage particles (*transduction*). This happens when a virus particle is formed that accidentally contains a very small

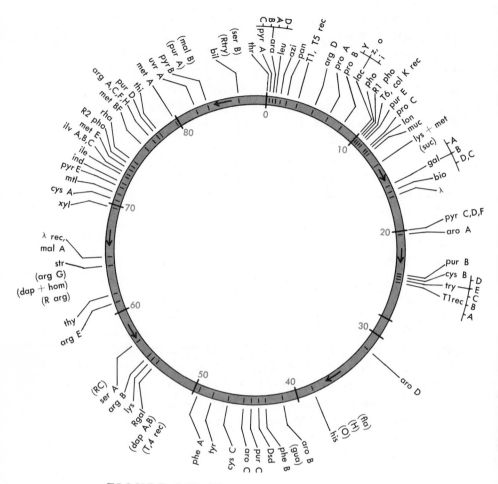

FIGURE 7–13   The genetic map of E. coli. The symbols mark the
locations of genes. A key to the various gene abbre-
viations is found in Table 7–1. Those genes whose
locations are only approximately known are shown in
parentheses. The numbers divide the map into time
intervals corresponding to the time in minutes which
it takes each male chromosomal segment to move into
a female cell. Thus 89 minutes are now thought to
be required for complete transfer. The arrows mark
the points at which various Hfr chromosomes break
prior to transfer into a female cell; the direction of
the arrows indicates transfer direction. [Redrawn
from A. L. Taylor and M. S. Thoman, Genetics, **50**,
667 (1964), with permission.]

portion (usually less than 1 to 2 per cent) of its host chromosome (a *transducing phage*). When this virus particle (usually biologically inactive because its viral chromosome is incomplete or totally missing) attaches to a host cell, the fragment of bacterial chromosome is injected into the cell. It then can engage in crossing over with the host chromosome; if the transducing phage has been grown on a bacterial strain genetically different from the strain subsequently infected with the phage, a genetically altered bacterium may be produced (Figure 7–14). For example, a suspension of phage particles P1 grown on a strain of *E. coli* that is able to grow on lactose contains a small number of particles carrying the gene (lac⁺) involved in lactose metabolism. Addition of these phages to an

FIGURE 7–14   *Passive transfer of genetic material from one bacterium to another by means of carrier phage particles (transduction).*

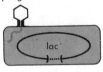

Infection of *E. coli* by phage P1

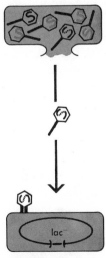

Formation of a large number of complete virus particles and a small number of defective phages carrying a small fragment of the bacterial chromosome.

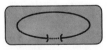

Insertion of the lac⁺ region in the host chromosome by crossing over.

Adsorption of a lac⁺ transducing P1 particle to a lac⁻ *E. coli* cell.

E. coli strain unable to use lactose (lac⁻) transforms a small number of the lac⁻ bacteria to the lac⁺ form, by means of genetic recombination.

Because transduction is very rare, it might be guessed that it would not be a useful tool for probing chromosome structure. In fact, it has been most helpful in telling us whether two genes are located close to each other and what their exact order is. This is because the number of bacterial genes carried by a single transducing particle is small so that only genes located very close to each other will be enclosed in the same transducing particle. Thus by determining the frequencies with which groups of genes can be transduced by the same phage particle we can establish very accurately their relative locations.

TRANSFER OF PURIFIED CHROMOSOME FRAGMENTS

Transformation is the name given to genetic recombination brought about by the introduction of purified chromosomes (DNA). It has provided the crucial biological system for the chemical identification of the genetic material (DNA). Transformation was originally discovered in 1928, when the observation was made that the addition of heat-killed cells of a pathogenic strain of *Diplococcus pneumoniae* to a suspension of live, nonpathogenic pneumonia cells caused a small fraction of the live bacteria to become pathogenic. The hereditary nature of this transformation was shown by using descendants of the newly pathogenic strain to transform still other nonpathogenic bacteria. This suggested that when the pathogenic cells are killed by heat, their chromosomes (now known to be DNA) are undamaged, and free chromosomal material, liberated somehow from the heat-killed cells, can pass through the cell wall of the living cells and subsequently undergo genetic recombination with the host chromosome (Figure 7–15).

Subsequent experiments have confirmed the genetic interpretation of the transformation phenomenon. The pathogenic character is caused by a gene S (smooth), which affects the chemistry of the bacterial cell wall and causes the formation of a carbohydrate capsule. When the R (rough) allele of this gene is present instead, no capsule is formed, and the cell is not pathogenic.

Although the first transformation experiments involved only changes in capsule chemistry, it is now clear that all genes can be transformed by means of the addition of extracted chromosomes. Because only small chromosomal fragments are gen-

FIGURE 7–15   *Transformation of the genetic character of a bacterial cell (Diplococcus pneumonia) by addition of heat-killed cells of a genetically different strain. Here we show an R cell receiving a chromosomal fragment containing the S gene. Most R cells, however, receive other chromosome fragments, and so the efficiency of transformation for a given gene is usually less than 1 per cent.*

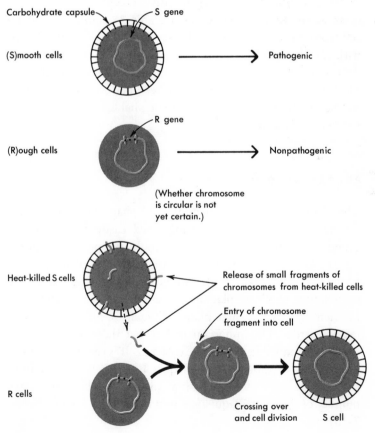

erally transformed in this way, this process can also reveal which genes are located close to each other. The fact that transformation of most types of bacteria is very inefficient has, up to now, severely restricted its general applicability to genetic problems. Thus transduction rather than transformation is our most efficient means of determining the precise order of *E. coli* genes. Transformation has, nevertheless, been very useful in locating the genes of the bacteria *Bacillus subtilis*, for which a useful transducing phage is not yet known.

Ever since transformation was first demonstrated, much speculation has existed whether it is possible in organisms larger than bacteria. Particular attention has been focused on the possibility of transforming mammals, especially man. So far, however, all results have been negative, except for some special cases where viral chromosomes are able to transform normal cells into cancer cells. Here, however, we may be dealing not with the change of an existing gene, but rather with the introduction of entirely new genetic material. In any case, though, too few good experiments have yet been performed to give us a feeling of whether this type of genetic analysis can be extended to higher organisms.

PHAGES ALSO MUTATE

The plaques formed by a given type of phage are quite characteristic and can often be distinguished easily from those of genetically distinct phages. For example, the plaques of phage T2 can easily be separated from those made by phage λ or by phage F2. More significantly, mutations occur that change the morphology of phage plaques. We do not usually know the biochemical basis of these plaque differences, but this does not really matter. The important fact is that these differences are usually reproducible and simple to score. It is easy to look at the morphology of thousands of plaques to see if any differ from the plaques made by the wild-type phage. In this way a large number of different plaque-type mutations were found (Figure 7–16).

Another class of mutations changes the ability of phage to

adsorb to bacteria. For example, wild-type T2 cannot multiply on *E. coli* strain B/2, because the B/2 mutation changes the cell surface, thereby preventing the attachment of T2. Mutant T2 particles can, however, multiply on B/2: They are called T2h, and are able to adsorb because they possess altered tail fibers.

Another very large and important class of mutants exists

FIGURE 7–16 Photograph of mutant phage plaques. Shown are a mixture of T2r⁺ (wild-type) plaques and T2r (a rapid lysis mutant) plaques. The mottled plaques arise from the simultaneous growth of both r and r⁺ phages in the same plaque. (From G. S. Stent, *Molecular Biology of Bacterial Viruses*, Freeman, San Francisco, 1963, p. 177, with permission.)

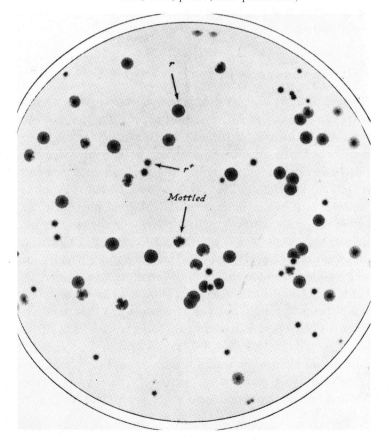

which have the ability to multiply at 25°C, but cannot multiply at 42°C (temperature-sensitive *conditional lethals*). Although we cannot now pinpoint the exact reason why these mutant phages do not multiply at the higher temperature, we suspect that the high temperature destroys the 3–D structure of a protein necessary for their reproduction. This type of mutation has proved useful because a large number of viral genes mutate to a temperature-sensitive form. When we isolate a mutant unable to multiply at the higher temperature, the mutation may be located in a large variety of different genes.

The existence of conditional lethal mutations has allowed phage geneticists to find mutations in essentially all the genes of phages T4 and λ. Despite the fact that genetic recombination between mutant viruses was not discovered until 1945, the phage T4 is now the best and most completely characterized genetic object.

PHAGE CROSSES

More than one phage particle at a time can grow in a single bacterium. If several particles adsorb at once, the chromosomes from all of them enter the cell and duplicate to form large numbers of new copies. So long as the chromosomes exist free (unenclosed by a protective coat) they can cross over with similar chromosomes (Figure 7–17). This is shown by infecting cells with two or more genetically distinct phage particles and finding recombinant genetic types among the progeny particles. For example, it is easy to obtain mutant T4 particles differing from the wild type by two mutations, one in an h gene, which allows them to grow on *E. coli* strain B/4 (a strain resistant to wild-type T4 particles) and the other in an r gene, which causes them to form larger and clearer plaques than wild-type T4 particles. These double mutant phages are designated T4hr, and the wild-type is called T4h⁺r⁺. When an *E. coli* cell is infected simultaneously with a T4h⁺r⁺ and a T4hr phage, four types of progeny particles are found: the parental genotypes h⁺r⁺ and hr, and the recombinant genotypes hr⁺ and h⁺r (Figure 7–18).

The frequency with which recombinants are found depends upon the particular mutants used in the cross. Crosses between some pairs of markers give almost 50 per cent recombinant phage; crosses between others give somewhat lower recombinant values, and sometimes almost no recombinants are found. This immediately suggests that viruses also have unbranched genetic maps, a suggestion now completely confirmed by intense analysis of a large number of independently isolated mutations. At present our best known map is that of phage T4 (Figure

FIGURE 7–17   *Genetic recombination following infection of a bacterium with several genetically distinct phage particles.*

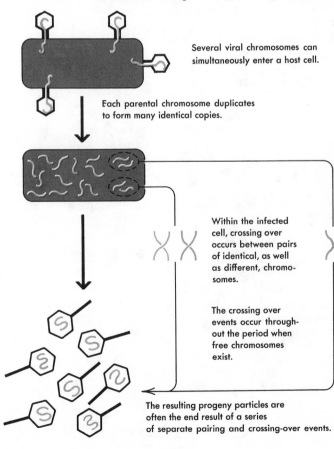

Several viral chromosomes can simultaneously enter a host cell.

Each parental chromosome duplicates to form many identical copies.

Within the infected cell, crossing over occurs between pairs of identical, as well as different, chromosomes.

The crossing over events occur throughout the period when free chromosomes exist.

The resulting progeny particles are often the end result of a series of separate pairing and crossing-over events.

7–19), a circular map, like that of *E. coli*. We do not know
whether all viruses will have circular maps; hints now exist that
several viruses previously thought to have strictly linear maps
will be found to have circular ones.

FIGURE 7–18   *Plaques found after infecting bacteria with T2 hr and
T2h⁺r⁺ phages. The technique used to see all four
progeny types (hr, h⁺r⁺, h⁺r, hr⁺) is to look for plaques
on a mixture of strain B and strain B/2. Only phages
possessing the h gene can kill both B and B/2 cells.
Phages with the h⁺ gene kill only B cells, and their
plaques look turbid because of the presence of live
B/2 cells. (From G. S. Stent, Molecular Biology of
Bacterial Viruses, Freeman, San Francisco, 1963, p.
185, with permission.)*

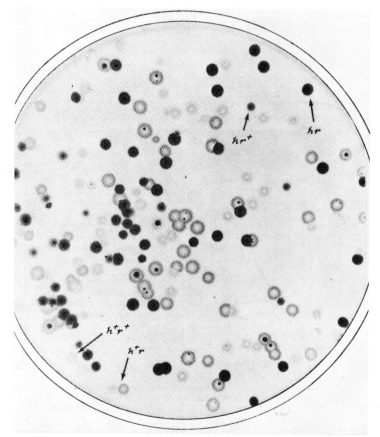

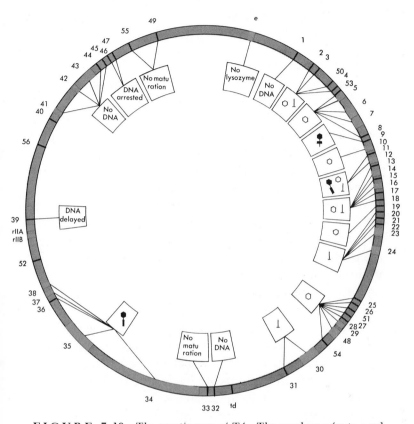

FIGURE 7–19 *The genetic map of T4. The numbers refer to a collection of 56 genes in which conditional lethal mutations have been located. Their existence as distinct genes has been shown by complementation studies (see Chapter 8). The minimal length is shown for some of the genes (color segments). The length of other genes (black segments) has not yet been worked out. The boxes show either deficiencies in synthesis associated with some mutant genes or incomplete viral components seen by EM investigation of infected cells. The genes in the upper left of the circle control functions in the first half of the life cycle. The remaining genes function in the last half of the cycle. Nothing is known about how this differential timing is accomplished.*

VIRAL CROSSES INVOLVE MULTIPLE PAIRINGS

Thus the genetic structure of viral chromosomes appears to be essentially similar to that of cellular chromosomes. Nonetheless, it is worth pointing out a distinct feature of viral crosses. In conventional meiosis each chromosome pairs just once, whereas in a viral cross, pairing and crossing over may occur repeatedly throughout the period when free chromosomes are present. Thus a given chromosome may participate in several pairing and crossing over events. This point is simply demonstrated by infecting a cell with three virus particles, each with a distinct genetic marker, and finding single progeny particles that have derived chromosomal regions from all three particles. The products of a phage cross are essentially, then, the products of a large number of distinct pairings and crossings over. There is great variation among viruses in the amount of crossing over; for example, a chromosome of phage T4 crosses over, on the average, 5 to 10 times, and a phage λ chromosome only 0.5 times, during each growth cycle. The existence of many distinct crossovers does not, however, restrict our ability to map the genetic markers, since the general rule still holds that genes located close together seldom recombine.

Another way in which a viral cross differs from conventional meiosis involving cell fusion is that viruses are not separated into male and female particles. Differentiation into sexes can be considered a device to bring about cell fusion between genetically distinct organisms. Virus particles, however, do not have to fuse, since genetic recombination occurs when two viral chromosomes of different genotypes enter a single host cell. Moreover, in cells infected with several genetically distinct viruses, crossing over can occur between both genetically identical and different chromosomes; thus only a fraction of the crossovers in a cell infected with different viruses result in recombinant chromosomes of a new genotype. Evidence also exists that crossing over occurs after infection with a single virus particle. This phenomenon cannot be revealed by genetic analysis, since all the progeny chromosomes are genetically identical, and so experiments with isotopically labeled virus (see Chapter 9) are necessary for its demonstration.

SUMMARY

Chromosomes control the hereditary properties of all cells and are linear collections of specific genetic factors called genes. Each gene can affect the character of a cell in a highly specific way. This is shown by the striking cellular effects of hereditary changes in gene structures (mutations): Various mutations can alter, for example, the eye color or body size of an organism. Although spontaneous mutations occur only rarely, it is possible to increase mutation rates by applying specific chemicals or radiation (mutagens).

Most of the early work in genetics was with large and complicated diploid plants and animals. Now, however, the most favorable objects for use in studying what a gene is and how it functions are the haploid microorganisms like the bacteria and their viruses, the bacteriophages (phages). They have the advantage of very short life cycles and ease of growth under controllable laboratory conditions.

Bacterial mutations involving growth factors and resistance to specific antibiotics and viruses are particularly useful because of the ease of separating wild-type and mutant particles. The same is true for phage mutations involving host range and temperature requirements.

The location of genes on chromosomes is revealed by a study of the segregation of genes in genetic crosses. Recombination of alleles can be caused by both random assortment of chromosomes and crossing over of homologous chromosomes. We can determine whether given genes are located on different or the same chromosomes by whether they assort randomly, as chromosomes do, or whether they exhibit (more than 50 per cent) linkage. Crossing over of homologous chromosomes provides a basis for determining the relative positions of genes on chromosomes (chromosome mapping). The more frequently crossovers occur between two genes, the farther apart the genes must be. When three genes are considered at once (three-factor cross), the least frequent recombinant type results from a double crossover; the determination of this recombinant type provides a check for the results of several two-factor crosses dealing with the same three factors.

Most genetic crosses designed to reveal what genes are are now performed with bacteria and phages, where typical meiosis does not occur. Bacterial crosses usually involve crossovers between a chromosome fragment and an intact chromosome. Genetic recombination occurs in bacteria as a result of mating between male (Hfr) and female cells (conjugation), attachment of phage particles containing the genes of former bacterial hosts (transduction), and the introduction of foreign chromosomal (DNA) extracts (transformation). Phage crosses take place when a bacterium is infected with two or more genetically distinct phages; they involve many cycles of pairing and crossing over. Despite the difficulties which these phenomena present to the study of phage and bacterial genetics, the chromosomes of the bacterium E. coli and the phage T4 are quickly becoming the best understood of all genetic material.

REFERENCES

Sager, R., and F. J. Ryan, *Cell Heredity*, Wiley, New York, 1961. A discussion of modern genetics, emphasizing microorganisms.

Hayes, W., *The Genetics of Bacteria and Their Viruses: Studies in Basic Genetics and Molecular Biology*, Wiley, New York, 1964. A comprehensive description of the genetic systems of viruses and bacteria showing how they have been used to elucidate many of the fundamental principles of molecular genetics.

Jacob, F., and E. L. Wollman, *Sexuality and the Genetics of Bacteria*, Academic, New York, 1961. Though now slightly out of date in its discussion of advanced topics, the book remains an excellent discussion of the heredity of E. coli.

Stent, G. S., *Molecular Biology of Bacterial Viruses*, Freeman, San Francisco, 1963. An example of that rare item—a nearly perfect book. Here are lucidly presented both the past and present ideas about bacterial viruses.

Adelberg, E. A. (ed.), *Papers on Bacterial Genetics*, Little, Brown,

Boston, 1960. A collection of significant reprints on the development of bacterial genetics.

Stent, G. S. (ed.), *Papers on Bacterial Viruses*, Little, Brown, Boston, 1960. A collection of many of the papers that shaped the development of current research with bacterial viruses.

8

GENE

STRUCTURE

AND

FUNCTION

FOR MANY YEARS IT WAS GENERALLY thought that crossing over occurred between genes, not within the genes themselves. The chromosome was viewed as a linear collection of genes held together by some nongenetic material, somewhat like a string of pearls. Now, however, we realize that this viewpoint is completely wrong and the exact opposite may be true—all crossing over may occur by breakage and reunion of the genetic molecules themselves. The original impression arose from the fact that crossing over between two regions is much easier to detect if the regions are far apart on a chromosome. If they are very close, recombination is extremely rare and can be detected only by examining a very large number of progeny, too large to make study of intragenic recombination practicable when genetic work was restricted to higher organisms. Even with the intensively studied fruit fly *Drosophila*, it is difficult to look at more than 50,000 progeny from a single cross. Newer techniques, however, permit rapid screening of millions of the progeny from crosses between genetically different molds, yeast, bacteria, or viruses. With these organisms it has been simple to show that crossing over can cause recombination of material within a gene. Each gene contains a number of different sites at which mutations occur and between which crossing over occurs. This result provides a powerful method for investigating topological structures of genes.

230

RECOMBINATION WITHIN GENES ALLOWS
CONSTRUCTION OF A GENE MAP

Up to now, the most striking results on the genetic structure of the gene itself have come from the work with the rIIA and rIIB genes of the bacterial virus T4. These are two adjacent genes which influence the length of the T4 life cycle; mutations in both thereby affect the size of plaques produced in a bacterial layer growing on an agar plate. The presence of either an rIIA or an rIIB mutation can cause a shorter life cycle of T4 phage within an *E. coli* cell. T4-infected cells on an agar plate normally do not break open and release new progeny phage until several hours after they have been infected. Cells infected with rII mutants, however, always break open more rapidly, hence the designation r (II stands for the fact that there do exist other genes which cause rapid cell lysis). Thus rII mutants produce larger plaques than wild-type phage. The rII mutants were chosen to work with because of the possibility of detecting a very small number of wild-type particles among a very large number of mutants. Although the wild-type and the rII mutants grow equally well on *E. coli* strain B, there is another strain, *E. coli* K(λ), on which only the wild-type can multiply. Thus when the progeny of a genetic cross between two different rII mutants are added to K12(λ), only the wild-type recombinants form plaques. Even as few as one wild-type recombinant per 10^6 progeny is easily detected.

Over two thousand independent mutations in the rIIA and rIIB genes have been isolated and used in breeding experiments. In a typical cross, *E. coli* strain B bacteria were infected with two phage particles, each bearing an independently isolated rIIA (or rIIB) mutation. As the virus particles multiplied, genetic recombination occurred. The progeny were then grown on *E. coli* K(λ) to test for the wild type. Normal particles were found in a very large fraction of the crosses, indicating recombination within the gene (Figure 8–1). If recombination occurred only *between* genes it would be impossible to produce wild-type recombinants by crossing two phage particles with mutations in the same gene. A large spectrum of recombination values was found, just as in crosses

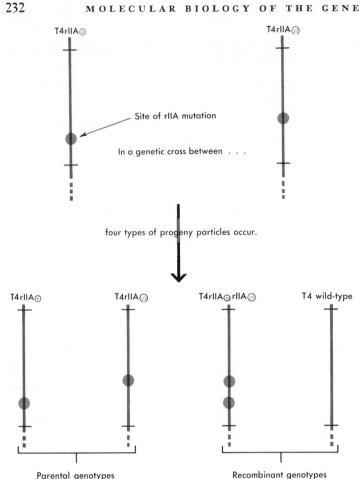

FIGURE 8-1   *The use of T4rII mutations in the demonstration of crossing over within the gene. Equal numbers of wild-type and double r recombinants occur. The wild-type recombinants are easily found, because they are the only progeny genotype which will form plaques on K12(λ). It is much harder to identify the double rIIA$_6$rIIA$_{27}$ recombinants; inasmuch as their plaques are indistinguishable from single r plaques. To detect them, it is necessary to isolate a large number of progeny r viruses with the r phenotype and use them for new genetic crosses with both parent r strains. The double r mutants will not produce wild-type recombinants with either of the single r mutants.*

between mutants for separate genes. This spread of values indicates that some mutations occur closer together than others, and allows for the construction of genetic maps for the two rII genes. Examination of these genetic maps yields the following striking conclusions:

1. A large number of different sites of mutation (mutable sites) occur within the gene. This number is on the order of 1000 to 1500 altogether for the rIIA and rIIB genes (Figure 8–2).

2. The rIIA and rIIB genetic maps are unambiguously linear, strongly hinting that the gene itself has a linear construction.

3. Most mutations are changes at only one mutable site. Genes containing such mutations are able to be restored to the original wild-type gene structure by the process of undergoing a second (reverse) mutation at the same site as the first mutation.

4. Other mutations cause the deletion of significant fractions of the genetic map. These are the result of a physical deletion of part of the rII gene (Figure 8–3). Mutations deleting more than one mutable site are highly unlikely to mutate back to the original gene form.

The genetic fine structure of a number of other viral and bacterial genes has also been extensively mapped. The lengths of these maps vary from gene to gene, suggesting that some gene products are larger than others. Though no other study has been as extensive as the rII work, each points to the same conclusions—that all genes have a very large number of sites at which mutation can occur, and that these mutable sites are arranged in a strictly linear order. The geneticist's view of a gene is thus: *a discrete chromosomal region which (1) is responsible for a specific cellular product and (2) consists of a linear collection of potentially mutable units (mutable sites), each of which can exist in several alternative forms and between which crossing over can occur.*

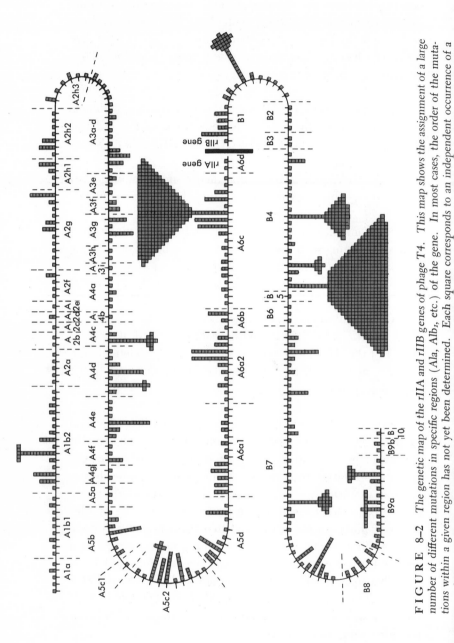

FIGURE 8-2 The genetic map of the rIIA and rIIB genes of phage T4. This map shows the assignment of a large number of different mutations in specific regions (Ala, Alb, etc.) of the gene. In most cases, the order of the mutations within a given region has not yet been determined. Each square corresponds to an independent occurrence of a

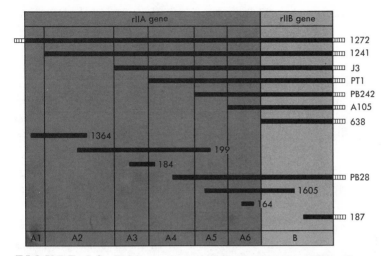

FIGURE 8–3   *Deletion mutations within the rII region of T4. About 10 per cent of the spontaneous rII mutations do not map at a distinct point. They are due to deletions of a large number of adjacent mutable sites. Some deletions, for example 1272, involve both the rIIA and rIIB genes. The small rectangles indicate that the deletion most likely extends into the adjacent gene. The existence of deletion mutations has considerably facilitated genetic mapping. By crossing a newly isolated rII mutant with a number of deletion mutations covering increasingly larger regions, it is quickly possible to assign an approximate map location to the new mutant. In this map the size of the rIIB gene has been arbitrarily reduced.*

THE COMPLEMENTATION TEST DETERMINES IF TWO MUTATIONS ARE IN THE SAME GENE

Since mutations in both the rIIA and rIIB genes result in a larger sized plaque, it is natural to ask why they are considered two genes: Would it not be simpler to consider them parts of the same gene? Our answer is straightforward. If *E. coli* strain K12(λ) is infected simultaneously with a T4rIIA and a T4rIIB mutant, the chromosomes of both viruses multiply, and progeny virus is produced (Figure 8–4). In contrast, simultaneous infection of the K12(λ) with either two different T4rIIA or two different T4rIIB mutants results in no virus multiplication. This demonstrates that rIIA and rIIB genes carry out two different functions, each necessary for multiplication on K12(λ).

In infection with a single T4rIIA mutant, the rIIB gene functions normally, but no active form of the rIIA product is available, so that no viral multiplication is possible. Likewise, in infection with a single rIIB mutant, an active rIIA product results, but only an inactive form of the rIIB product arises. Virus multiplication only occurs when we simultaneously infect a bacterium with an rIIA phage mutant and an rIIB phage mutant because each mutant chromosome is able to produce

FIGURE 8-4 *The demonstration that the rII region consists of two distinct genes which can complement each other during simultaneous infection.*

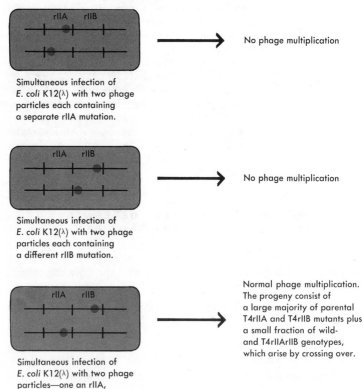

Simultaneous infection of
E. coli K12(λ) with two phage
particles each containing
a separate rIIA mutation.

No phage multiplication

Simultaneous infection of
E. coli K12(λ) with two phage
particles each containing
a different rIIB mutation.

No phage multiplication

Simultaneous infection of
E. coli K12(λ) with two phage
particles—one an rIIA,
the other an rIIB mutation.

Normal phage multiplication.
The progeny consist of
a large majority of parental
T4rIIA and T4rIIB mutants plus
a small fraction of wild-
and T4rIIArIIB genotypes,
which arise by crossing over.

the gene product that its infecting partner is unable to make. Two chromosomes thus can *complement* each other when the mutations are present in distinct genes—*the complementation test.* (This experiment is not affected by the possibility of intragenic crossing over between mutants to produce wild-type phage, because the number of such recombinants is very small; in contrast, complementation between different mutant genes yields a normal number of progeny particles.)

It is easy to perform complementation tests with phage mutants. All that is necessary is to infect a bacterium with two different mutants at once. This automatically creates a cell containing one copy of each mutant chromosome. It is more difficult to carry out complementation tests with normally haploid cells, like *E. coli.* But fortunately, genetic tricks too complicated to be described here enable special strains to be constructed with some chromosome sections present twice (partially diploid strains). These have often been useful in telling us that a chromosomal region thought to contain only one gene actually produces several gene products, and so must contain a corresponding number of genes.

GENETIC CONTROL OF PROTEIN FUNCTION

A direct relationship between genes and enzymes was hypothesized as early as 1909 from a study of the metabolism of phenylalanine in patients suffering from certain hereditary diseases; but it was not until the decade following 1941, when a variety of growth factor mutants became available in *Neurospora* and *E. coli,* that the one gene–one enzyme hypothesis became an established fact. One of the first proofs involved the biosynthesis of the amino acid arginine. Its pathway starts with glutamic acid and proceeds by eight chemical reactions, each catalyzed by a distinct enzyme (Figure 8–5). For each of these eight steps mutant cells have been isolated that fail to carry out that specific enzymatic reaction. This suggests that a separate gene controls the presence of each enzyme, a hypothesis confirmed by the absence of the specific active enzyme in cell extracts prepared from such mutant cells. The biosynthesis of histidine (Figure 8–6) provides another beautiful example of this relationship: There exist specific mutations resulting in the absence of each of the ten enzymes necessary for this biosynthesis.

FIGURE 8–5   *Pathway of arginine biosynthesis in* E. coli.

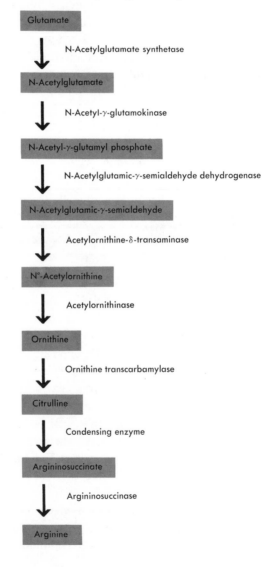

Enzymes are not the only proteins directly controlled by genes. Each specific protein is controlled by a gene unique for that protein. One of the first clean proofs of this idea came from the study of the hemoglobin present in people suffering

FIGURE 8–6   *The pathway for histidine biosynthesis in* Salmonella typhimurium. *This bacterium, which is closely related to* E. coli, *appears to have a chromosome with a similar gene arrangement.*

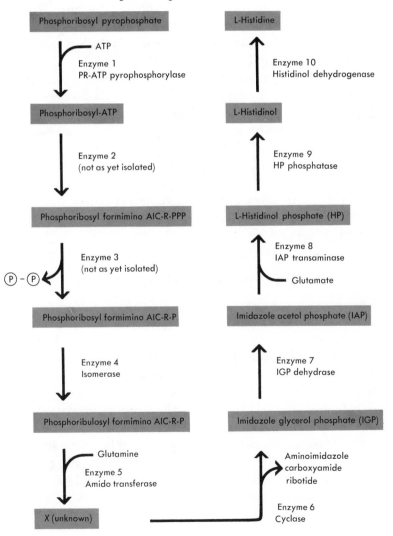

from sickle-cell anemia. This is a disease whose genetic basis is well worked out. If the sickle (s) gene is present in both homologous chromosomes, a severe anemia results, characterized by the red blood cells having a sickle shape. If only one s gene is present, and the allele in the homologous chromosome is normal (+), the anemia is less severe, and the red blood cells almost normal in shape. The type of hemoglobin in red blood cells is likewise correlated with the genetic pattern. In the ss case, all the hemoglobin is of an abnormal type, characterized by a solubility different from that of normal hemoglobin, whereas in the +s condition, half the hemoglobin is normal and half sickle.

Even now it is often hard to identify the protein product of a given gene. One of the most annoying cases involves the rII region of T4. We still do not know the biochemical changes that underlie the larger plaques produced by rII mutant phages and, despite much effort, no one has yet found a specific protein absent in E. coli cells infected with T4rII mutants and present in cells infected with wild-type phage. Thus there is now a strong tendency to concentrate further genetic analysis on those genes for which we already know how to isolate the corresponding protein.

ONE GENE–ONE POLYPEPTIDE CHAIN

Until recently, the above ideas were stated by the slogan "one gene–one protein (enzyme)." Now we realize that a more correct statement is "one gene–one polypeptide chain." When a protein contains more than one polypeptide chain, each chain is made separately. Only after their synthesis do they aggregate to form the final protein. Generally, the two or more polypeptide chains needed to form a functional protein are controlled by adjacent genes. This is, however, not always the case. The α and β hemoglobin chains are not controlled by linked genes. The complementation test thus tells us not whether two genes control different proteins, but rather, if they control two different polypeptide chains.

RECESSIVE GENES FREQUENTLY DO NOT PRODUCE FUNCTIONAL PRODUCTS

Most mutant genes are recessive with respect to wild-type genes. This fact, puzzling to early geneticists, is now partially understood in terms of the gene-enzyme relation. The recessive phenotype often results from the failure of mutant genes to produce *any* functional protein (enzyme). In heterozygotes, however, there is always present one "good" gene, and correspondingly, a number of good gene products. Because the wild-type gene is present only once in heterozygotes, the possibility exists that there are always fewer good copies of the relevant protein in heterozygotes than in individuals with two wild-type genes. If this were the case, we might guess that the heterozygous phenotype would tend to be intermediate between the two homozygous phenotypes. Usually, however, this does not happen, for one of two reasons. Either there are still enough good enzyme molecules to catalyze the metabolic reaction even though the total number is reduced, or the recessive gene is not noticeable, because control mechanisms cause the wild-type gene in a heterozygote to produce more gene products than does each wild-type gene in a homozygote. In Chapter 14 we shall discuss how the rate at which a gene acts may be controlled.

GENES WITH RELATED FUNCTIONS ARE OFTEN ADJACENT

Until ten years ago, geneticists believed that the chromosomal location of genes was purely random; there seemed to be no tendency for genes with related effects to be located near each other. Now, however, there are strong indications from viral and bacterial genetics that a sizable fraction of genes are situated in groups carrying out related functions. There are two main reasons for this change.

First, many geneticists now study mutations directly affecting the biosynthesis of known cellular molecules. Until the advent of work with microorganisms, most genetic markers involved very complex characters, like eye color or wing shape. The development of wings or eyes is, from a chemical viewpoint, fantastically complicated; clearly there is a large variety of *unrelated chemical reactions* whose absence might lead to a misshapen wing. It is thus not surprising that genes affecting the wings occur in many places on all *Drosophila's* four different chromosomes. In contrast, a mutant character that shows itself as the inability to synthesize a relatively simple molecule like the amino acid serine is most likely due to the absence of one of a much smaller number of *related chemical reactions*. If related genes are, indeed, next to each other on a chromosome, we are more likely to observe this phenomenon when we are studying mutations that we can assign immediately to a particular category of chemical upset.

The second main reason why we now frequently find adjacent genes with related functions is the availability of the complementation test. This often tells us that a chemical phenomenon is more complicated than originally guessed. The splitting of the rII region into the rIIA and rIIB genes is a typical case. Numerous situations now exist where a region previously thought to contain a single gene has been shown by complementation tests to perform a number of different, yet related, tasks. Subsequent biochemical investigations have then revealed that several chemical reactions (enzymes) are involved. One of the most spectacular examples involves the ability of E. coli to synthesize histidine. Twenty years ago we would have guessed that a series of mutations blocking histidine synthesis and mapping in the same region all fell in the same gene. Today, however, ten different genes in this region have been identified (Figure 8–7), each concerned with a different enzyme in the biosynthesis of histidine starting from phosphoribosyl pyrophosphate. Likewise, the region concerned with tryptophan biosynthesis contains a cluster of five different genes, each concerned with a distinct step (enzyme) in the biosynthesis of tryptophan.

At first it was thought that the order of genes in the cluster corresponded to the order of their respective enzymes in the biosynthetic pathway. Now, however, there are several known exceptions to the rule. For example, the first two enzymes in histidine biosynthesis are located at opposite ends of the cluster. Clusters of related genes are not always connected with the biosynthesis of essential metabolites. Degradation of many specific food molecules, such as the sugars galactose and lactose, also involves several consecutive chemical reactions; these also tend to be controlled by adjacent genes. Galactose breakdown requires three specific chemical steps, and lactose utilization at least two, probably three, different genes. Another striking example of adjacent related genes concerns genetic control of various structural proteins found in the protective coat of phage T4: The genes affecting the synthesis of head proteins are in one region, and those affecting the tail fibers in another.

The grouping together of related genes is connected with the fact, which we shall examine in detail in Chapter 14, that all genes do not function at the same time. Mechanisms exist that tell genes whether or not to work. For example, the genes controlling lactose metabolism function only when a cell is growing on lactose; when lactose is absent, there is no need for these genes to work. The switching on and off of the genes is controlled by a specific molecule, the lactose repressor. As we

FIGURE 8–7 *Clustering of the genes involved in the biosynthesis of histidine by the bacterium Salmonella typhimurium. The gene order was determined by transduction experiments. Each gene is responsible for the synthesis of one of the 10 enzymes needed to transform phosphoribosyl pyrophosphate into histidine. Here the genes are designated by numbers 1–10. Enzyme 1 is responsible for catalyzing the first reaction in the biosynthesis, enzyme 2 for the second step, etc. **The names of these enzymes are given in Figure 8–6.***

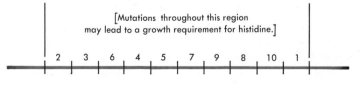

Histidine region

[Mutations throughout this region may lead to a growth requirement for histidine.]

2   3   6   4   5   7   9   8   10   1

shall see in Chapter 14, the ability of these repressor molecules to simultaneously control the synthesis of several proteins is dependent upon the fact that the corresponding genes are physically adjacent.

PROOF THAT GENES CONTROL AMINO ACID SEQUENCES IN PROTEINS

The first experimental demonstration that genes control amino acid sequences involved sickle-cell hemoglobin. Wild-type hemoglobin molecules are constructed from two different kinds of polypeptide chains: α chains and β chains. Each chain has a molecular weight of about 16,100. Two α chains and two β chains are present in each molecule, giving hemoglobin a molecular weight of about 64,500. The α and β chains are controlled by two distinct genes, so a single mutation will affect either the α or the β chain but not both. Sickle hemoglobin differs from normal hemoglobin by the change of one amino acid in the β chain: at position 6 (Figure 8-8), the valine residue found in the wild-type hemoglobin is replaced by glutamic acid. Except for this one change the entire amino acid sequence is identical in normal and mutant hemoglobin peptides. This shows that a mutation in a gene results in a specific change in the template for hemoglobin, and strongly hints that all the information required to order hemoglobin amino acid sequences is present in the genes. Strongly supporting this belief are the analyses of amino acid sequences in hemoglobin isolated from persons suffering from other forms of anemia; here sequence analysis shows that each specific anemia is characterized by a single amino acid replacement at a unique site along the polypeptide chain.

The impracticality of large-scale breeding experiments with mammals makes it impossible to correlate the changes in hemoglobin sequences with the location of the various mutations along the genetic map. It is, however, possible to do this form of analysis with altered enzymes found in microorganisms whose genetics are well known.

COLINEARITY OF THE GENE AND ITS POLYPEPTIDE PRODUCT

The best understood example of the relationship between the order of the mutable sites in a gene and the order of their corresponding amino acid replacements involves the *E. coli* enzyme tryptophan synthetase, one of the several enzymes in-

FIGURE 8–8 *A summary of the established amino acid substitutions in human hemoglobin variants.*

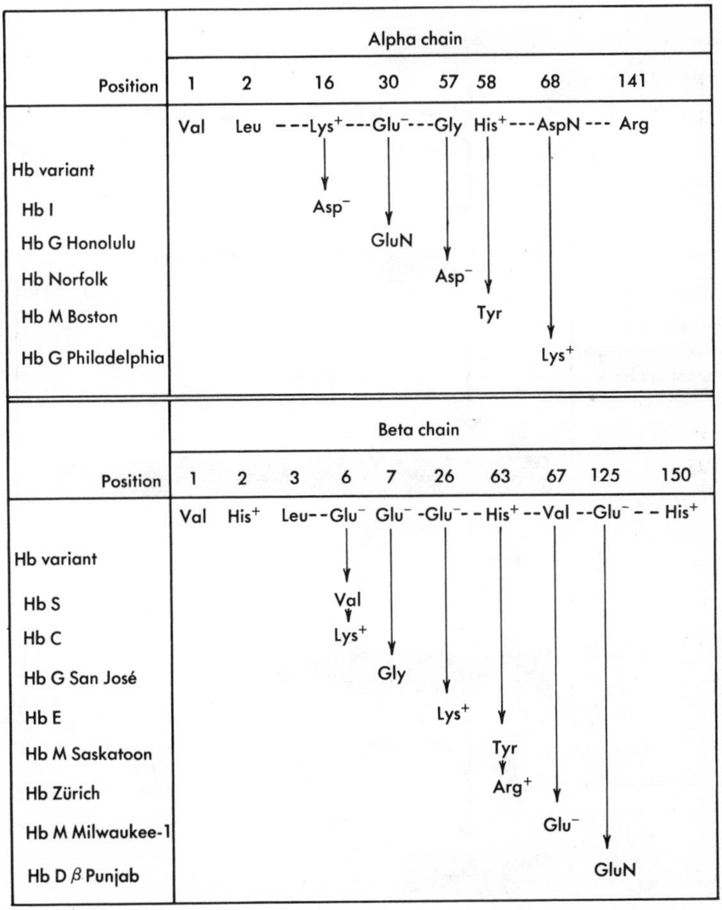

	Alpha chain							
Position	1	2	16	30	57	58	68	141
	Val	Leu	---Lys+---	Glu-	---Gly	His+	---AspN---	Arg
Hb variant								
Hb I			Asp-					
Hb G Honolulu				GluN				
Hb Norfolk					Asp-			
Hb M Boston						Tyr		
Hb G Philadelphia							Lys+	

	Beta chain									
Position	1	2	3	6	7	26	63	67	125	150
	Val	His+	Leu--	Glu-	Glu-	-Glu--	His+	--Val	--Glu-	His+
Hb variant										
Hb S				Val						
Hb C				Lys+						
Hb G San José					Gly					
Hb E						Lys+				
Hb M Saskatoon							Tyr			
Hb Zürich							Arg+			
Hb M Milwaukee-1								Glu-		
Hb D β Punjab									GluN	

volved in tryptophan synthesis (Figure 8–9). This enzyme consists of two easily separable polypeptide chains, A and B, neither of which is enzymatically active by itself. A large number of mutants unable to synthesize tryptophan have been isolated; they lack a functional A chain and so are enzymatically inactive. When these mutants were genetically analyzed, it was found that changes at a large number of different mutable sites can give rise to inactive A chains. Accurate mapping of these

FIGURE 8–9   *Last steps in the pathway of tryptophan biosynthesis.*

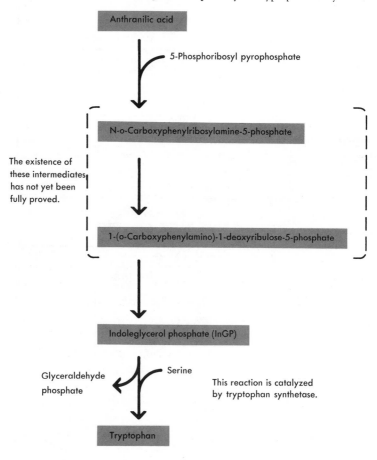

mutants revealed that they all could be unambiguously located on the linear genetic map shown in Figure 8–10. It was possible to isolate the inactive A chains from many of these mutants and to begin to compare their amino acid sequences with the sequence of the wild-type A chain, which contains 280 amino acids. Because of its length, the entire sequence of the A chain is not yet known; now only a 75-amino acid segment has been precisely established. This partial sequence, however, provides sufficient information for us to see how the location of a mutation within a gene is correlated with the location of amino acid replacements in its polypeptide chain product. Since both genes and polypeptide chains are linear, the simplest hypothesis is that amino acid replacements are in the same relative order as the mutationally altered sites in the corresponding mutant genes. This was most pleasingly demonstrated in 1964. The location of each specific amino acid replacement is exactly correlated (colinearity) with its location along the genetic map (Figure 8–10). Thus each amino acid in a polypeptide chain is controlled (coded) by a specific region of the gene.

A MUTABLE SITE CAN EXIST
IN SEVERAL ALTERNATIVE FORMS

Enzymatically inactive tryptophan synthetase molecules resulting from different mutations of the *same* mutable site (as shown by failure to give wild-type recombinants) do not always contain the same amino acid replacement. For example, depending upon the exact mutant strain examined, a change at the same mutable site will result in glycine being replaced by either glutamic acid or valine. This result means that a mutable site can exist in at least three alternative forms. In the next chapter, we shall discuss other evidence which tells us that the mutable sites are the deoxynucleotide building blocks from which the genes (regions of DNA molecules) are constructed. Since only four types of deoxynucleotides exist, this leads us to expect that genetic evidence will never show more than four alternative configurations for a mutable site.

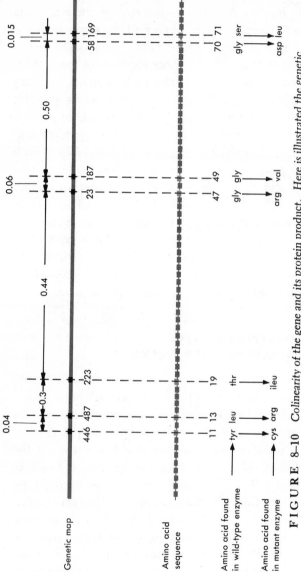

FIGURE 8–10 *Colinearity of the gene and its protein product. Here is illustrated the genetic map for one-fourth of the gene coding for the amino acid sequences in the E. coli protein tryptophan synthetase A. The symbols ←0.04→, etc. refer to map distances (frequencies of recombination) between the various tryptophan synthetase mutations A446, A487, etc. The numbers in the amino acid sequence refer to their position in a 75-residue segment of the A protein. Following convention, the amino terminal end of the segment is on the left.*

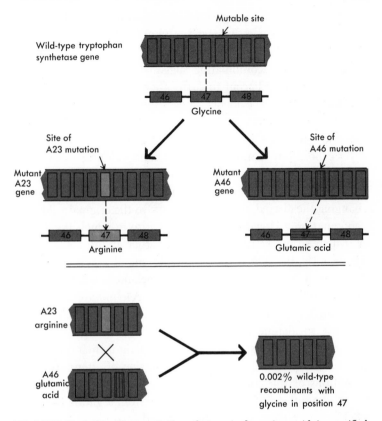

FIGURE 8–11   *Demonstration that a single amino acid is specified by more than one mutable site (see text for details).*

SINGLE AMINO ACIDS ARE SPECIFIED BY SEVERAL ADJACENT MUTABLE SITES

A one-to-one relationship between mutable sites and specific amino acids does not exist.   Instead, there is genetic evidence showing that some, if not all, amino acids are jointly specified by several adjacent sites.   The relevant evidence comes from the study of residue 47 of the tryptophan synthetase fragment illustrated in Figure 8–10.   Treatment with a mutagen of the wild strain has given rise to mutant A23, in which glycine is replaced by arginine, and the mutant A46, in which glutamic acid replaces glycine.   The difference between A23 and A46 does not involve changes to alternatve forms of the same mutable site, since a genetic cross between A23 and A46 yields a number of wild-type (glycine in position 47) recombinants (Figure 8–11). If these changes were at the same mutable site, no wild-type recombinants could be produced. The very low frequency of the wild-type recombination suggests that the mutable sites involved may be adjacent to each other.

Another type of evidence suggesting that several mutable sites code for a single amino acid comes from observing how A23 and A46 themselves mutate upon treatment with mutagens. After exposure to a mutagen, both strains can give rise to new strains containing tryptophan synthetase molecules with glycine in position 47. These reverse mutations most likely involve changing the altered mutable sites back to the original wild-type configuration. However, strains also arise in which the amino acid in position 47 is replaced by another amino acid. Most significantly, the type of possible replacement differs for strains A23 and A46. Strain A23, besides back-mutating to glycine, mutates to threonine and serine, whereas A46 mutates to alanine and valine, in addition to glycine. The failure of A23 ever to give rise to alanine or valine, whereas A46 never mutates to threonine or serine, is very difficult to explain if their differences from wild types are based on the possession of alternative configurations of the same mutable site. Instead, if the changes are at two different sites, then a change from arginine to valine might require changes at both sites and so occur at too low a level to be detected under ordinary mutagen treatment.

These experiments by themselves place only the lower limit (two) of the number of mutable sites coding for a single amino acid. Much more extensive results would be necessary before an upper limit could be assigned on the basis of these types of experimentation. In the next chapter we shall talk about other evidence which tells us that three mutable sites (nucleotides) specify a given amino acid.

UNIQUE AMINO ACID SEQUENCES ARE NOT REQUIRED FOR ENZYME ACTIVITY

The ability of a chain to be enzymatically active does not demand a unique amino acid sequence. This is shown by examination of the new mutant strains obtained by treating

strains A23 and A46 with mutagens. The fact that the possession of either glycine or serine in position 47 yields a fully active
enzyme (Figure 8–12), whereas threonine in the same position
yields an enzyme with reduced activity, demonstrates that the
activity of an enzyme does not demand a unique amino acid
sequence. In fact, a variety of evidence now indicates that
amino acid replacements in many parts of a polypeptide chain
can occur without seriously modifying catalytic activity. Most

FIGURE 8–12 *Evidence that many amino acid replacements do not
result in loss of enzymatic activity (see text for
details). We have arbitrarily shown the mutations
occurring at the same mutable site.*

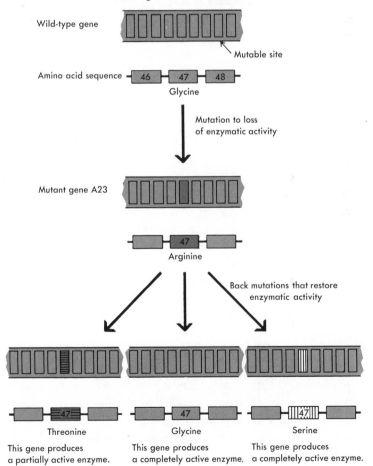

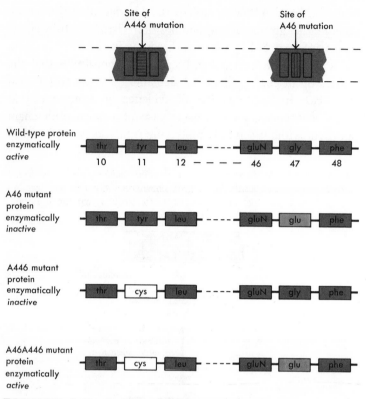

FIGURE 8–13   *Reversal (suppression) of mutant phenotype by a second mutation at a second site in the same gene.*

likely, however, one sequence is best suited to a cell's particular needs, and it is this sequence that is coded for by the wild-type allele. Even though other sequences are almost as good, they will tend to be selected against in evolution unless they are equally functional.

"REVERSE" MUTATIONS SOMETIMES CAUSE A SECOND AMINO ACID REPLACEMENT

The conclusion that a unique amino acid sequence is not necessary for enzyme activity is extended by the finding that some mutations, which convert inactive mutant enzyme to an active form, work by causing a second amino acid replacement in the mutant enzyme. If we start with cells of mutant A46, which

produces inactive tryptophan synthetase because of the substitution of arginine for glycine, distant second site mutations
that result in active enzyme occasionally emerge. For example,
the second site mutation A446 is located one-tenth of a gene
length away from the first (Figure 8–13). The double mutant
A46A446 produces active enzyme molecules containing two
amino acid replacements: the original glycine-to-arginine shift,
and a tyrosine-to-cysteine shift located 36 amino acids away.

The second shift can be studied independently of the first
by obtaining recombinant cells with only the A446 mutation.
Most interestingly, the A446 change when present alone also results in an inactive enzyme. We thus see that a combination of
two wrong amino acids can produce an enzyme with an active
3-D configuration. Only sometimes do two wrong amino acids,
however, cancel out each other's faults. For example, double
mutants containing A446 and A23, or A446 and A187, do not
produce active enzyme. It does not now seem wise to speculate
on how the various amino acid residues are folded together in
the 3-D configuration, and why only some combinants are
enzymatically active. This kind of analysis must await the
establishment of the 3-D structure of tryptophan synthetase.

SUMMARY

Crossing over occurs within the gene, thereby making possible
the mapping of mutations within the gene. Like the order of
genes on a chromosome, the arrangement of mutable sites in a
gene is strictly linear. There appear to be many mutation sites
within an average gene (500 to 1500). Sometimes it is initially
difficult to determine whether a chromosomal region contains
more than one gene; this usually can be resolved by introducing
more than one chromosome (or chromosomal fragment) mutant
for that region into a cell. If two mutants can complement
each other, their mutations must be in different genes (the
complementation test).

Genes control a cell's phenotype by determining which proteins the cell can synthesize. Each gene is responsible for the
synthesis of a specific polypeptide. Genes work by controlling
the sequence of amino acids in proteins. This is clearly shown
by the discovery that many mutations cause the production of

protein molecules that differ from normal protein by a single amino acid replacement. Mutant genes are usually recessive to the wild type because they most often express themselves by the failure to produce a protein product; in such heterozygotes, the wild-type gene dominates by producing enough of its product to bring about the wild-type phenotype.

Good evidence is accumulating that the gene and its polypeptide product are colinear: Mutations that map at an end of a gene affect the amino acid sequence at an end of the polypeptide, and so forth. Genes controlling a series of related biochemical reactions are often adjacent to each other. Various mutants of tryptophan synthetase A demonstrate that a mutable site can exist in at least three alternative states (we shall see in the next chapter that the number is thought to be exactly four). Experiments with these mutants also reveal that each amino acid is under the joint control of more than one (as we shall see, three) mutable site, and that an enzyme does not require a unique amino acid sequence in order to be active.

REFERENCES

Pontecorvo, G., *Trends in Genetic Analysis*, Columbia University Press, New York, 1958. A very readable discussion of the fine-structure analysis of the gene.

Benzer, S., "The Fine Structure of the Gene," *Sci. Am.* January, 1962, pp. 70–84. A lucid presentation of the author's classic investigations of rII gene of phage T4.

Hartman, P. E., and S. R. Suskind, *Gene Action*, Prentice-Hall, Englewood Cliffs, N.J., 1964. A very clear description of how genes work; introduces many of the experimental details that have led to the general principles.

Wagner, R. P., and H. K. Mitchell, *Genetics and Metabolism*, 2nd ed., Wiley, New York, 1964. A more advanced text illustrating a large number of different gene-enzyme relations.

Ingram, V. M., *The Hemoglobins in Genetics and Evolution*, Columbia University Press, New York, 1963. A description of the variety of ways in which hemoglobin has been used to establish important biological principles. Particularly relevant to this chapter is the discussion of the abnormal hemoglobin molecules.

Yanofsky, C., "Gene-Enzyme Relationships," in I. C. Gunsalus and R. Y. Stanier (eds.), *The Bacteria*, Academic, New York, 1964, Vol. 5, pp. 373–417. An excellent review that emphasizes the author's work on tryptophan synthetase.

9

THE REPLICA-

TION AND

GENETIC

ORGANIZATION

OF DNA

GENETICS TELLS US THAT THE INFORMA-
tion that directs amino acid sequences
in proteins is carried by long-chain
polymeric molecules, the deoxyribonucleic acids (DNA).* Though DNA
was first recognized in chromosomes
about 70 years ago, it was definitely
identified as having a genetic function
only 20 years ago, and even then many
geneticists thought that some information might also reside in the protein
component of chromosomes. Now,
however, there is no reason to believe
that any genetic information is carried in other than nucleic acid molecules.

This poses the chemical question of
how the information is transferred at
the molecular level. In addition, we
must ask how the DNA molecules are
exactly copied during chromosome duplication. These questions could not
be immediately attacked in 1943, when
the genetic role of DNA was established. At that time, only fragmentary
information concerning its structure
existed. It was known to be a very
long, large molecule (Figure 9–1), but
the extent of its complexity was unclear. Consequently, there was much
apprehension not only that DNA structure would vary from one gene to another, but that even in the simplest

* As we shall see in Chapter 12, the
chromosomes of some viruses do not contain
DNA but instead are composed of the chemically very similar compound ribonucleic acid
(RNA).

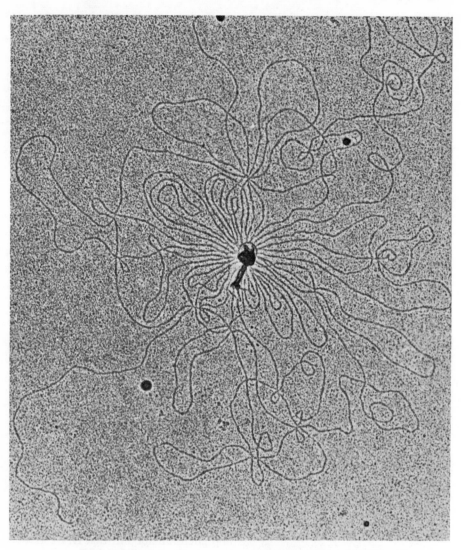

FIGURE 9-1   Electron micrograph of T2 DNA x 100,000. [Reproduced from A. K. Kleinschmidt et al., Biochim. Biophys. Acta, 61, 857 (1962), with permission.]

case, the solution of its structure would pose almost insuperable problems. Moreover, there existed an apprehension that, even when the structures of one or more DNA molecules were known, we would not be presented with any obvious clues about how it acted as a template for its self-replication or how it could control the sequence of amino acids in proteins. Fortunately, these fears were unfounded. Only ten years elapsed between the identification of DNA as the transforming substance and the 1953 elucidation of the double-helical structure of most DNA molecules. Moreover, the basic features of the double helix were simple and immediately told how DNA stores genetic information; even more pleasing, they suggested a chemical mechanism for the self-replication of DNA. From this moment on, the way in which geneticists investigated the gene entered a completely new phase. Their hypotheses no longer needed to be based only on genetic crosses. Instead, it made sense always to ask how the structure of DNA affects the interpretation of their genetic crosses. As a consequence, many subjects (e.g., the action of mutagens) previously refractory to a systematic treatment became open to rational analysis.

THE GENE IS (ALMOST ALWAYS) DNA

The first serious assignment of the primary genetic role to DNA arose from experiments (discussed in Chapter 7) involving the genetic transformation of pneumonia bacteria. Soon after the discovery that cell extracts were effective in transformation, careful chemical studies were begun to determine which type of molecule was responsible. Since virtually everybody believed that genes were proteins, there was initially great surprise when Avery and his co-workers reported in 1943 that the active genetic principle was deoxyribonucleic acid (DNA) (Figure 9–2). A major experimental result prompting their conclusion was the observation that the transforming activity of the extract was destroyed by deoxyribonuclease, an enzyme which specifically degrades DNA molecules to their nucleotide building blocks, and has no effect on the integrity of protein molecules or ribonucleic acid (RNA). The addition of either the enzyme ribonuclease (which degrades RNA) or various proteolytic (protein-destroying) enzymes had no influence on transforming activity.

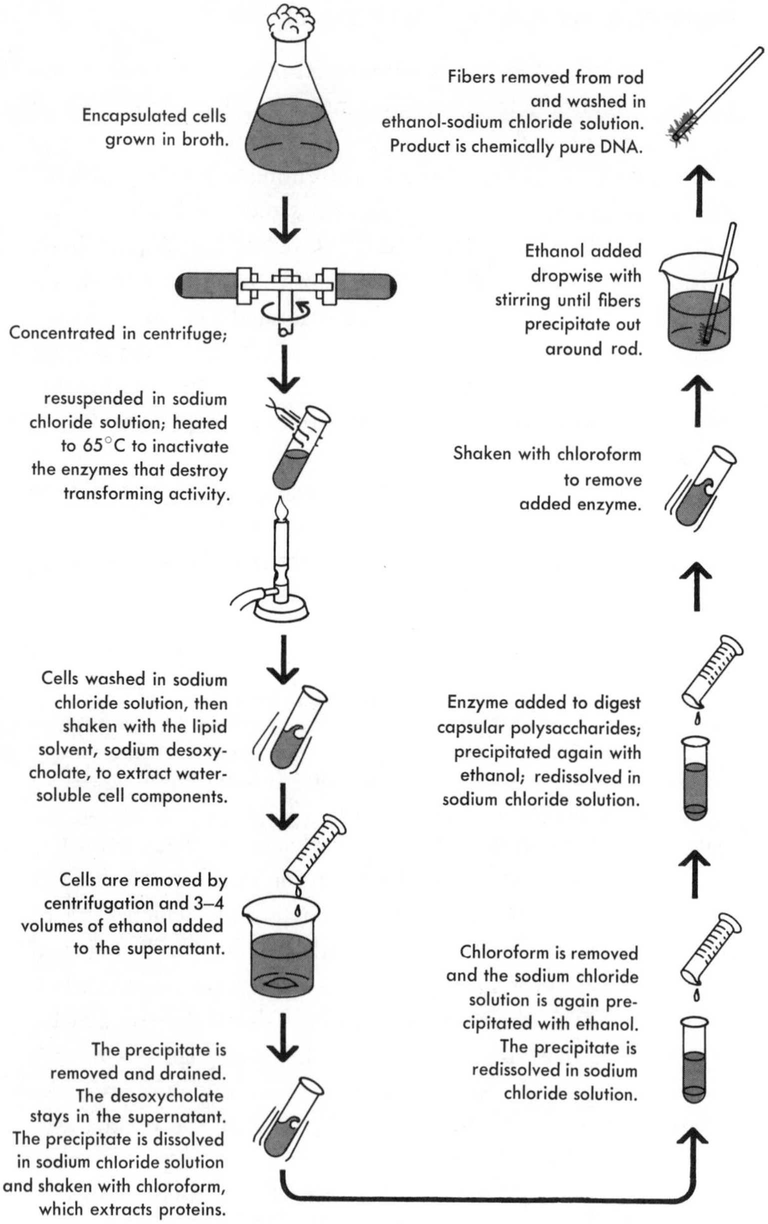

Encapsulated cells
grown in broth.

Fibers removed from rod
and washed in
ethanol-sodium chloride solution.
Product is chemically pure DNA.

Concentrated in centrifuge;

Ethanol added
dropwise with
stirring until fibers
precipitate out
around rod.

resuspended in sodium
chloride solution; heated
to 65°C to inactivate
the enzymes that destroy
transforming activity.

Shaken with chloroform
to remove
added enzyme.

Cells washed in sodium
chloride solution, then
shaken with the lipid
solvent, sodium desoxy-
cholate, to extract water-
soluble cell components.

Enzyme added to digest
capsular polysaccharides;
precipitated again with
ethanol; redissolved in
sodium chloride solution.

Cells are removed by
centrifugation and 3–4
volumes of ethanol added
to the supernatant.

Chloroform is removed
and the sodium chloride
solution is again pre-
cipitated with ethanol.
The precipitate is
redissolved in sodium
chloride solution.

The precipitate is
removed and drained.
The desoxycholate
stays in the supernatant.
The precipitate is dissolved
in sodium chloride solution
and shaken with chloroform,
which extracts proteins.

FIGURE 9–2 *The chemical method used in the original isolation
of a chemically pure transforming agent. (Redrawn
from F. W. Stahl, The Mechanics of Inheritance,
Prentice-Hall, Englewood Cliffs, N.J., 1964, Fig. 2.3,
with permission.)*

THE AMOUNT OF CHROMOSOMAL
DNA IS CONSTANT

Even though the transformation results were clear-cut, there was initially great skepticism about their general applicability; people doubted that they would be found relevant to anything but certain strains of bacteria. Thus the momentous nature of Avery's discovery was only gradually appreciated.

One important confirmation came from studies on the chemical nature of chromosomes. DNA was found to be located almost exclusively in the nucleus, and essentially never where detectable chromosomes were absent. Moreover, the amount of DNA per diploid set of chromosomes was constant for a given organism, and equal to twice the amount present in the haploid sperm cells. Another type of evidence that favored DNA as the genetic molecule was the observation that it is metabolically stable. It is not rapidly made and broken down like many other cellular molecules: Once atoms are incorporated into DNA they do not leave it as long as healthy cell growth is maintained.

VIRAL GENES ARE ALSO NUCLEIC ACIDS

Even more important confirmatory evidence came from chemical studies with viruses and virus-infected cells. It was possible by 1950 to obtain a number of viruses essentially pure and to determine which types of molecule were present in them. This work led to the very important generalization that *all* viruses contain nucleic acid. Since there was, at that time, a growing realization that viruses contain genetic material, the question immediately arose of whether the nucleic acid component was the viral chromosome. The first crucial experimental test of the question came from isotopic study of the multiplication of T2, a virus containing a DNA core and a protective shell built up by the aggregation of a number of different protein molecules. In these experiments the protein coat was labeled with a radioactive isotope S^{35}, and the DNA with the radioactive isotope P^{32}. The labeled virus was then used for following the fates of the phage protein and nucleic acid as virus multiplication proceeded, particularly to see which labeled atoms from the parental virus appeared in the progeny phage.

Clear-cut results emerged from these experiments (Figure 9–3): Much of the parental nucleic acid and none of the parental protein was detected in the progeny phage. Moreover, it was possible to show that little of the parental protein ever enters the bacteria—instead it stays attached to the outside of the bacterial cell, performing no function after the DNA component has passed in. This point was neatly shown by violently agitating infected bacteria after the entrance of the DNA: The protein coats were shaken off without effect-

FIGURE 9–3   *Demonstration that only the DNA component of T2 carries genetic information and that the protein coat functions as a protective shell which facilitates DNA transfer to new host cells.*

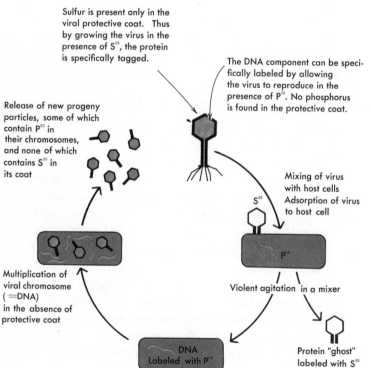

Sulfur is present only in the viral protective coat. Thus by growing the virus in the presence of S^{35}, the protein is specifically tagged.

The DNA component can be specifically labeled by allowing the virus to reproduce in the presence of P^{32}. No phosphorus is found in the protective coat.

Release of new progeny particles, some of which contain P^{32} in their chromosomes, and none of which contains S^{35} in its coat

Mixing of virus with host cells Adsorption of virus to host cell

S^{35}

P^{32}

Multiplication of viral chromosome (=DNA) in the absence of protective coat

Violent agitation in a mixer

DNA Labeled with P^{32}

Protein "ghost" labeled with S^{35}

ing the ability of the bacteria to form new virus particles. With some viruses it is now possible to do an even more convincing experiment. For example, purified DNA from the mouse virus polyoma can enter mouse cells and initiate a cycle of viral multiplication producing many thousands of new polyoma particles. The primary function of viral protein is thus to protect its genetic nucleic acid component in its movement from one cell to another. Thus no reason exists for the assignment of any genetic role to protein molecules.

DNA IS USUALLY A DOUBLE HELIX

The most important feature of DNA is that it usually consists of two very long, thin polymeric chains twisted about each other in the form of a regular double helix (Figures 9–4 and 9–5). The diameter of the helix is about 20 A and each chain makes a complete turn every 34 A. Each chain is a polynucleotide (Figure 3–10), a regular polymeric collection of nucleotides in which the sugar of each nucleotide is linked by a phosphate group to the sugar of the adjacent nucleotide. There are 10 nucleotides on each chain every turn of the helix. The distance per nucleotide base is thus 3.4 A. Four main nucleotides exist, each of them containing a deoxyribose residue, a phosphate group, and a purine or pyrimidine base (Figure 3–9). There are two pyrimidines, thymine (T) and cytosine (C), and two purines, adenine (A) and guanine (G). In the polynucleotide chain the joining together of the sugar and phosphate groups always involves the same chemical groups. Hence, this part of the molecule, called the *backbone*, is very regular. In contrast, the order of the purine and pyrimidine residues along the chain is highly irregular and varies from one molecule to another. Both the purine and pyrimidine bases are flat, relatively water-insoluble molecules which tend to stack above each other perpendicular to the direction of the helical axis.

The two chains are joined together by hydrogen bonds between pairs of bases. Adenine is always paired with thymine and guanine with cytosine (Figure 4–14). Only these arrangements are possible, for two purines would occupy too much space to allow a regular helix and, correspondingly, two pyrimidines would occupy too little. The strictness of these pairing rules results in a complementary relation between the sequences of bases on the two intertwined chains. For example, if we have

FIGURE 9–4 A space-filling model of double-helical DNA. The size of the circles reflects the van der Waals radii of the different atoms. (Courtesy of N. H. F. Wilkins.)

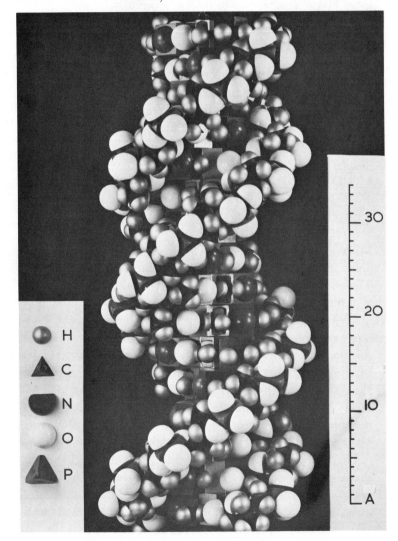

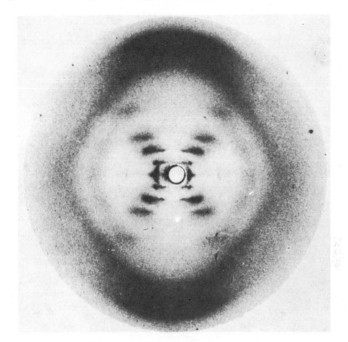

FIGURE 9–5   *The key x-ray photograph involved in the elucidation of the DNA structure. This photograph, taken at Kings College, London, in the winter of 1952–1953, by Rosalind Franklin, experimentally confirmed the then current guesses that DNA was helical. The helical form is indicated by the crossways pattern of x-ray reflections (photographically measured by darkening of the x-ray film) in the center of the photograph. The very heavy black regions at the top and bottom tell that the 3.4-A thick purine and pyrimidine bases are regularly stacked next to each other, perpendicular to the helical axis. [Reproduced from R. E. Franklin and R. Gosling, Nature, 171, 740 (1953), with permission.]*

a sequence ATGTC on one chain, the opposite chain must have the sequence TACAG. A stereochemical consequence of the formation of the $A \cdots T$ and $G \cdots C$ base pairs is that the two polynucleotide chains run in opposite directions. Thus, if the helix is inverted by 180°, it superficially looks the same (Figure 9–6).

An important chemical feature of the structure is the position of the hydrogen atoms in the purine and pyrimidine bases.

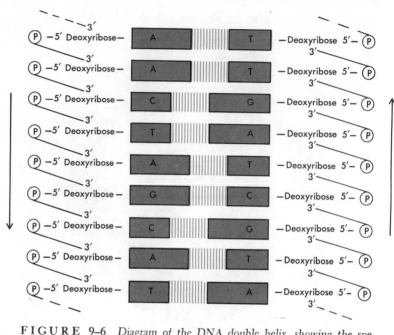

FIGURE 9–6   Diagram of the DNA double helix, showing the specific pairing of the bases, the unrestricted sequence of
bases along any one chain, and the reversed direction of the 3′-5′-phosphodiester linkages of the two
chains. The heavy lines indicate the bases, and the
interrupted lines the hydrogen bonds between base
pairs (A, adenine; G, guanine; T, thymine; C, cytosine).
(Redrawn from W. Hayes, The Genetics of Bacteria
and Their Viruses, Blackwell, Oxford, 1964, p. 229,
with permission.)

Before 1953, many people thought that some of the hydrogen
atoms were highly mobile, randomly moving from one ring nitrogen or oxygen atom to another, and so could not be assigned a
fixed location. Now we realize that, although these movements (called tautomeric shifts) do occur, they are generally
quite rare, and most of the time the H atoms are found at
precise locations. The N atoms attached to the purine and
pyrimidine rings are usually in the *amino* (NH₂) form and only
very, very rarely assume the *imino* (NH) configuration. Likewise, the oxygen atoms attached to the C-6 atoms of guanine
and thymine normally have the keto (C=O) form and only
rarely take up the enol (COH) configuration. As we shall see,

these relatively stable locations are essential to the biological function of DNA. For if the H atoms had no fixed locations, adenine could often pair with cytosine, and guanine with thymine.

In contrast to the ratios of A/T and G/C, which must always be 1:1 to satisfy the base-pairing rules, there are wide variations in the A + T/G + C contents of different DNA molecules (Table 9–1). Higher plants and animals all have an excess of A + T over G + C in their DNA, whereas among the viruses, bacteria, and lower plants, there is much more variation, and both A + T-rich and G + C-rich species occur. These variations, however, are not purely random, and the base ratios of taxonomically related organisms are quite similar. No one yet knows the reason for the wide base-ratio spread. It may be a consequence of but certainly not a prerequisite for extensive evolution. Witness extreme differences between higher plants and animals despite roughly similar percentages of the four main bases. This fact tells us that variation in the *sequences* of the bases is, by itself, sufficient to

TABLE 9–1 *Examples of the spread of A + T/G + C ratios in the DNA molecules of taxonomically diverse organisms*

Source of DNA	$\frac{A+T}{G+C}$	Source of DNA	$\frac{A+T}{G+C}$
Pseudomonas aeruginosa (a bacterium)	.51	Paracentrotus lividos (sea urchin)	1.86
Escherichia coli	.97	Locust migratoria (an insect)	1.41
Bacillus megaterium (a bacterium)	1.66	Trout	1.34
Mycobacterium tuberculosis (a bacterium)	.60	Domestic chicken	1.36
Saccharomyces cerevisiae (a yeast)	1.80	Horse	1.33
Aspergillus niger (a fungi)	1.00	Man	1.40
Scendesmus quadricauda (an algae)	.57	Phage T2	1.84
Rhabdonema adriaticum (an algae = diatom)	1.71	Phage λ	1.06
Wheat	1.22		

produce the gene differences between plants and animals.

DNA molecules with a high G + C content are more resistant to thermal collapse than A + T-rich molecules. When double helical DNA molecules are heated above physiological temperatures (to near 100°C), their hydrogen bonds break and the complementary strands often separate from each other (DNA denaturation). Because the G····C base pair is held together by three hydrogen bonds, higher temperatures are necessary to separate G + C-rich strands than to break apart A + T-rich molecules.

Denaturation is not necessarily an irreversible phenomenon. If a heated DNA solution is slowly cooled, a single strand can often meet its complementary strand and reform a regular double-helical molecule. This ability to renature DNA molecules permits us to show that artificial hybrid DNA molecules can be formed by slowly cooling mixtures of denatured DNA from two different species. For example, hybrid molecules can be formed containing one strand from a man and one from a mouse. Only a fraction (25 per cent) of the DNA strands from a man can form hybrids with mouse DNA. This is, of course, not surprising since it merely means that some genes of a man are very similar to those of a mouse, whereas others have quite different nucleotide sequences. It now appears that this molecular technique may be quite useful in establishing the genetic similarity of the various taxonomic groups.

THE COMPLEMENTARY SHAPE IMMEDIATELY SUGGESTS SELF–REPLICATION

Earlier, in the discussion of how templates must act, the point was emphasized that, in general, two identical surfaces will not attract each other and that it is instead much easier to visualize the attraction of oppositely shaped or charged groups. Thus, without any detailed structural knowledge, we might guess that a molecule as complicated as the gene could not be directly copied. Instead, replication would involve the formation of a molecule complementary in shape, and this in turn would serve as a template to make a replica of the original template. Some geneticists, in the days before detailed knowledge of protein or nucleic acid structure existed, wondered whether DNA might serve as a template for a specific protein that in turn served as a template for a corresponding DNA molecule.

The realization that it is possible to form a DNA molecule in which the specific genetic surfaces (the purine and pyrimidine bases) of the two polynucleotide strands are complementary in shape and charge immediately tells us to reject the possibility, which we already suspected to be chemically tricky if not impossible, of having specific protein formation as the essential aspect of DNA replication. Instead, it is immensely simpler to imagine that DNA replication involves strand separation and formation of complementary molecules on each of the free single strands (Figure 9–7). Under this scheme, one of the two

FIGURE 9–7   *The replication of DNA.*

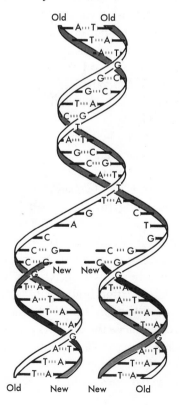

strands of each DNA molecule would serve as the template for the formation of its complement.

No difficulty arises from the need to break the hydrogen bonds joining the base pairs in the parental templates. Though they are highly specific, they are at the same time relatively weak and no enzymes are needed either to make or to break them. Thus they are the ideal means of specifically holding together a template and its complementary replica. Nor does the need to untwist the DNA molecule to separate the two intertwined strands present a real problem. The DNA molecule is very thin (20 A), and rotation about its axis involves almost no energy.

BASE PAIRING SHOULD PERMIT VERY ACCURATE REPLICATION

Earlier we stated that the chemistry of the specific amino acid side groups argued against their employment as accurate templates. Just the opposite, however, is true of the purine and pyrimidine bases, for each of them can form several hydrogen bonds. These bonds are ideal template forces, for they are highly specific, unlike the van der Waals interactions, whose attractive forces are both weaker and virtually independent of specific chemical groupings.

The average energy of a hydrogen bond is about 4 kcal/mole, or eight times the average energy of thermal motion of molecules at room temperature. This value allows us to estimate the ratio of the frequency with which two suitable groups will hydrogen bond to the nonbonding frequency. Under ordinary cellular conditions the ratio of bonding to nonbonding is about 10^4. This means that two molecules held together by several hydrogen bonds are almost never found in the nonbonded form. For example, the frequency with which cytosine will attach to adenine during DNA replication is about 10^{-8} times the frequency of its bonding to thymine ($10^{-4} \times 10^{-4}$ since two hydrogen bonds are involved). Since the $G \cdots C$ pair is held together by three hydrogen bonds, its replication should be even more accurate.

This argument is not affected by the fact that the bases also can form almost equally strong hydrogen bonds with the hydrogen and oxygen atoms of water. It does not matter if, say, the potential thymine site is temporarily filled with several water molecules. They cannot be chemically joined to the growing polynucleotide chain, and they will soon diffuse away and be replaced by the suitable hydrogen-bonding nucleotide.

It is not yet possible to give a similar quantitative argument for why two purines or two pyrimidines never accidentally bond to each other. Though both arrangements seriously distort the sugar-phosphate backbone and clearly are energetically unfavorable, the large number of atoms involved makes the precise calculation of energy differences impossible now. Part of the difficulty arises from the fact that the precise locations of the atoms in DNA are not known at the 0.1-A level. Furthermore, it is unclear what effect this distortion would have on the binding of the enzyme that catalyzes the formation of the internucleotide covalent bonds.

DNA REPLICATION DOES NOT INVOLVE
SYNTHESIS OF SPECIFIC PROTEINS

The proof of this statement is given by study of DNA synthesis in highly purified, cell-free systems. There exists in all dividing cells the enzyme DNA polymerase, which functions during

TABLE 9–2 *A comparison of the base composition of enzymatically synthesized DNA and their DNA templates*

| Source of DNA template | Base composition of the enzymatic product | | | | $\dfrac{A + T}{G + C}$ in product | $\dfrac{A + T}{G + C}$ in template |
	Adenine	Thymine	Guanine	Cytosine		
Micrococcus lysodeiticus (a bacterium)	0.15	0.15	0.35	0.35	0.41	0.39
Aerobacter acrogenes (a bacterium)	0.22	0.22	0.28	0.28	0.80	0.82
Escherichia coli	0.25	0.25	0.25	0.25	1.00	0.97
Calf thymus	0.29	0.28	0.21	0.22	1.32	1.35
Phage T2	0.32	0.32	0.18	0.18	1.78	1.84

DNA synthesis to link together by 3–5 phosphodiester bonds the precursor deoxynucleotides (Figure 9–8). This enzyme works only in the presence of DNA, which is needed to order the four nucleotides in the polynucleotide product. The DNA polymerase itself recognizes only the regular sugar-phosphate portion of the nucleotide precursors and so cannot determine sequence specificity. This is neatly demonstrated by allowing the enzyme to work in the presence of DNA molecules that contain varying amounts of A····T and G····C base pairs. In every case, the enzymatically synthesized product has the base ratios of the primer DNA (Table 9–2). During this cell-free synthesis, no synthesis of protein or any other molecular class occurs—thus

FIGURE 9–8　*Enzymatic synthesis of DNA.*

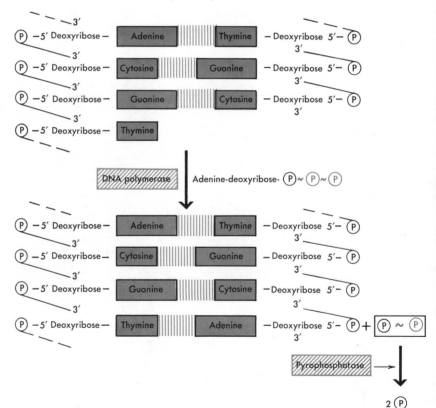

unambiguously eliminating any non-DNA compounds as intermediate carriers of the genetic specificity of the genes. Instead, there is no doubt that DNA is the direct template for its own formation. We might expect that the enzymatic product, like the primer, has a double-helical structure, and this is in fact the case.

SOLID EVIDENCE IN FAVOR OF DNA STRAND SEPARATION

To prove this point, methods had to be found to separate physically parental from daughter DNA molecules. This separation was first accomplished through use of heavy isotopes such as N^{15}. Bacteria are grown in a medium containing the heavy isotope N^{15}. Their DNA is more dense than the light DNA containing N^{14} of bacteria grown under normal conditions. Heavy DNA can be separated from light DNA by equilibrium centrifugation in concentrated solutions of heavy salts such as cesium chloride. When high centrifugal forces are applied, the solution becomes more dense at the outside of the centrifuge cell. If the correct initial solution density is chosen, the individual DNA molecules will move to the central region of the centrifuge cell where their density equals that of the salt solution. Thus the heavy molecules will band at a higher density than the light molecules. If bacteria containing heavy DNA are transferred to light medium (containing N^{14}) and allowed to grow, the precursor nucleotides available for use in DNA synthesis will be light; hence, DNA synthesized after transfer will be distinguishable from DNA made before transfer.

If DNA replication involves strand separation, definite predictions can be made about the density of the DNA molecules found after various growth intervals in light medium. After one generation of growth, all the DNA molecules should contain one heavy and one light strand and thus be of intermediate hybrid density. This result is exactly what is observed. Likewise, after two generations of growth, half the DNA molecules are light and half hybrid (Figure 9–9), just as strand separation predicts.

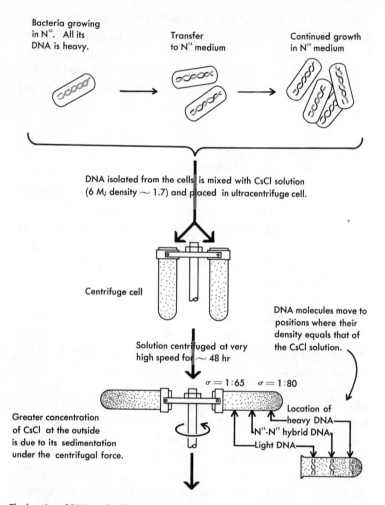

Bacteria growing in N^{15}. All its DNA is heavy.

Transfer to N^{14} medium

Continued growth in N^{14} medium

DNA isolated from the cells is mixed with CsCl solution (6 M; density ~ 1.7) and placed in ultracentrifuge cell.

Centrifuge cell

DNA molecules move to positions where their density equals that of the CsCl solution.

Solution centrifuged at very high speed for ~ 48 hr

$\sigma = 1:65$ $\sigma = 1:80$

Greater concentration of CsCl at the outside is due to its sedimentation under the centrifugal force.

Location of heavy DNA

N^{14}-N^{15} hybrid DNA

Light DNA

The location of DNA molecules within the centrifuge cell can be determined by ultraviolet optics. DNA solutions absorb strongly at 2600 A.

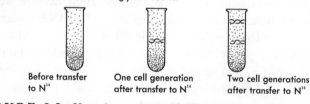

Before transfer to N^{14}

One cell generation after transfer to N^{14}

Two cell generations after transfer to N^{14}

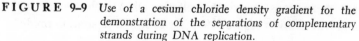

FIGURE 9–9 Use of a cesium chloride density gradient for the demonstration of the separations of complementary strands during DNA replication.

REPLICATION GOES HAND IN HAND
WITH STRAND SEPARATION

It is theoretically conceivable that replication is a two-step process. First the strands would completely unwind and separate; then the free single strands would act as templates and form new double helices. Alternatively, it is possible that replication would commence as soon as untwisting began. The latter scheme predicts that we should be able to find Y-shaped DNA molecules if we look at DNA in the process of duplication. Y-shaped DNA molecules are in fact found. Figure 9–10 shows several examples of Y-shaped regions revealed by radioautographs of *E. coli* chromosomes.

SINGLE–STRANDED DNA ALSO IS
REPLICATED BY BASE PAIRING

At first it was thought that all DNA molecules are double-stranded except during replication, when small portions near the Y region are temporarily in a non-hydrogen-bonded, single-stranded form. Many people were surprised, therefore, when conclusive experiments revealed that the DNA of several groups of small bacterial viruses exists normally as single-stranded molecules in which $A \neq T$ and $G \neq C$. This discovery immediately posed the question of whether an additional copying mechanism exists in which a single DNA strand serves as a template for an identical copy. This type of replication cannot be accomplished by the formation of a double helix in which identical bases hydrogen bond to each other, because such a structure is stereochemically impossible. If self-replication were to exist, it would have to use connector molecules of the type we discussed when we considered whether a polypeptide chain could be the template for an identical copy. There would have to exist four different connectors each having two identical surfaces that could make several hydrogen bonds with a specific base. The connectors could line up and connect the nucleotides to form a new polynucleotide chain identical to the first.

There is no evidence, however, for the existence of such con-

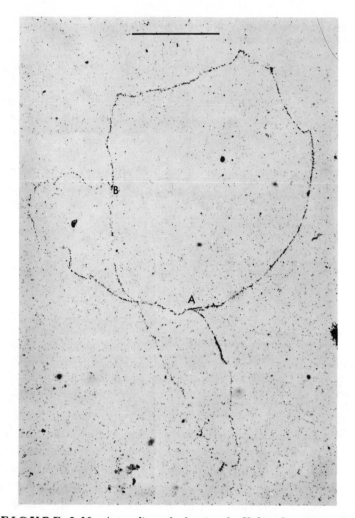

FIGURE 9-10   Autoradiograph showing the Y-shaped growing point of an E. coli chromosome. The DNA was labeled with H³-thymidine for two generations of DNA replication. The figure-8 appearance is the result of looking at a circular chromosome which has been two-thirds duplicated. The symbol A marks the growing point, B the finishing point. The scale shows 100 μ. (Compare with Figure 9–14.) [Reproduced from J. Cairns, Cold Spring Harbor Symp. Quant. Biol., 28, 44 (1963), with permission.]

nectors.   Instead we find that as soon as the single-stranded DNA molecule (which we shall call the "+" strand) enters its host cell, the strand serves as a template for the formation of a complementary "−" strand (Figure 9–11).   The resulting double helix in turn serves as a template for the formation of new single "+" strands, which then become incorporated into new virus particles.   Thus, the fundamental mechanism for ordering nucleotides during polynucleotide synthesis of single-stranded DNA is basically the same as that used for double-helical DNA.   Nucleotide selection always occurs by attraction of the complementary base pair.   The difference does exist, however, that with the single-stranded viruses, only one (the "−") of two strands in the double helix functions as a template for progeny particle DNA.   How this choice is made is not yet known.

Despite the existence of single-stranded DNA in some viruses, most cellular DNA must exist as double helices.   This follows from the facts that (1) the two complementary chains do not

FIGURE 9–11   *The replication of a single-stranded DNA molecule. Each double helix generally serves as the template for the formation of a large number of new "+" strands.*

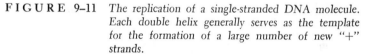

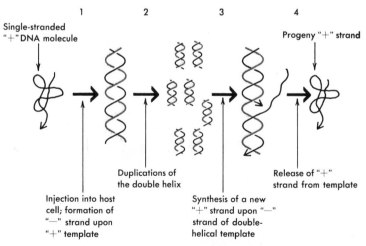

1   2   3   4

Single-stranded
"+" DNA molecule

Progeny "+" strand

Duplications of
the double helix

Release of "+"
strand from template

Injection into host
cell; formation of
"−" strand upon
"+" template

Synthesis of a new
"+" strand upon "−"
strand of double-
helical template

have identical base sequences and hence (as we shall see later) code for entirely different amino acid arrangements, and (2) in bacteria (and probably in many higher cells) there is usually only one copy of a given gene. Thus, if the single-stranded form were the usual form and the double helix existed only briefly during DNA duplication, then following mitosis the two daughter cells would contain completely different sets of genetic information.

SINGLE DNA MOLECULES ARE THE CHROMOSOMES OF VIRUSES AND E. COLI

Early estimates of the molecular weights of DNA centered at about a million, a size that we shall later see is that of the average gene. It was thus natural to equate single DNA molecules with single genes. Most recently, however, it has been discovered that these first reports were misleading because of the breakage of DNA during its isolation and study. It is now clear that virtually all undegraded DNA molecules contain the infor-

FIGURE 9–12   *Autoradiograph of several T2 chromosomes. The total length is 52 μ. (Courtesy of J. Cairns.)*

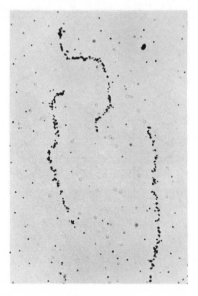

mation of several genes. Our most convincing MW values come from DNA-containing viruses. For example, the bacterial virus T2 contains one DNA molecule of MW $= 1.2 \times 10^8$ (Figure 9–12), and the bacterial virus λ contains a single molecule of MW $= 3.2 \times 10^7$. In these cases, we must equate the chromosome, not the gene, with single DNA molecules. This must also be done for the single chromosome of *E. coli*. From this cell there can be isolated a single DNA molecule of MW about 2×10^9 whose extended length is almost a millimeter (Figure 9–10). It is not known exactly how many DNA molecules are contained in the chromosomes of higher plants and animals. Because there are suggestions that they contain more than one growing point during DNA replication, the presence of at least several molecules seems likely. In any case, some DNA molecules are larger by several powers of 10 than any other biological molecule.

DNA MOLECULES SOMETIMES HAVE A CIRCULAR SHAPE

Initially our experimental evidence, largely from electron microscopy, suggested that all DNA molecules were linear and had two free ends. Now, however, as it becomes possible to look at undegraded DNA molecules, the generalization is beginning to emerge that some DNA molecules can exist in either linear or circular form. For example, when the phage λ DNA molecule is isolated from the free phage, it is linear in shape. However, by controlled heating and recooling it can be reversibly converted to a circular form (Figure 9–13). Another circular DNA form is found in polyoma virus where the DNA is a circular double helix inside the virus. Circles are also found in single-stranded viruses. $\phi \times 174$ possesses a single-stranded circle that remains a circle as it is converted in replication to a double-stranded form.

At first the possibility was considered that these circles might represent features peculiar to viruses and their replication. This hypothesis was clearly disproved by the discovery that the *E. coli* chromosome (DNA molecule) can also be found as a circle. It is, therefore, necessary to ask, in general, why DNA molecules should be capable of forming a circle. The most appealing hypothesis now is that the circular DNA form is a device for preventing unwanted DNA replication. During cell division each chromosome must replicate once, not twice or more. One conceivable way to achieve this objective would be to have the DNA molecule in a circular form except for one brief period in each division cycle when the circle breaks and replication starts at one of the free ends. As yet the molecular basis for this aspect of the control of DNA replication is completely unknown. We do not know the chemistry of converting a linear molecule to its circular form. Nor do we know how, given a circular form, the necessary untwisting of the complementary strands occurs. In some region, probably the junc-

FIGURE 9-13   *Electron micrograph (by B. Chandler, University of Wisconsin) of circular λ DNA molecule. The reference line represents 1 μ. The contour length is 16.3 μ. [Reproduced from H. Ris and B. C. Chandler, Cold Spring Harbor Symp. Quant. Biol., 28, 2 (1963), Fig. 1, with permission.]*

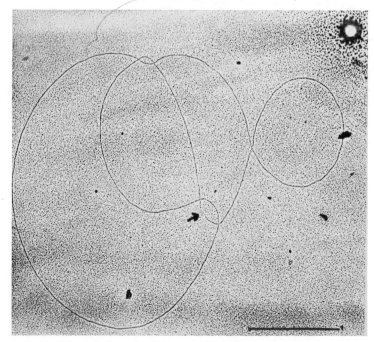

tion point, a molecular swivel would clearly have to exist which would rotate as the complementary strands separate from each other (Figure 9–14).

THE AVERAGE GENE CONTAINS ABOUT 1500 NUCLEOTIDE PAIRS

There are several ways to reach this conclusion. The most direct one divides the number of nucleotides in a chromosome by the number of genes located along it. For example, over 50 genes in the bacterial virus T4 chromosome are already described and the chromosome has a molecular weight of 120 million, giving an average molecular weight of 2.4 million per gene. This is clearly an upper estimate, since it is possible that a significant fraction of the T4 genes has not yet been discovered. In the bacterial virus λ some 20 genes have been mapped. Since the DNA molecular weight is 32 million, this gives us an upper limit to the gene size of 1.5 million.

A similar size range is given by genetic mapping experiments. For example, the rIIA gene of T4 occupies about 1 per cent of the total genetic map; if it is of average size, there are about 100 genes in T4. The validity of this method depends upon the assumption that crossing over occurs with equal frequency at all spots along the chromosome. If this is not true, then regions in which much crossing over takes place will genetically seem much farther apart than regions of equal physical size that have limited recombination.

Fortunately, however, complications of this type do not appear to be very serious; there is frequently a correlation between genetic map length and true physical length. For example, the T4 gene that codes for the small protein lysozyme (MW~12,000) occupies a region only about one-fourth the map length of the rIIA region. This correlates nicely with the fact that the average protein has an MW of 30,000 to 50,000. Unfortunately, the protein produced by the rIIA gene has not yet been found. We do not know whether it is of average size, and so our argument is only suggestive.

Our first argument is, however, the more rigorous except

for the complication that not all the genes in T4 are known. Hence, we must ask whether the rate at which new genes are being discovered hints that the final gene number will be 120, 200, or conceivably 1000 per cent of our present values. It now

FIGURE 9-14 *A plausible model for the replication of a circular DNA molecule. Synthesis always moves in a fixed direction commencing at a specific beginning point. Because the complementary strands are helically twisted about each other, the parent helix must rotate as the strands separate. This means that some form of molecular swivel must exist at the point where replication begins. [Reproduced from J. Cairns, Cold Spring Harbor Symp. Quant. Biol., 28, 43 (1963), with permission.]*

Swivel at point where
replication starts

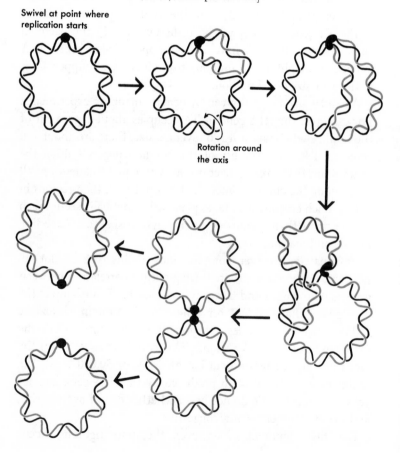

Rotation around
the axis

looks as if the number will be at most doubled (the rate of discovery is slowing down), and the average gene size may be slightly less than a million. Since the average MW of a pair of bases is slightly over 600, this means that an average gene is a linear arrangement of about 1500 base pairs.

CROSSING OVER IS DUE TO BREAKAGE AND REJOINING OF INTACT DNA MOLECULES

Until recently, not even a superficial understanding of the molecular basis of crossing over existed. The classical picture of crossing over, developed in the 1930s from cytological observations, hypothesized that, during meiosis, the paired, coiled chromosomes were sometimes physically broken at the chromatid level as a result of tension created by their contraction. The broken ends then could relieve the tension by crossways reunion, thereby creating two reciprocally recombinant chromatids as well as two parental chromatids (Figure 9–15). According to this model, recombination occurs after chromosome duplication is complete, that is, at the four-strand stage. This hypothesis fell into disfavor about 1955, when geneticists found that crossing over occurred within the gene, by then realized to be a DNA molecule. A seemingly unpleasant consequence was the necessity of postulating that the effective breakage points lay between the same nucleotides in the two homologous chromatids. Otherwise recombination would generate new DNA molecules differing in length from the parental molecules.

To avoid these dilemmas, enthusiasm developed for a hypothesis relating recombination to chromosome duplication. This alternative hypothesis proposed that, during replication of the paired chromosomes, the new DNA strand being formed along the paternal chromosome (for example) switches to the maternal one that it thereafter copies. If the complementary replica of the maternal strand also switches templates when it reaches the same point, two reciprocally recombinant strands would be formed. This hypothetical process is called *copy choice*. A fundamental distinction between the two hypotheses lies in their prediction of the physical origin of recombinant chromosomes.

Following breakage and reunion, the recombinant chromosomes inherit physical material from the two parental chromosomes. In contrast, the recombinant chromosomes produced by copy choice are synthesized from new material.

These alternate hypotheses were recently tested by experiments using isotopically heavy (C^{13}, N^{15}) parental phage λ particles (Figures 9–16 and 9–17). Here again the heavy isotopes were used to allow a cesium chloride gradient to distinguish between parental and daughter DNA strands. Genetic crosses

FIGURE 9–15   Diagrammatic representation of two possible mechanisms of crossing over.

(a) Breakage and reunion

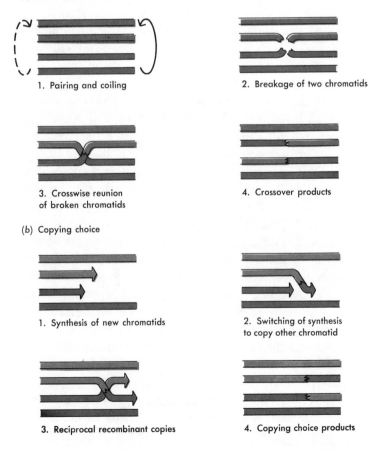

1. Pairing and coiling

2. Breakage of two chromatids

3. Crosswise reunion of broken chromatids

4. Crossover products

(b) Copying choice

1. Synthesis of new chromatids

2. Switching of synthesis to copy other chromatid

3. Reciprocal recombinant copies

4. Copying choice products

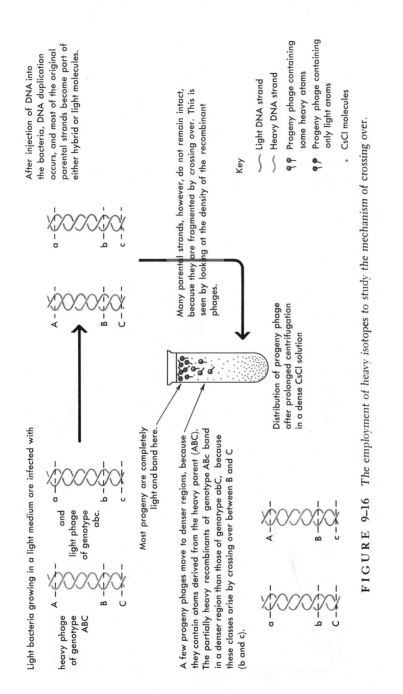

Light bacteria growing in a light medium are infected with

heavy phage of genotype ABC and light phage of genotype abc.

Most progeny are completely light and band here.

A few progeny phages move to denser regions, because they contain atoms derived from the heavy parent (ABC). The partially heavy recombinants of genotype ABc band in a denser region than those of genotype abC, because these classes arise by crossing over between B and C (b and c).

Distribution of progeny phage after prolonged centrifugation in a dense CsCl solution

After injection of DNA into the bacteria, DNA duplication occurs, and most of the original parental strands become part of either hybrid or light molecules.

Many parental strands, however, do not remain intact, because they are fragmented by crossing over. This is seen by looking at the density of the recombinant phages.

Key

〰 Light DNA strand

〰 Heavy DNA strand

Progeny phage containing some heavy atoms

Progeny phage containing only light atoms

• CsCl molecules

FIGURE 9-16 The employment of heavy isotopes to study the mechanism of crossing over.

283

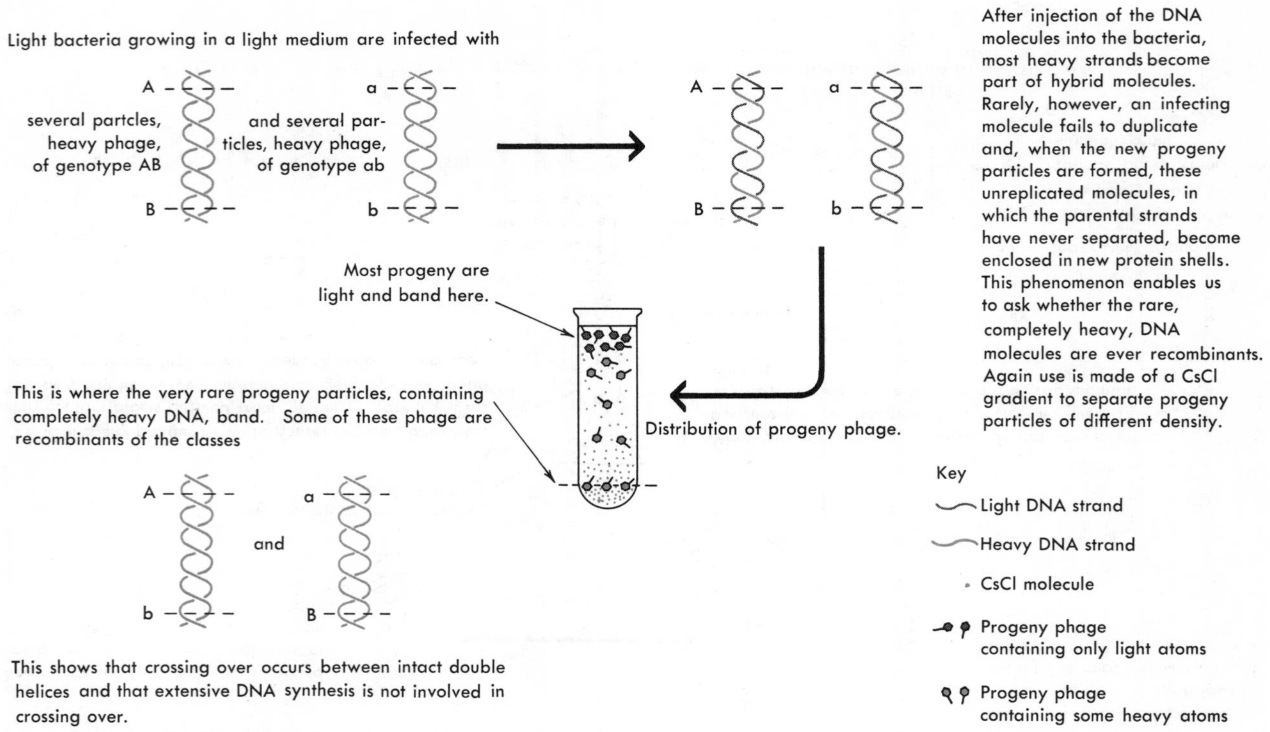

FIGURE 9–17 An experimental demonstration that crossing over and DNA duplication are independent phenomena.

between heavy (or between heavy and light) phage particles were made in E. coli cells growing in a light (C^{12}, N^{14}) medium. Under these conditions, all of the newly synthesized viral DNA molecules are derived from light precursors; thus, if copy choice is the correct mechanism, all the recombinant particles should be light. On the contrary if recombinants are derived by breakage and reunion, some of the recombinant phage particles will contain heavy atoms derived from the parental chromosomes. The progeny particles of these crosses were placed in dense CsCl solutions, and rapidly centrifuged to separate particles of different density. Phage particles of varying density were then collected and genetically tested to see which were recombinants. The experimental results were clear-cut and, to the surprise of most molecular biologists, showed that some recombinant particles contained heavy atoms. Breakage and reunion of double-helical DNA molecules must therefore be the primary mechanism of crossing over in bacteriophage. How this happens at the molecular level is still a mystery. Particularly puzzling is the chemical basis of the pairing process. We do not as yet know any obvious reason why two homologous DNA molecules, particularly if they are in the double-helical form, should attract each other.

THE GENETIC CODE IS CARRIED BY THE SEQUENCE OF BASES

Since the sugar-phosphate backbone is the same in all DNA molecules, it necessarily cannot carry any genetic information. The information must instead be carried in the sequence of the four (A, G, C, T) bases. This requirement, however, poses no real restriction on the effective amount of information that DNA carries. Since each molecule is very long, the number of sequence permutations is 4^n, where n is the number of nucleotides in a given molecule. A virtually infinite number of genetic messages can be coded with the four letters A, T, G and C of the nucleic acid alphabet. The possible number of different genes of MW = 10^6 is 4^{1500}, a value very much larger than the number of different genes that have existed in all the chromosomes present since the origin of life.

GENETIC FINE STRUCTURE REFLECTS
THE BASE–PAIR ARRANGEMENT

The genetic mapping of the rIIA gene revealed the existence of at least 500 sites at which mutation can occur and between which genetic recombination (crossing over) is possible. The magnitude of this number immediately tells us that these sites are the specific base pairs along the gene (Figure 9–18).

Many mutations are base-pair switches from, for example, AT to GC, CG, or TA (Figure 9–19). Thus, by studying the fine

FIGURE 9–18   *The relationship of mutations in the rII region of the chromosome of phage T4 to the structure of DNA.*

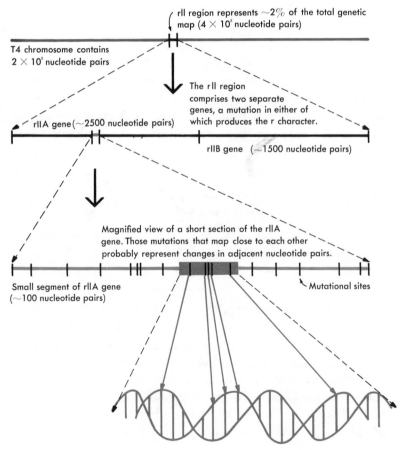

rII region represents ~2% of the total genetic map (4 × 10³ nucleotide pairs)

T4 chromosome contains 2 × 10⁵ nucleotide pairs

The rII region comprises two separate genes, a mutation in either of which produces the r character.

rIIA gene (~2500 nucleotide pairs)

rIIB gene (~1500 nucleotide pairs)

Magnified view of a short section of the rIIA gene. Those mutations that map close to each other probably represent changes in adjacent nucleotide pairs.

Small segment of rIIA gene (~100 nucleotide pairs)

Mutational sites

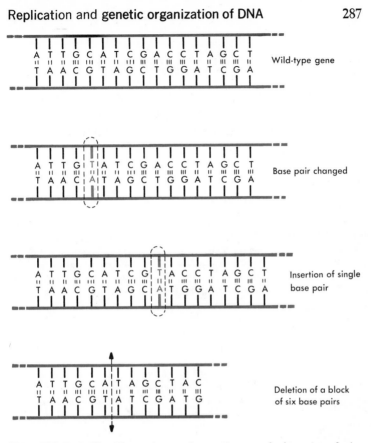

FIGURE 9–19 *Three classes of mutations result from introducing defects in the sequence of bases (A, T, G, C) that are attached to the backbone of the DNA molecule. In one class a base pair is simply changed from one into another (i.e., G, C, A, T). In the second class a base pair is added or removed. In the third class a group of nucleotides is deleted (or inserted).*

details of the genetic map very carefully, it is possible to obtain important information about the sequence of base pairs along the DNA molecule. One important reservation, however, is necessary. There is no a priori reason to believe that all changes in the genetic code will necessarily cause functional changes in the corresponding proteins. The number of observed mutable sites is thus likely to seriously underestimate the number of nucleotide pairs.

Most single base switches are reversible, and often the rate of the "back" mutation to the normal nucleotide arrangement has an order of magnitude similar to that of the rate of change to the mutant arrangement. These mutations most likely reflect failures in the replication process. Either the correct hydrogen bonds do not form (Figure 9–20) or an adenine mistakingly pairs with guanine (or cytosine with thymine). There are other rare locations where the rates of forward mutation greatly exceed the reverse step. The origin of these highly mutable nucleotide pairs—"hot spots"—is still obscure.

FIGURE 9–20   *This demonstrates how the specificity of base pairing in DNA is determined by hydrogen bonding. The hydrogen atoms are indicated by solid circles, the bonds by ||||. (a) shows why the pairing of cytosine with an adenine molecule, having the most stable distribution of its hydrogen atoms, cannot lead to hydrogen bonding. (b) shows how the shift of a hydrogen atom in an adenine molecule, from the 6-amino group to the N_1 position, permits hydrogen bonding with cytosine. The normal position of the hydrogen atom is indicated by the small open circle. (The dimensions shown are only approximate.) (Redrawn from W. Hayes, The Genetics of Bacteria and Their Viruses, Blackwell, Oxford, 1964, p. 228, with permission.)*

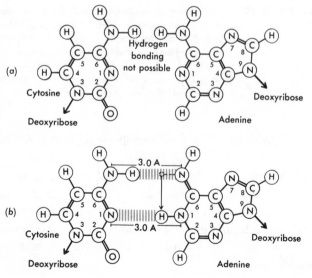

Except for the hot spots, the general rate of spontaneous mutations agrees with our earlier guess about the accuracy of the base pairing during replication. The average rate of detectable mutation per gene duplication is about 10^{-6}. This figure can be extended to the nucleotide level only if we can guess what fraction of base pairs must remain unchanged for the maintenance of normal gene function. If we suppose that all the base pairs are essential, then in a gene containing 1000 nucleotides, the error at the nucleotide level is approximately 10^{-9} mistakes per nucleotide replication. Only for the rII genes are there sufficient data present to estimate the fraction of base pairs whose change leads to a detectable mutation. The 500 mutable sites known at present probably reflect at least one-fourth and possibly one-half of the total genetic map. Detectable mutations in the rII gene, however, occur at a higher rate than in many other loci. Here the total mutation frequency (even if we exclude the hot spots) is about 10^{-4} to 10^{-5}. This may mean that in most other genes, many fewer nucleotide changes lead to detectable mutations than in the rII genes. If so, the general mistake level may be as high as 10^{-7} per nucleotide replication.

Other spontaneous mutations involve the loss (deletions) or gain (insertions) of nucleotides. Sometimes hundreds to thousands of nucleotides are involved in deletions, and in rare cases whole genes are lost. Reverse (back) mutation to the normal gene arrangement is clearly impossible for large deletions and occurs only at low rates for simple one-nucleotide deletions and insertions.

It is now also possible to make intelligent statements about how some chemical mutagens produce changes in the genetic code. For example, nitrous acid (HNO_2) is a very powerful mutagen because it acts directly on the nucleic acids replacing NH_2 groups by keto groups. Thus it directly alters the genetic code by converting one base into another (Figure 9–21). Other substances cause mutations as a result of their incorporation into the DNA molecule itself. These latter compounds are base analogues, whose structures are very similar to the normal DNA bases and which can be expected to be incorporated into DNA without destroying its capacity for replication. However be-

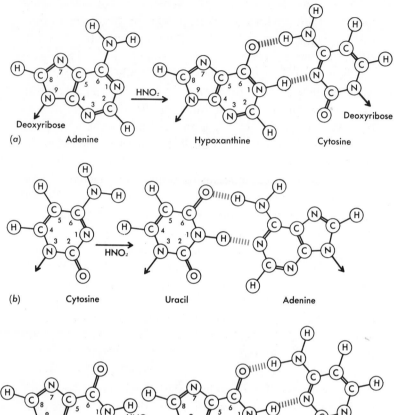

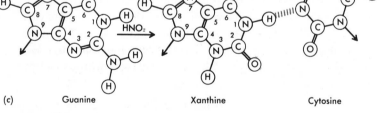

FIGURE 9–21 The oxidative deamination of DNA bases by nitrous acid, and its effects on subsequent base pairing. (a) Adenine is deaminated to hypoxanthine, which bonds to cytosine instead of to thymine. (b) Cytosine is deaminated to uracil, which bonds to adenine instead of to guanine. (c) Guanine is deaminated to xanthine, which continues to bond to cytosine, though with only two hydrogen bonds. Thymine, and the uracil of RNA, do not carry an amino group and so remain unaltered. (Redrawn from W. Hayes, *The Genetics of Bacteria and Their Viruses*, Blackwell, Oxford, 1964, p. 280, with permission.)

cause of their different structures, they often do not form base pairs as accurately as the normal bases and so cause mistakes during the replication process itself. One of the most powerful base analogue mutagens is 5-bromouracil, an analogue of thymine. It is believed to cause mutations because its hydrogen atom at position 1 is not as firmly fixed as the corresponding hydrogen atom in thymine. Sometimes it is found bonded to the oxygen atom attached to carbon atom 6 (Figure 9–22). When this happens, the 5-bromouracil can pair with guanine.

THE GENETIC CODE IS READ
IN GROUPS OF THREE

There cannot be a one-to-one correspondence between the DNA bases and the amino acids. This is an obvious consequence of the fact that there are 20 amino acids and only 4 bases. Each amino acid must thus be coded for by groups of nucleotides. Genetic evidence tells us that groups of three nucleotides are fundamental units and that the code is read linearly starting from one end. These results arise from crosses between mutants with deletions (or insertions) of single nucleotides. Deletion or insertion mutations generally lead to completely nonfunctional genes. In contrast, simple nucleotide switches often lead to "leaky" genes, in which the mutant protein has partial enzymatic activity because of a single amino acid replacement. The virtually complete absence of enzymatic activity in the deletion (insertion) mutants tells us that their protein product is completely changed.

This striking qualitative difference arises from the fact that during protein synthesis the reading of the genetic code starts from one end of the protein template and occurs in consecutive blocks of three bases. As a result, if a deletion or insertion occurs, the reading frame is completely upset (Figure 9–23). For example, if normally the gene sequence ATTAGACAC . . . is read as (ATT)(AGA)(CAC) . . . , then the insertion of a new nucleotide ATTCAGACAC . . . leads to reading in the following groups (ATT)(CAG)(ACA)(C . .). A similar consequence follows from a deletion. Crossing of two deletion (or insertion) mutants yields double mutants in which the reading frame is still misplaced.

Partially active genes, however, can be produced by crosses overs between an insertion and a nearby deletion. Crossing over between the deletion and insertion restores the correct reading frame except in the region between (Figure 9–23). When the resulting protein product is normal except for several amino acid replacements, it may have some enzymatic activity. It is also sometimes possible to obtain functional genes by producing recombinants containing three closely spaced insertions

FIGURE 9–22   *The base-pairing attributes of 5-bromouracil.   (a) In the normal keto state, with a hydrogen atom in the N_1 position, bromouracil bonds to adenine. (b) In the rare enol state, a tautomeric shift of this hydrogen atom determines specific pairing with guanine. (Redrawn from W. Hayes, The Genetics of Bacteria and; Their Viruses, Blackwell, Oxford, 1964, p. 278, with permission.)*

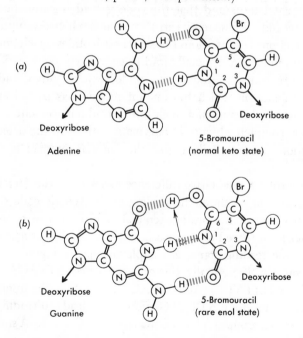

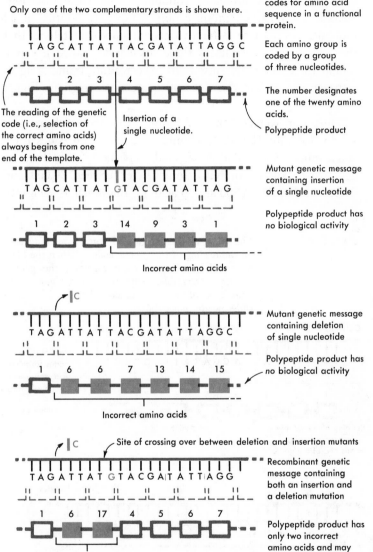

Only one of the two complementary strands is shown here.

Normal genetic message codes for amino acid sequence in a functional protein.

Each amino group is coded by a group of three nucleotides.

The number designates one of the twenty amino acids.

The reading of the genetic code (i.e., selection of the correct amino acids) always begins from one end of the template.

Insertion of a single nucleotide.

Polypeptide product

Mutant genetic message containing insertion of a single nucleotide

Polypeptide product has no biological activity

Incorrect amino acids

Mutant genetic message containing deletion of single nucleotide

Polypeptide product has no biological activity

Incorrect amino acids

Site of crossing over between deletion and insertion mutants

Recombinant genetic message containing both an insertion and a deletion mutation

Polypeptide product has only two incorrect amino acids and may have biological activity

Incorrect amino acids

FIGURE 9–23 *The effect of mutations that add or remove a base is to shift the reading of the genetic message.*

(deletions). Recombinants containing four close insertions (deletions), however, produce only completely nonfunctional proteins. It is these latter two experiments that tell us that the reading group contains three nucleotides, since by combining three deletions (insertions) the reading frame is again restored except for the deletion (insertion) region (Figure 9–24).

Thus, our average gene containing 1500 nucleotide pairs is subdivided into 500 reading units, each of which codes for a single amino acid. This corresponds very nicely with the average size of known proteins, somewhere between 30,000 and 50,000 MW (300 to 500 amino acids). Inasmuch as each esti-

FIGURE 9–24   *The effect of the addition of three nucleotide pairs on the reading of the genetic code. When the three nucleotides are added close together, the genetic message is scrambled only over a short region. The same type of result is achieved by the deletion of* **three nearby nucleotides.**

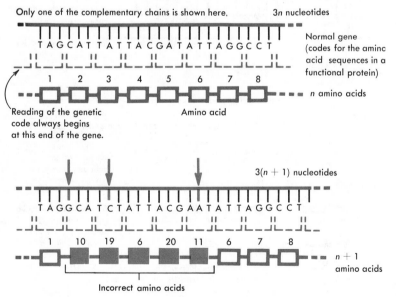

Only one of the complementary chains is shown here.   3n nucleotides

TAGCAT TATTA CGATAT TAGGCCT   Normal gene
(codes for the amino
acid sequences in a
functional protein)

1   2   3   4   5   6   7   8

Reading of the genetic   Amino acid   n amino acids
code always begins
at this end of the gene.

3(n + 1) nucleotides

TAGGCA TCTATT ACGAATAT TAGGCCT

1   10   19   6   20   11   6   7   8   n + 1
amino acids

Incorrect amino acids

Polypeptide chain contains four incorrect amino acids; its chain length is increased by one amino acid. It may have some biological activity depending upon how the five wrong amino acids influence its 3-D structure.

mate (average gene size and average protein size) is uncertain by 50 to 100 per cent, this level of agreement is almost better than the experimental evidence demands.

SUMMARY

The primary genetic material is DNA. It usually consists of two polynucleotide chains twisted about each other in a regular helix. Each chain contains a very large number of nucleotides. There are four main nucleotides and their sequence along a given chain is very irregular. The two chains are joined together by hydrogen bonds between pairs of bases. Adenine (purine) is always joined to thymine (pyrimidine) and guanine (purine) always bonds to cytosine (pyrimidine). The existence of the base pairs means that the sequences of nucleotides along the two chains are not identical but complementary. If the sequence of one chain is known, that of its partner is automatically known.

Cellular duplication of DNA occurs with the two strands separated, allowing the single strands to act as templates for the formation of complementary strands. The strands do not completely separate before the synthesis of the new strands. Instead duplication goes hand in hand with strand separation. The monomeric precursors for DNA synthesis are the deoxynucleoside-triphosphates, which are enzymatically joined together in the presence of a single-stranded DNA template by the enzyme DNA polymerase. Selection of the correct nucleotides by hydrogen bonding to the correct base pair is a very accurate process. The average probability of an error in the insertion of a new nucleotide under optimal conditions may be as low as 10^{-8} to 10^{-9}.

Individual DNA molecules may be very large. In fact, the E. coli chromosome is probably a single DNA molecule with an MW of about 2 to 4 × 10^9. Most DNA molecules correspond not to single genes, but to a collection of genes. Our best estimate now is that the average gene size is about MW = 10^6 (1500 nucleotide pairs).

The genetic information of a gene (the genetic code) resides in the sequences of the four main bases. Many mutations consist of changes in single base pairs at definite locations along the DNA molecule. Other mutations involve insertion or deletion of one to many nucleotide pairs. Groups of three nucleotides along the gene code for individual amino acids in the polypeptide chain product. Thus a gene with 1500 nucleotide pairs determines the sequence of a polypeptide chain containing 500 amino acids.

REFERENCES

Stahl, F. W., *The Mechanics of Inheritance*, Prentice-Hall, Englewood Cliffs, N.J., 1964. A discussion of genetics that starts with DNA. Particularly valuable are the excellent questions accompanying each chapter.

Kornberg, A., *Enzymatic Synthesis of DNA*, Wiley, New York, 1962. A summary of many of the relevant experiments about the synthesis of DNA in a test tube.

"Synthesis and Structure of Macromolecules," *Cold Spring Harbor Symp. Quant. Biol.*, 28, 1963. An excellent collection of papers presented in a June, 1963, meeting, most of which are highly relevant to the material in this and subsequent chapters.

Baldwin, R. L., "Molecular Aspects of the Gene: Replication Mechanisms," in I. C. Gunsalus and R. Y. Stanier (eds.), *The Bacteria*, Academic, New York, 1964, Vol. 5, pp. 327–372. A clear survey of current ideas about DNA duplication in vivo and in vitro.

Crick, F. H. C., "The Genetic Code," *Sci. Am.*, October, 1962, pp. 66–74. A description of the original experiments with phage T4 revealing that the genetic code is read in groups of three nucleotides.

Ingram, V. M., *The Biosynthesis of Macromolecules*, Benjamin, New York, 1965. An excellent discussion from a more advanced chemical level of many of the topics discussed in Chapters 9, 10, 11, and 13 of this book.

10

THE TRAN-
SCRIPTION OF
RNA UPON
DNA
TEMPLATES

WE ARE NOW READY TO APPROACH THE problem of how DNA controls the sequence of amino acids in proteins. Compared with DNA replication, we should anticipate this selection procedure to be a more chemically sophisticated task, since many of the amino acid side groups neither form specific hydrogen bonds nor have surfaces obviously complementary in shape to any nucleotide or nucleotide group. Yet somehow the correct amino acids are inserted into a given polypeptide chain with less than 1 error per 1000 amino acids. It is, then, not surprising that the solution of this problem (commonly known as the coding problem) has required much theoretical insight, produced many unanticipated results, and employed a greater variety of experimental approaches than those needed in understanding the mechanism of DNA replication.

THE CENTRAL DOGMA

We should first look at the evidence that DNA itself is not the direct template that orders amino acid sequences. Instead, the genetic information of DNA is transferred to another class of molecules, which then serve as the protein templates. These intermediate templates are molecules of ribonucleic acid (RNA), large polymeric molecules chemically very similar to DNA. Their relation to DNA and protein is usually summarized by the formula (often called the central dogma)

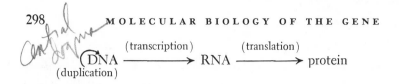

$$\text{DNA} \xrightarrow{\text{(transcription)}} \text{RNA} \xrightarrow{\text{(translation)}} \text{protein}$$

(duplication)

where the arrows indicate the direction of transfer of the genetic information. The arrow encircling DNA signifies that it is the template for its self-replication; the arrow between DNA and RNA indicates that all cellular RNA molecules are made on DNA templates.[1] Correspondingly, all protein sequences are determined by RNA templates. Most importantly, both these latter arrows are unidirectional, that is, RNA sequences are never copied on protein templates; likewise, RNA never acts as a template for DNA.

PROTEIN SYNTHESIS IN ABSENCE OF DNA

Many experiments now exist which show that proteins can be constructed in the absence of DNA. The most obvious demonstration comes from nucleated cells, where most protein synthesis occurs in the cytoplasm; almost all the DNA is found in the chromosomes within the nucleus. This observation unambiguously tells us that an intermediate template must carry genetic information to the cytoplasmic sites of synthesis. No such simple in vivo demonstration can exist for bacterial cells that lack a nucleus, but the use of in vitro cell-free systems (see below) shows that DNA's lack of direct participation is a general phenomenon.

The intermediate is clearly RNA. In the first place, there is evidence from many types of nucleated cells that all cellular RNA synthesis is restricted to the DNA-containing nucleus (Figure 10–1).[2] No RNA strands are made in the cytoplasm, from which DNA is absent.[3] RNA is thus synthesized where it

---

[1] Although this statement holds for normal cellular RNA, it does not hold for cells infected with certain RNA viruses (see Chapter 12).

[2] This statement does not hold for certain virus-infected cells (see Chapter 12).

[3] This statement must now be qualified to take into account the recently discovered facts that both the mitochondria and chloroplasts contain small amounts of DNA which may serve as templates for the RNA molecules involved in the synthesis of specific mitochondria and chloroplast proteins.

should be if it is made on DNA. After their synthesis, many of the RNA molecules move to the cytoplasm in which most protein synthesis is taking place. Some protein synthesis also occurs in the nucleus, and correspondingly, some RNA is not transported away but instead remains in the nucleus.

In the second place, the amount of protein synthesized is directly related to the cellular content of RNA. Cells rich in RNA synthesize much protein, whereas little protein is made in RNA-poor cells. For example, the RNA-rich pancreas (Figure 10–2) synthesizes large quantities of proteolytic enzymes which are secreted into the digestive tract. Correspondingly, little RNA is found in muscle cells, in which little protein is made.

FIGURE 10–1 (a) Autoradiograph of a cell (Tetrahymena) exposed to radioactive cytidine for 15 min. Superimosed on a photograph of a thin section of the cell is a photograph of an exposed silver emulsion. Each dark spot represents the path of an electron emitted from an H^3 (tritium) atom that has been incorporated into RNA. Almost all the newly made RNA is found within the nucleus. (b) An autoradiograph of a similar cell, exposed to radioactive uridine for 12 min and then allowed to grow for 88 min in the presence of non-radioactive cytidine. Practically all the label incorporated in the first 12 min has left the nucleus and moved into the cytoplasm. [Photographs courtesy of D. M. Prescott, University of Colorado Medical School; reproduced from Progr. Nucleic Acid Res., III, 35 (1964), with permission.]

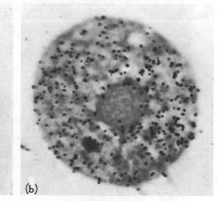

(a)   (b)

The significance of this correlation is strengthened by isotopic experiments designed to locate accurately the synthetic sites within the cytoplasm. In these experiments cells are very briefly exposed to amino acids labeled with radioactive isotopes. During these short intervals ("pulses"), some radioactive amino acids become incorporated into proteins. The cells are then quickly broken open to see in which cellular fraction the newly made protein (identified by its possession of radioactive amino

FIGURE 10–2   *Electron micrograph (×105,000) of a portion of a cell in the pancreas of a bat, showing a mitochondrion and large numbers of ribosomes. Some ribosomes exist free; others (especially in the upper right) are attached to a membranous component, the endoplasmic reticulum. (Courtesy of K. R. Porter.)*

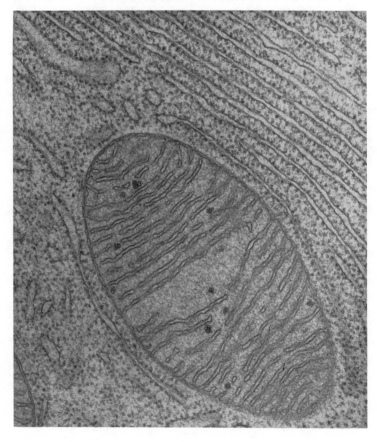

acids) is found. In all cells the results are the same: Newly synthesized polypeptide chains are found associated with spherical RNA-containing particles, the ribosomes (Figure 10-3). Likewise, a small amount of protein can be made in vitro in carefully

FIGURE 10-3 *Sucrose gradient demonstration that protein synthesis occurs on ribosomes. [Redrawn from A. Rich, Sci. Am., 209, 46–47 (December 1963).]*

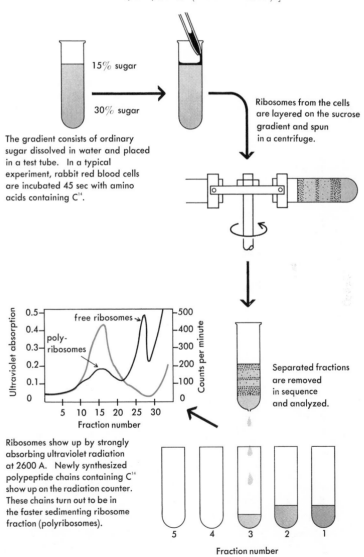

15% sugar

30% sugar

The gradient consists of ordinary sugar dissolved in water and placed in a test tube. In a typical experiment, rabbit red blood cells are incubated 45 sec with amino acids containing C¹⁴.

Ribosomes from the cells are layered on the sucrose gradient and spun in a centrifuge.

Separated fractions are removed in sequence and analyzed.

Ribosomes show up by strongly absorbing ultraviolet radiation at 2600 A. Newly synthesized polypeptide chains containing C¹⁴ show up on the radiation counter. These chains turn out to be in the faster sedimenting ribosome fraction (polyribosomes).

free ribosomes

poly-ribosomes

Ultraviolet absorption

Counts per minute

Fraction number

5 4 3 2 1

Fraction number

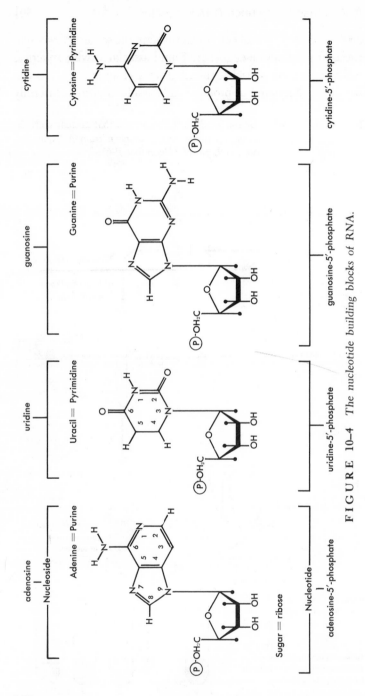

FIGURE 10–4 *The nucleotide building blocks of RNA.*

302

prepared extracts of cells, and here also use of radioactive isotopes shows attachment of much of this new protein to the
RNA-rich ribosomes.

RNA IS CHEMICALLY VERY SIMILAR TO DNA

Mere inspection of RNA structure shows how it could be exactly
synthesized on a DNA template. Chemically it is very similar
to DNA. It is also a long, unbranched molecule containing four
types of nucleotides (Figure 10–4) linked together by 3′–5′ phosphodiester bonds (Figure 10–5). Two differences in its chemical groups distinguish RNA from DNA. The first is a minor
modification of the sugar component (Figure 10–6). The sugar
of DNA is deoxyribose, whereas RNA contains ribose, identical
to deoxyribose except for the presence of an additional OH
(hydroxyl) group. The second difference is that RNA contains
no thymine but instead contains the closely related pyrimidine
uracil. Despite these differences, however, polyribonucleotides
have the potential for forming complementary helices of the
DNA type. Neither the additional hydroxyl group nor the absence of the methyl group found in thymine affects RNA's
ability to form double-helical structures held together by hydrogen-bonded base pairs.

RNA IS USUALLY SINGLE–STRANDED

RNA molecules do not usually have complementary base ratios
(Table 10–1). The amount of adenine does not often equal the

T A B L E 10–1 *The base composition of RNA from various
sources*

RNA Source	Proportion of the four main bases			
	Adenine	Uracil	Guanine	Cytosine
E. coli	24	22	32	22
Proteus vulgaris (a bacterium)	26	19	31	24
Euglena (a protozoan)	22	21	30	27
Turnip yellow mosaic virus	23	22	17	38
Poliomyelitis virus	30	25	25	20
Rat kidney	19	20	30	31

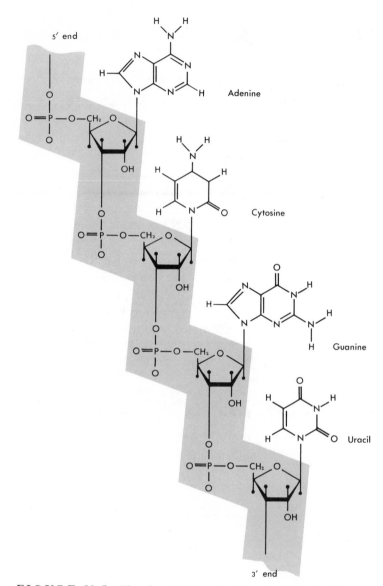

FIGURE 10–5 *The chemical formula of a polyribonucleotide.*

amount of uracil, and the amounts of guanine and cytosine also usually differ from each other. This tells us that most RNA does not possess a regular hydrogen-bonded structure, but, unlike double-helical DNA, exists as single polyribonucleotide strands.

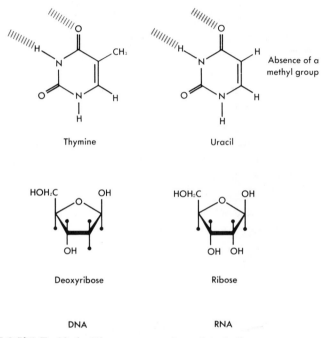

FIGURE 10–6 *The structures of uracil and ribose.*

Because of the absence of regular hydrogen bonding, these single-stranded molecules do not have a simple regular structure like DNA. As a consequence their 3-dimensional form(s) is (are) not yet known and may not be solved for many years. This structural uncertainty initially caused much pessimism, for there was general belief that we should have to see the template before we could attack the problem of how it selected amino acids during protein synthesis. Fortunately, as we show later, this hunch was wrong.

ENZYMATIC SYNTHESIS OF RNA UPON DNA TEMPLATES

The fact that RNA, like DNA, is a long, unbranched chain using four different nucleotides immediately suggests that the genetic information of DNA chains is transferred to a complementary sequence of RNA nucleotides. According to this hypothesis, the DNA strands at one or more stages in the cell cycle separate and function as templates onto which complementary ribonucleotides are attracted by DNA, like base-pairing [adenine with thymine (uracil) and guanine with cytosine]. It further tells us that some control mechanism must dictate whether the separated DNA strands will function as templates for a complementary DNA strand or a complementary RNA strand.

Direct evidence for the hypothesis comes from the discovery of the appropriate enzyme RNA polymerase, which exists in virtually all cells. This enzyme links together ribonucleotides by catalyzing the formation of the internucleotide 3′–5′ phosphodiester bonds that hold the RNA backbone together (Figure 10–7). It does so, however, only in the presence of DNA, a fact that suggests that DNA must line up the correct nucleotide precursors in order for RNA polymerase to work. Proof for this idea comes from seeing how the RNA base composition varies with the addition of DNA molecules of

FIGURE 10–7   *Enzymatic synthesis of RNA upon a DNA template.*

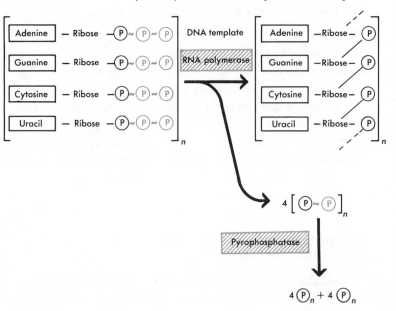

T A B L E 10–2 *Comparison of the base composition of enzymatically synthesized RNAs with the base composition of their double-helical DNA templates*

Source of DNA template	Composition of the RNA bases, % Adenine	Uracil	Guanine	Cytosine	$\frac{A+U}{G+C}$ observed	$\frac{A+T}{G+C}$ in DNA
T2	0.31	0.34	0.18	0.17	1.86	1.84
Calf thymus	0.31	0.29	0.19	0.21	1.50	1.35
E. coli	0.24	0.24	0.26	0.26	0.92	0.97
Micrococcus lyso- deikticus (a bacterium)	0.17	0.16	0.33	0.34	0.49	0.39

different AT/GC ratios. In every enzymatic synthesis, the RNA AU/GC ratio is similar to the DNA AT/GC ratio (Table 10–2).

Further experiments directly demonstrate that the template is a single DNA strand. One of the clearest experiments uses DNA from the virus ϕx174. This virus belongs to one of the very special viral classes that contain single-stranded DNA instead of the customary double helical form. Only one of the two possible complementary DNA strands is present, and when it is used as the template for RNA polymerase, the enzymatic product has a complementary base sequence (Table 10–3). Moreover, in this special case the RNA product remains attached to its DNA template, allowing the isolation of a hybrid DNA-RNA double helix. This result contrasts with

T A B L E 10–3 *Base composition of enzymatically synthesized RNA using single-stranded ϕx174 DNA as primer*

	ϕx174 DNA, %	Observed values of RNA product, %	Predicted RNA composition, %
Adenine	0.25	0.32	0.33
Uracil	0.33 (thymine)	0.25	0.25
Guanine	0.24	0.20	0.18
Cytosine	0.18	0.23	0.24
Total	1.00	1.00	1.00

experiments using double-helical DNA. Here the RNA product quickly detaches from its template and the two DNA strands again come together in specific register. Apparently the double helix made from two complementary DNA strands is energetically more stable than the hybrid DNA-RNA structure, so that the free single DNA strand quickly displaces the RNA product soon after RNA polymerase has moved over the corresponding template region.

We thus see that the fundamental mechanism for the synthesis of RNA is very similar to that of DNA. In both cases the immediate precursors are nucleoside triphosphates that use the energy in one of their pyrophosphate bonds to drive the reaction toward synthesis. Also in both cases, a single enzyme works on all four possible nucleotides, whose correct selection is dictated by the obligatory need to base-pair with a polynucleotide template. The transcription of RNA on DNA may therefore be as accurate as the self-replication of DNA. In any case the very rare mistakes that do occur in RNA transcription are not passed on to many subsequent cell generations, since cellular RNA is not a self-replicating molecule.

ONLY ONE DNA STRAND ACTS AS AN RNA TEMPLATE

If each of the two DNA strands serves as an RNA template, each gene would produce two RNA products with complementary sequences, which should code for two different proteins. Since our genetic evidence tells us that each gene controls only one protein, we must assume that either only one of the two strands is made or, if both are synthesized, for some special reason, only one is functional. It appears that the former possibility is correct—in vivo only one of the two possible gene products is found. This can clearly be seen by examining the RNA synthesized in vivo under the direction of the virus SP8, which multiplies in the bacterium Bacillus subtilus. The two complementary DNA strands of the SP8, unlike those of most viruses, have quite different base compositions, and can be relatively easily separated. It is thus possible to ask whether the RNA products have base sequences complementary to one or both the DNA strands.

To answer this question, use was made of our ability to form artificial DNA-RNA hybrid molecules by mixing RNA molecules with single-stranded DNA molecules formed by heating of double-helical DNA. Heating DNA molecules to temperatures just below 100°C breaks the hydrogen bonds holding the complementary strands together; they then quickly separate from each other (DNA denaturation). If the temperature is gradually lowered, the complementary strands again form the correct hydrogen bonds and the double-helical form is regained (renaturation of DNA). If, however, this gentle cooling is done in the presence of single-stranded RNA that has been synthesized on homologous DNA, then DNA-RNA hybrids form as well as renatured DNA double helices (Figure 10–8). These DNA-RNA hybrids are very specific and only form if some of the nucleotide sequences in the DNA are complementary to the RNA nucleotide sequences. This technique lets us ask whether the in vivo RNA products will form hybrids with only one or with both of the complementary SP8 DNA strands. A clear result emerges: Only one DNA strand is copied (Figure 10–9). No one yet knows how this choice is made.

Differential copying of the two strands of a DNA molecule can also be observed in vitro. This result depends on the use of DNA templates which have not been severely damaged. If the DNA has denatured to produce single strands or if it is broken so that single-stranded regions are produced, then both strands are copied. When, however, intact molecules of T4 DNA (MW ~ 1.2 × 10⁸) are used as in vitro templates, the DNA strand which is copied is the same strand copied during in vivo viral reproduction.

This unique copying of the DNA strand allows us to understand why the base ratios of RNA need not be complementary even though RNA is made on a DNA template. In a given DNA strand, there is no reason why the A should equal T or G equal C. These ratios need be one-to-one only when the corresponding bases on the two complementary chains are added together. Thus, in general, we must assume that only in the

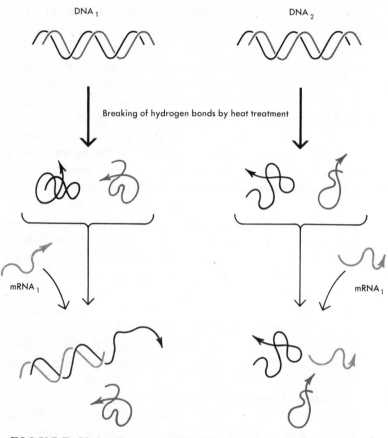

FIGURE 10-8   The use of DNA-RNA hybrids to show the comple-
mentarity in nucleotide sequences between an RNA
molecule and one of the two strands of its DNA
template.   The left side of the diagram shows the
formation of a hybrid molecule between an RNA
molecule and one of the two strands of the template.
The specificity of this method is shown on the right
side of the diagram.   Here the same RNA molecule
is mixed with unrelated DNA.   No hybrid molecules
are formed.

exceptional DNA molecule will the single strands be found on
close inspection to have the complementary ratios.   Correspondingly, only rarely will single-stranded RNA molecules be found
in which A accurately equals U and G equals C.

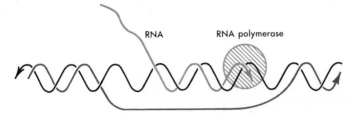

FIGURE 10–9   *Transcription of an RNA molecule upon a unique strand of its DNA template. The attachment of the enzyme RNA polymerase to a DNA molecule opens up a short section of the double helix, thereby allowing free bases on one of the DNA strands to base pair with the ribonucleoside—⑪～⑪～⑪ precursors. As RNA polymerase moves along the DNA template, the growing RNA strand peels off, allowing hydrogen bonds to reform between two complementary DNA strands.   Thus   almost   immediately   after   the synthesis of an RNA strand commences, its front end becomes available to bind to a ribosome (see Chapter 11).*

SYNTHESIS OF RNA CHAINS
OCCURS IN A FIXED DIRECTION

Each RNA chain, like a DNA chain, has a direction defined by the orientation of the sugar-phosphate backbone. The chain end terminated by the 5′-carbon atom is called the 5′ end, while the end containing the 3′ carbon atom is called the 3′ end (Figure 10–5). Until recently, there was no evidence whether RNA chains grow in the 3′ to 5′ direction or vice versa. If they grow 5′ to 3′, then we expect the beginning nucleotide to possess a ⑪～⑪～⑪ group (Figure 10–10). On the contrary, if the chains grow 3′ to 5′, then the nucleotide at the growing end will contain the ⑪～⑪～⑪ group. At this time (March, 1965), evidence is beginning to accumulate that the direction of growth is 5′ to 3′. When growing chains are examined, the newly inserted nucleotides are found at the 3′ ends, while the ⑪～⑪～⑪ groups are found attached to the nucleotides which commenced chain growth.

Work with the metabolic inhibitor 3′-deoxyadenosine confirms the 5′-to-3′ direction of growth. When it is added to cells,

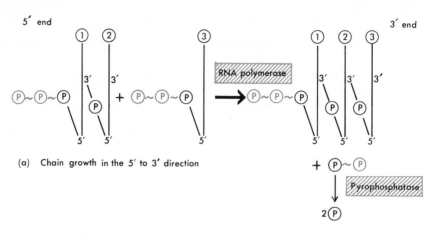

(a)   Chain growth in the 5' to 3' direction

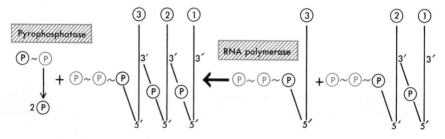

(b)   Chain growth in the 3' to 5' direction

FIGURE 10–10   *Alternative directions for the synthesis of an RNA chain. Newly performed experiments suggest that chains always grow in the 5' to 3' direction.*

it is first phosphorylated to 3'-deoxyadenosine—Ⓟ~Ⓟ~Ⓟ and then joined to the 3' growing end. Because it contains no 3'-OH group, further nucleoside—Ⓟ~Ⓟ~Ⓟ cannot attach, and RNA synthesis stops.

GENETIC MESSAGES MUST BE GIVEN TO START (STOP) THE SYNTHESIS OF SPECIFIC RNA MOLECULES

The RNA products transcribed on DNA molecules are very much smaller than the DNA templates. It is thus believed that RNA polymerase can attach to more than one place on a DNA molecule and begin synthesis. It then moves along the DNA template, transcribing a specific nucleotide sequence, falling off the template when a unique stop signal is given. The number of starting signals is believed to be very large; for phage T4, over 50 different starting points are believed to exist. No evidence is now available about the molecular basis of the start signals. Perhaps a specific nucleotide sequence is complementary in shape to a region of the enzyme RNA polymerase. This could allow the enzyme to attach to the DNA in such a way as to preferentially copy one of the two strands.

SUMMARY

DNA molecules are not the direct templates for protein synthesis. The genetic information of DNA is first transferred to molecules of RNA. In turn RNA molecules act as the primary templates that order amino acid sequences in proteins. (DNA → RNA → protein). RNA's covalent structure is chemically very similar to DNA, and its genetic information also is stored in the sequences of its four main bases. In contrast to DNA, however, most RNA molecules are single-stranded. The synthesis of RNA upon DNA templates shows many similarities to the DNA duplication process. Most importantly the selection process involves formation of complementary base pairs. The enzyme, RNA polymerase, links together the monomeric precursors, which are the ribonucleoside triphosphates (ATP, GTP, CTP and UTP). In a given gene only one of the two DNA strands is copied. The molecular basis of this differential transcription is not known.

REFERENCES

Chantrenne, H., The Biosynthesis of Proteins, Pergamon, New York, 1961. Though already somewhat out of date, it provides an excellent introduction to the biochemical study of protein synthesis.

Prescott, D. M., "Cellular Sites of RNA Synthesis," in J. N. Davidson and W. E. Cohn (eds.), Progress in Nucleic Acid Research, Academic, New York, 1964, Vol. 3, pp. 35–57. A very clear discussion of the techniques of cell biology which have established the nucleus as the site of most RNA synthesis.

Hurwitz, J., and J. T. August, "The Role of DNA in RNA Synthesis," in J. N. Davidson and W. E. Cohn (eds.), *Progress in Nucleic Acid Research*, Academic, New York, 1963, Vol. 1, pp. 59–92. A summary of experiments showing how DNA acts as a template for RNA synthesis.

Marmur, J., C. Greenspan, F. Palecek, F. M. Kahan, J. Levine, and M. Mandel, "Specificity of the complementary RNA formed by *B. subtilis* Infected with Bacteriophage SP8," *Cold Spring Harbor Symp. Quant. Biol.*, 28, pp. 191–199 (1963). A description of an experiment showing that, in vivo, only one of the two DNA strands is a template for RNA synthesis.

Spiegelman, S. S., "Hybrid Nucleic Acids," *Sci., Am.*, May, 1964, pp. 48–56. Here are clearly explained many of the experimental techniques that have been so elegantly used to demonstrate homology in nucleotide sequences between DNA and RNA.

11

INVOLVEMENT

OF RNA IN

PROTEIN

SYNTHESIS

WE NOW BEGIN TO LOOK AT HOW SINGLE-stranded RNA molecules function during protein synthesis. When the general validity of the central dogma (DNA → RNA → protein) was becoming obvious in the mid-1950s, there was general belief that all RNA was template RNA. Hope also existed that, when the RNA general structure was solved, mere inspection might tell us how RNA ordered amino acid sequences. Now, however, we realize that these views were very naive and that protein synthesis is a much more complicated affair than the synthesis of nucleic acid. Moreover, not all RNA molecules are templates. In addition to a template class, there exist two additional classes of RNA, each of which plays a vital role in protein synthesis.

AMINO ACIDS HAVE NO SPECIFIC AFFINITY FOR RNA

The fundamental reason behind this complexity has been mentioned before. There is no specific affinity between the side groups of many amino acids and the purine and pyrimidine bases found in RNA. For example, the hydrocarbon side groups of the amino acids alanine, valine, leucine, and isoleucine do not form hydrogen bonds and would be actively repelled by the amino and keto groups of the various nucleotide bases. Likewise, it is hard to imagine the existence of specific RNA surfaces with unique affinities for

315

the aromatic amino acids phenylalanine, tyrosine, and trypto-phan. It is thus impossible for these amino acids in unmodified form to line up passively in specific accurate order against an RNA template prior to peptide bond formation.

AMINO ACIDS ATTACH TO RNA TEMPLATES BY MEANS OF ADAPTORS

Before the amino acids line up against the RNA template, they are chemically modified to possess a specific surface capable of combining with a specific number of the hydrogen-bonding groups along the template. This chemical change consists of the addition of a specific adaptor molecule to each amino acid through a single covalent bond. It is this adaptor component that combines with the template; at no time does the amino acid side group itself need to interact with the template. Adding a specific adaptor residue to an amino acid is much more economical than chemically modifying the side group itself. The latter process might require many enzymes for just a single amino acid. Conceivably a similar number would be required to change the adapted side group back to its original configuration after it becomes part of a polypeptide chain. On the other hand, only a single enzyme is needed either to attach or to detach an amino acid from its specific adaptor.

SPECIFIC ENZYMES RECOGNIZE SPECIFIC AMINO ACIDS

There need not be any obvious relation between the shape of the amino acid side group and the adaptor surface. Instead the crucial selection of an amino acid is done by a specific enzyme. The enzyme that catalyzes the attachment of the amino acid to its adaptor must be able to bind specifically to both the amino acid side group and the adaptor. For this task, proteins are extremely suitable, because their active regions can be rich in either hydrophilic or hydrophobic groups. There is no difficulty in folding a suitably sequenced polypeptide chain to produce a cavity that is specific for the side group of one specific amino acid. For example, tyrosine can be distinguished from phenylalanine by an enzyme having a specific cavity containing an atom that can form a hydrogen bond to the OH group on tyrosine. Here the formation of one specific hydrogen bond yields about 4 to 5 kcal/mole of energy. This energy would be lost if phenylalanine were chosen instead. Thus, with the help of a physical chemical theory, we can predict that the probability that tyrosine is found in the "tyrosine cavity" is about 1000 times greater than the probability that phenylalanine is found in the tyrosine cavity.

There is more difficulty in immediately seeing how a similar accuracy can be achieved in distinguishing between amino acids differing only by one methyl residue, a group incapable of either salt linkages or hydrogen bonding. For example, glycine must be distinguished from alanine and valine from isoleucine. There is, of course, no difficulty in understanding why the larger alanine side group cannot fit into the smaller glycine cavity. Likewise, isoleucine will not fit into the cavity designed for the smaller amino acid valine. The problem arises when we ask why glycine will not sometimes fit into the alanine cavity or valine into the isoleucine hole. If this should happen, there would be loss of the van der Waals forces arising out of a snug fit around a methyl group. These forces are now thought to be about 2 to 3 kcal/mole, by themselves too small in value to account for the general accuracy by which amino acids are ordered during protein synthesis. Now we suspect that the maximum frequency at which a wrong amino acid is inserted into a growing polypeptide chain is about 1 in 1000. This means that the energy gained by selecting the correct amino acid must be at least 4 to 5 kcal, a value about twice that provided by only the van der Waals energy. This difference provided an apparent paradox until consideration was also given to the relative difficulty of inserting glycine and alanine molecules into an aqueous solution: The water molecules in the liquid phase are held together by a relatively regular arrangement of hydrogen bonds ($O-H \cdot \cdot \cdot O$). Virtually all the hydrogen and oxygen atoms in water are hydrogen bonded. This arrangement is disturbed by the presence of the non-hydrogen-bond-forming CH_3 groups whose introduction necessarily causes the loss of the energy gained by forming hydrogen bonds. We should thus look at an aqueous solution as a collection of molecules that will try to expel unwanted hydrophobic groups. This tendency provides the added energy difference (2 kcal/mole) to allow the correct selection of alanine (isoleucine), since there is a very marked difference in the rate at which water solutions will expel alanine (isoleucine) in comparison to the more water soluble glycine (valine).

THE ADAPTOR MOLECULES
ARE THEMSELVES RNA MOLECULES

The molecules to which the amino acids attach are a group of relatively small RNA molecules called soluble RNA (sRNA).[1] It is really not surprising that the adaptors are also RNA molecules, since a prime requirement for a useful adaptor is the ability to attach specifically to the free keto and amino groups on the single-stranded template RNA molecules. This attachment is ideally accomplished by having the adaptor also be a single-stranded RNA molecule, since this opens the possibility of having very specific hydrogen bonds (perhaps of the base-pair variety) to hold the template and adaptor together temporarily. The sRNA adaptors for the 20 different amino acids all have different structures, each uniquely adapted for fitting onto a different nucleotide sequence on the template. A large number of different types of sRNA thus exist.

Each of the sRNAs contains approximately 80 nucleotides (MW~25,000) linked together in a single covalently bonded chain (Figure 11–1). One end of the chain (3' end) always terminates in a CCA sequence (cytidylic acid, cytidylic acid, adenylic acid). The terminal nucleotide of the other end (5') is guanylic acid. Even though there is only one chain, most of the bases are hydrogen bonded to each other, using the DNA-type base pairing (A with U, G with C). This is accomplished by hairpin folds that bring bases on the same chain into a DNA-like double-helical arrangement. The configuration is possible

---

[1] Some authors prefer the name *transfer* RNA (tRNA) for the adaptor molecule.

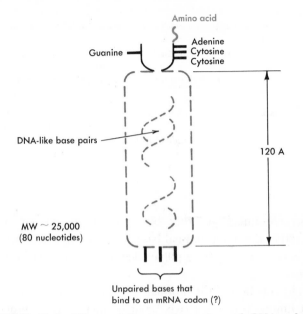

FIGURE 11-1   *Diagrammatic view of an amino-acyl sRNA molecule.*

because the number of adenine residues is approximately equal
to the number of uracil residues. Likewise, the guanine number almost equals the cytosine number. The correspondence is
not exact, however, and some nucleotides that do not internally
base pair are available to fit to the template.

YEAST ALANINE sRNA CONTAINS 77 NUCLEOTIDES

During December, 1964, the first nucleotide sequence of a
specific sRNA molecule (from yeast) was worked out. This
sRNA specifically attaches to alanine and therefore is called
alanine sRNA. It contains 77 nucleotides arranged in a unique
sequence (Figure 11-2). The most striking aspect of this
sequence is the high content (9/77) of unusual bases (Figure
11-3). ("Unusual" means a base other than A, G, C, or U.)
Many of these unusual bases differ from normal bases by the
presence of one or more methyl (CH₃) groups. Most if not
all the methyl groups are enzymatically added after the nucleo-

5'
G-G-G-C-G-U-G-U-MeG-G-C-G-C-G-U-A-G-DiHU-C-G-G-DiHU-A-G-
1   10   20

C-G-C-DiMeG-C-U-C-C-C-U-U-I-G-C-MeI-ψ-G-G-G-A-G-A-G-U-C-
        30   40   3'

U-C-C-G-G-T-ψ-C-G-A-U-U-C-C-G-G-A-C-U-C-G-U-C-A-C-C-A
50   60   70   77

FIGURE 11–2   *The nucleotide sequence of alanine sRNA from
yeast. Here we follow the convention that the
nucleotide at the 5' end is written first. The chemical
formulas for the various rare bases are shown in Figure
11–3.*

tides are linked together by 3'–5' phosphodiester linkages.
Whether the other unusual bases also arise by enzymatic modification of a preexisting polynucleotide has not yet been established.

The function of the unusual bases is not yet clear. They are
not limited to alanine sRNA but occur in varying proportions
in all sRNA molecules. Our only hint as to their role is the fact
that several unusual bases cannot form conventional base
pairs. Some of the unusual bases may thus have the function
of disrupting double-helical hairpin regions, thereby exposing
free keto and amino groups which can then form secondary
bonds. Depending upon the specific bases, the free groups
may form secondary bonds to template RNA, to a ribosome,
or to the enzyme needed to attach a specific amino acid to its
specific sRNA molecule.

THE 3–D SHAPE OF sRNA IS NOT YET KNOWN

The exact nucleotide sequence of alanine sRNA by itself does
not provide sufficient information to guess unambiguously its
3-D structure. When the sequences of several more sRNA
molecules become known, it may be possible to find common
features which will tell us their 3-D shapes. Until then, we can
only speculate about which sRNA nucleotides bind to template
RNA. Most likely, three specific bases (the anticodon) bind

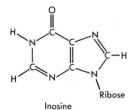

Inosine

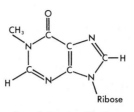

1-methylinosine (Me I)

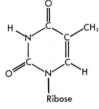

N²-dimethylguanosine (DiMeG)

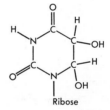

1-methylguanosine (MeG)

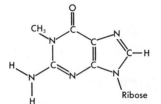

Ribothymidine (T)

Dihydrouridine (DiHU)

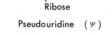

Pseudouridine (Ψ)

FIGURE 11-3 *The structures of the rare nucleotides found in yeast alanine sRNA.*

to the template. This follows from the fact, mentioned in Chapter 9, that the genetic code uses three-letter words (codons). Whether the three nucleotides in an anticodon are adjacent will not be known until more information becomes available on sRNA structure.

ADDITION OF THE ADAPTOR
ALSO ACTIVATES THE AMINO ACID

The amino acids are always linked to sRNA by means of their terminal adenylic acid residues (at the -CCA end). The link is a covalent bond between the amino acid carboxyl group and the terminal ribose component of the RNA (Figure 11–4). The use of the amino acid carboxyl group to attach to the adaptor has several interesting implications. In the first place, before the carboxyl can form a peptide bond, the sRNA adaptor must be released. Thus peptide bond formation and adaptor removal occur in a coordinated fashion. In the second place, the bond linking the sRNA to its specific amino acid is a high-energy bond: Thus these complexes can be considered "activated" precursors. The energy in the amino acid-sRNA bond (an aminoacyl bond), can be used in the formation of the lower-energy peptide bond.

The energy required for forming the amino-acyl bond has come from a high-energy pyrophosphate linkage ($(P)\sim(P)$) in ATP. Prior to the formation of the AA$\sim$sRNA compounds, the amino acids are activated by enzymes (amino-acyl synthetases) to form amino acid adenylates (AA$\sim$AMP) in which the amino acid carboxyl group is attached, by high-energy bonding, to an

$$AA + ATP \overset{\text{amino acyl}}{\underset{\text{synthetase}}{\rightleftharpoons}} AA \sim AMP + (P) \sim (P) \qquad (11-1)$$

adenylic acid (AMP) group (Figure 11–4). The AA$\sim$AMP intermediate normally remains tightly bound to the activating enzyme until collision with an sRNA molecule specific for the amino acid. Then the same activating enzyme transfers the amino acid to the terminal adenylic acid residue of the sRNA.

$$AA \sim AMP + sRNA \overset{\text{amino acyl}}{\underset{\text{synthetase}}{\rightleftharpoons}} AA \sim sRNA + AMP \qquad (11-2)$$

We thus see that the activating enzymes are able specifically to recognize (bind to) both a given amino acid and its sRNA adaptor. For this purpose, the enzymes must have two different combining sites: one that recognizes the side group of an amino acid, and another that recognizes the sRNA specific for that

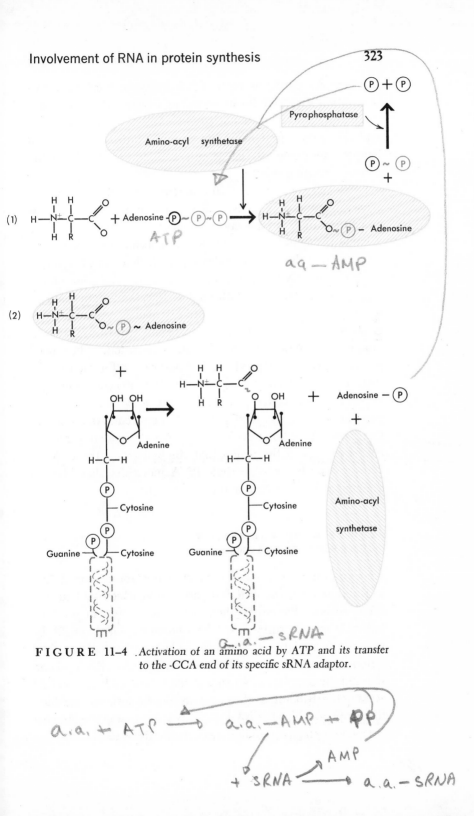

FIGURE 11-4 .Activation of an amino acid by ATP and its transfer to the -CCA end of its specific sRNA adaptor.

amino acid. Similarly, each sRNA molecule must have two recognition sites: one for its activating enzyme, the other for a specific group of template nucleotides. It follows that the amino acid side group itself never has to come into contact with a template molecule. It needs only to bind specifically to the correct activating enzyme.

Every cell needs at least 20 different kinds of activating enzymes and at least 20 kinds of sRNA molecules. There must be at least one of each for every amino acid. Though at first it was thought that only 20 different sRNA molecules were used, now it is clear that there are several cases in which at least two different types of sRNA molecules are specific for the same amino acid. This is connected with the fact that the genetic code often uses more than one nucleotide sequence (codon) for a given amino acid (degeneracy; see Chapter 13); there may be a unique sRNA molecule for each functional codon. There need not be, however, a separate activating enzyme for each of the several sRNAs corresponding to a given amino acid. Since the sRNA binds to the templates and to the activating enzymes at two distinct sites, it is possible for sRNA molecules that differ in their template-binding nucleotides to possess indentical nucleotide sequences in the region that combines with the enzyme. Thus it may be possible that sRNA molecules that bind to different codons can bind to the same enzyme.

PEPTIDE BOND FORMATION OCCURS ON RIBOSOMES

Once the amino acids have acquired their adaptors, they diffuse to the ribosomes, the spherical particles on which protein synthesis occurs. Protein synthesis never occurs free in solution, but only on the surfaces of the ribosomes, which might be regarded as miniature factories for making protein. Their chief function is to orient properly the incoming AA~sRNA precursors and the template RNA so that the genetic code can be read accurately. Ribosomes thus contain specific surfaces that bind the template RNA, the AA~sRNA precursors, and the growing polypeptide chain in suitable stereochemical positions.

There are approximately 15,000 ribosomes in a rapidly growing *E. coli* cell. Each ribosome has a molecular weight of
slightly less than 3 million. Together the ribosomes account for
about one-fourth of the total cellular mass, and hence a very
sizable fraction of the total cellular synthesis is devoted to the
task of making proteins. Only one polypeptide chain can be
formed at a time on a single ribosome. Under optimal conditions, the production of a chain of MW = 40,000 requires about
ten seconds. The finished polypeptide chain is then released
and the free ribosome can be used immediately to make another
protein.

All ribosomes are constructed from two subunits, the larger
subunit approximately twice the size of the smaller one (Figure
11–5). Both subunits contain both RNA and protein. In *E.
coli* ribosomes the RNA/protein ratio is 2:1; in many other
organisms, it is about 1:1. Most of the protein serves a
structural role (as opposed to an enzymatic role). Both the
large and small subunits contain a number of different proteins
(MW~30,000) whose chief function is to help bring the
template RNA and the AA~sRNA precursors together correctly.

RIBOSOME–ASSOCIATED RNA DOES NOT USUALLY CARRY GENETIC INFORMATION

When ribosomes became implicated in protein synthesis (1953),
it seemed natural at first to suppose that their tightly bound
RNA component was the template that ordered the amino
acids. In fact, it was initially supposed that all cellular RNA
was located in the ribosomes and that the lighter, slowly sedimenting, soluble fraction (~20 per cent of total RNA) was a
degradation product of the ribosomal RNA templates. The
identification (1956) of the soluble RNA fraction as the
adaptor molecules corrected this faulty guess, but it did not
remove the belief that the remaining 80 per cent of cellular
RNA functioned as templates. In 1960, however, RNA isolated from purified ribosomes (rRNA or ribosomal RNA) was
unambiguously shown not to have a template role.

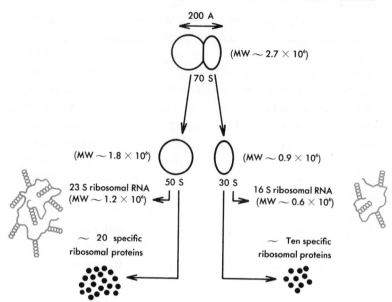

FIGURE 11–5   *The structure of the E. coli ribosome. It is usually called the 70-S ribosome since 70 S (Svedbergs) is a measure (the sedimentation constant) of how fast this ribosome sediments in the centrifuge. Likewise, the designations 30 S and 50 S are the sedimentation constants of the smaller and larger ribosome subunits; 16 S and 23 S are the sedimentation constants of the smaller and larger ribosomal RNA molecules. The binding of the 30-S and 50-S subunits to form a 70-S ribosome is dependent upon the Mg^{2+} concentration. At the Mg^{2+} levels found in growing E. coli cells, 70–90% of the 30-S and 50-S subunits have aggregated to form 70-S ribosomes. This aggregation is a reversible process, for if the Mg^{2+} level is reduced, the 70-S ribosomes fall apart to their 30-S and 50-S subunits. Why all ribosomes contain easily dissociable subunits is still a complete mystery.*

TEMPLATE RNA (mRNA) REVERSIBLY ASSOCIATES WITH RIBOSOMES

The active templates are instead an RNA fraction comprising only one to several per cent of total RNA. This RNA reversibly binds to the surface of the smaller ribosome subunit and, in media of low Mg^{2+} ion concentration, can be removed without affecting ribosome integrity. Because it carries the genetic message from the gene to the ribosomal factories, it is called messenger RNA (mRNA). By moving across the ribosomal site of protein synthesis, it brings successive codons into position to select the appropriate AA~sRNA precursors.

The existence of mRNA was first unambiguously established in experiments with T2-infected *E. coli* cells. After T2 DNA enters a host cell, it must turn out RNA templates for the many viral specific proteins needed for viral reproduction (see Chapter 12 for more details). Thus many biochemists were initially surprised by the 1959 finding that no new rRNA chains and hence no new ribosomes were synthesized following T2 infection. This result could only mean that T2-specific proteins are not synthesized on rRNA templates and further hinted that perhaps in normal cells rRNA chains were not the templates for protein synthesis. Searches begun when the T2 result became known quickly revealed the presence of mRNA, first in viral infected cells, and soon afterwards in normal *E. coli* cells.

rRNA EXISTS IN TWO SIZE CLASSES

Two size classes of rRNA are found in all ribosomes. They are an integral component and, unlike mRNA, cannot be removed without the complete collapse of the ribosome structure. The smaller rRNA molecule, found in the smaller ribosome subunit, has a molecular weight of about one-half million, whereas the larger molecule, a component of the larger ribosome subunit, has a molecular weight of about 1 million. Both are single-stranded and have unequal amounts of guanine and cytosine and of adenine and uracil. There is rough equivalence of base pairs, and many rRNA bases on the same chain are hydrogen bonded together using the type hairpin turns found in sRNA. The joint presence of both single-stranded and double-helical regions gives individual rRNA molecules irregular 3-D shapes. As a result, it has not yet been possible to obtain rRNA preparations in which the molecules are regularly arranged in space. Thus x-ray diffraction pictures of rRNA are much more distorted than the corresponding DNA diagrams and cannot tell us precise details of rRNA structure. Similar dilemmas exist for elucidation of sRNA structures and mRNA by x-ray analysis.

THE FUNCTION OF rRNA IS NOT YET KNOWN

The function of rRNA remains a major mystery. Not even a semisatisfactory hypothesis now exists of why ribosomes contain rRNA as well as protein. Part of the reason may be that the unpaired bases in rRNA are in some way involved in the binding of sRNA and mRNA to ribosomes. In cells, much of RNA's negative phosphate charge is neutralized by Mg^{2+} ions. It is thus possible that the divalent Mg^{2+} ions sometimes form temporary bridges between mRNA and rRNA, or mRNA and sRNA, thereby helping to keep their components correctly aligned during polypeptide synthesis.

On the other hand, it seems unlikely that this is the sole role of rRNA. There are hints, still very weak, that although rRNA chains isolated from ribosomes have no template role, newly synthesized rRNA, before being enclosed in a ribosome, may function as a template. This hypothesis is based on two observations: (1) The rRNA component of ribosomes contains a small fraction of methylated bases similar to those found in sRNA. These methylated bases arise, like those of sRNA, by methylation of intact polynucleotides. The rRNA is first synthesized, then methylated, and finally packaged in a functional ribosome. (2) Unmethylated rRNA, in contrast to methylated rRNA, can function as a template in in vitro experiments. Before methylation, rRNA chains can attach to ribosomes. Somehow the attachment of methyl groups blocks the binding of free rRNA to a ribosome. It is thus tempting to believe that, in vivo, rRNA functions for a short time as a template, perhaps for the various structural proteins of ribosomes and then, following methylation, becomes part of native ribosomes, where it serves a structural as opposed to a template role.

We must emphasize that this hypothesis is very speculative. Nonetheless, it is a useful conjecture, since it may soon be put to a decisive test. If it is true, then the addition of nonmethylated rRNA chains to an in vitro protein synthesis system (see Chapter 13) should result in the specific synthesis of the structural proteins of ribosomes.

ALL THREE FORMS OF RNA ARE MADE ON DNA TEMPLATES

Since both sRNA and rRNA chains have very special roles in protein synthesis, the idea was proposed (several years ago) that perhaps these RNA forms were not made on DNA templates, but were instead self-replicating, like the RNA in the single-stranded RNA viruses (see Chapter 12). Recently, however, this idea has been shown to be wrong by DNA-RNA hybridization experiments. In these experiments, rRNA (or sRNA) chains are mixed at a high temperature (near 100°C) with DNA isolated from the same organism. At this temperature, the double-helical regions of rRNA (sRNA) fall apart. Likewise, all DNA hydrogen bonds in DNA break, and complementary strands separate. When the temperature is then dropped slowly, stable double helices again form. In addition to reformation of many complementary DNA double helices, some single DNA strands specifically combine with rRNA (sRNA) chains to form hybrid DNA-RNA helices. These DNA-RNA complexes are very specific, for they do not form if DNA from an unrelated species is used. Hence, sRNA and rRNA are synthesized exactly as mRNA is, using DNA molecules as templates. Most interestingly, even though rRNA and sRNA together comprise over 98 per cent of all RNA, less than 1 per cent of the total DNA functions as their templates.

There is probably only one specific sequence of DNA nucleotides (a gene) coding for each of the 30 to 40 different sRNA molecules. In contrast, both the larger and smaller rRNA chains appear to be coded by several genes. Whether each of these separate genes for small or large rRNA has identical nucleotide sequences is not known. They certainly cannot possess radically different sequences since their rRNA products must have very similar 3-D shapes in order to fit in a ribosome.

The use of DNA to code for sRNA (and for rRNA if future

experiments reveal it never assumes a template role) tells us that all genes need not code for specific amino acid sequences. We must thus ask the question whether other RNA forms, as yet undiscovered, may play important metabolic roles. Certainly we now cannot automatically assume that, for each gene, there exists a corresponding protein.

mRNA MOLECULES EXIST IN A LARGE VARIETY OF SIZES

In contrast to sRNA molecules, which have molecular weights of about 2.5×10^4, and to rRNA molecules, which are either 5×10^5 or 10^6 in molecular weight, mRNA molecules vary greatly in chain length, and hence in molecular weight. Some of this heterogeneity reflects the large size spread in the length of polypeptide chain products. Not many polypeptide chains contain fewer than 100 amino acids, and so almost all mRNA molecules must contain at least 100×3 (because there are three nucleotides in a codon) nucleotides. In E. coli the average size of mRNA is 900 to 1500 nucleotides, corresponding to the fact that the average E. coli polypeptide chain contains from 300 to 500 amino acids.

Some molecules, however, code for more than one polypeptide chain. Their length is the sum of the lengths of the chains required to code for each protein for which they serve as templates. This summing provides another basis of variation in mRNA chain lengths. In most, if not in all, of these polygenic messengers, the polypeptide products have related functions. For example, there exists an mRNA molecule that codes for the ten specific enzymes needed to synthesize the amino acid histidine. It has approximately 12,000 nucleotides (MW~4,000,000) or an average of 1200 nucleotides coding for each enzyme.

RIBOSOMES ATTACH TO mRNA AT SPECIFIC POINTS

Free ribosomes cannot attach at any point along natural mRNA chains. Each specific natural mRNA chain contains one to several spots at which free ribosomes can stick. These sticky points are most likely the nucleotide sequences which code for

the first amino acids (the NH$_3$ terminal; see below) in polypeptide chains. There is at most one sticky point per polypeptide chain coded by a given messenger. If there were more
than one sticky point per polypeptide product, incomplete
polypeptides would be produced. Why a messenger can attach
only at specific points is not stereochemically clear. The explanation may be connected with the fact that all natural
messengers (as distinct from synthetic messenger; see Chapter 13) have considerable double-helical regions formed by
hairpin turns similar to those in sRNA and rRNA. Now it is
guessed that only single-stranded regions are sticky. If so, the
sequence of nucleotides within each natural mRNA must cause
it to assume a configuration in which long single-stranded
regions are effectively absent.

Once a ribosome has attached to a messenger and polypeptide
synthesis has commenced, the ribosome moves along the mRNA
in a fixed direction, with a new amino acid being added every
time the ribosome moves over a group of three nucleotides.
As yet, we are completely in the dark as to what causes mRNA
and ribosomes to move relative to each other. It is clear, however, that after synthesis has commenced, the ribosome becomes
attached to regions of mRNA to which it could not attach
prior to synthesis. In some way, the presence of an attached
ribosome temporarily disrupts nearby hairpin double-helical
regions, creating single-stranded regions which are able both
to stick to the ribosome and to select the correct AA~RNA
precursors.

THE DIRECTION OF mRNA READING IS 5′ TO 3′

After a ribosome has stuck to an mRNA molecule, it must always move in a fixed direction during protein synthesis. It
does not have the alternatives of moving either to the right or
to the left, which reflects the fact that RNA molecules have a
direction defined by the relative orientations of the 3′ and 5′
ends. The end which is read first is the 5′ end. Thus the end
synthesized first is read first. This opens up the possibility that
a ribosome can attach to an incomplete mRNA molecule still

in the process of synthesis on its DNA template. If, on the contrary, polypeptide synthesis went 3′ to 5′, then a length of mRNA corresponding to a complete polypeptide chain would have to be synthesized before it could stick to a ribosome. The fact, however, that protein synthesis goes 5′ to 3′ most likely means that long sections of mRNA, unattached to ribosomes, may not normally exist in rapidly growing cells.

AN mRNA MOLECULE WORKS ON SEVERAL RIBOSOMES SIMULTANEOUSLY

The section of an mRNA molecule that is in contact with a single ribosome is relatively short. This allows a given mRNA molecule to work on several ribosomes at once. Single mRNA molecules can move over the surfaces of several ribosomes simultaneously (the collection of ribosomes bound to a single mRNA chain is called a polyribosome) thus functioning as a template for several polypeptide chains at once. At

FIGURE 11–6 Schematic picture of a polyribosome during protein synthesis. The mRNA molecule is moving in the direction of the arrows.

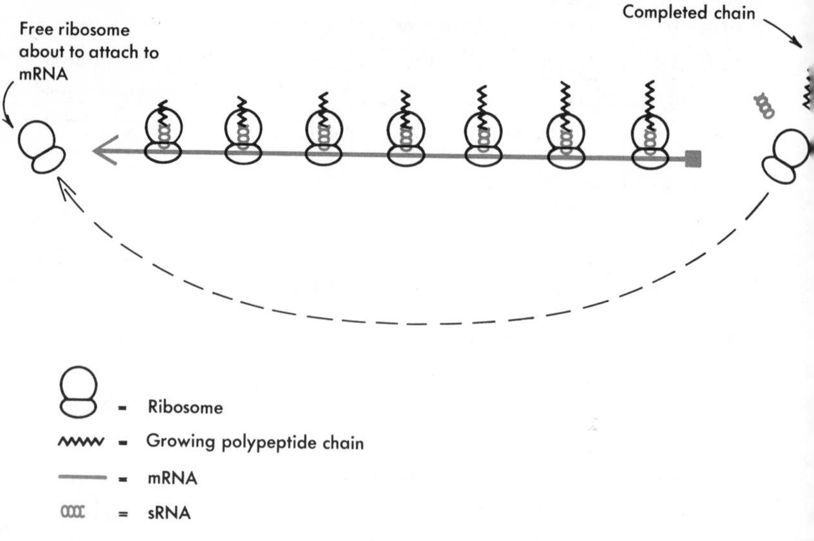

Free ribosome about to attach to mRNA

Completed chain

8 - Ribosome

ᴧᴧᴧᴧ - Growing polypeptide chain

——— - mRNA

ᴄᴄᴄᴄ = sRNA

a given time, the lengths of chains attached to successive ribosomes in the polyribosome vary in direct proportion to the fraction of the messenger tape to which each ribosome has already been exposed (Figure 11–6). This means that at any moment the polypeptide chains being produced along the length of the mRNA are shortest at the front of the strand, and gradually lengthen toward the end. There is great variation in polyribosome size, which depends upon the size of the mRNA chain. At maximum utilization of an mRNA chain, there is one ribosome for every 80 mRNA nucleotides. Thus the polyribosomes making the individual polypeptide chains (chain length—150) of the hemoglobin molecule usually contain 4 to 6 ribosomes (Figure 11–7), while approximately 12 to 20 ribosomes are attached to the mRNA molecules concerned with the synthesis of proteins in the 30,000 to 50,000 MW (300 to 500 amino acids) range.

The ability of a single mRNA to simultaneously function on several ribosomes explains why a cell needs so relatively little mRNA. Before polyribosomes were discovered, it was thought that the fact that mRNA comprised only 1 to 2 per cent of the total cellular RNA was paradoxical. This followed from the fact that, if the average MW chain were of MW about 5×10^5, then at a given instant, at most only 10 per cent of the ribosomes in a cell could be making protein.

STEPWISE CHAIN GROWTH BEGINS WITH THE AMINO TERMINAL END

At one end of each completed polypeptide chain there is an amino acid bearing a free carboxyl group, and at the other end there is one bearing a free amino group. Chains always grow by stepwise addition of single amino acids, starting with the amino terminal amino acid and ending with the carboxyl terminal amino acid (Figure 11–8). Chain initiation begins with the insertion of a specific AA~sRNA molecule into a hole formed jointly by the larger of the two ribosome subunits and with the first mRNA codon. Although the ribosome-bounded surface can accept any of the 20 specific AA~sRNAs, since it binds to

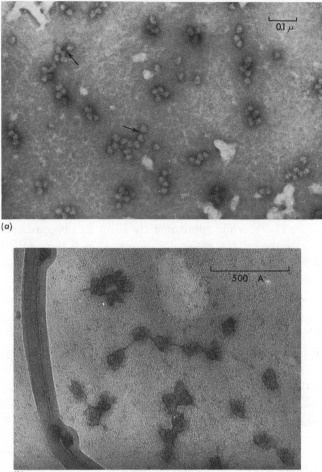

0.1 μ

(a)

500 A

(b)

FIGURE 11-7   Electron-microscope photographs of polyribosomes from rabbit reticulocytes. (a) shows that many of the observed polyribosomes contain 4–6 ribosomes. The smaller groups are most likely breakdown products produced during their isolation from cells. The arrows show material that seems to connect two ribosomes. (b) At higher magnification, the existence of a connecting thin mRNA strand is very clear. [Photographs by H. S. Slayter; reproduced from H. S. Slayter et al., J. Mol. Biol., 7, 652 (1963), with permission.]

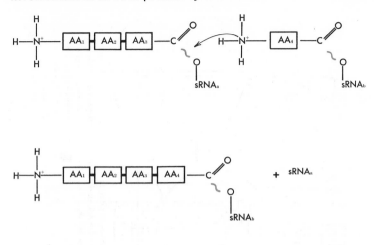

(Peptide bonds between amino acids
are indicated by a heavy line.)

FIGURE 11–8   *Stepwise growth of a polypeptide chain.   Initiation*
begins at the free NH$_3^+$ end with the carboxyl growing
point terminated by an sRNA molecule.

an unspecific region of the sRNA molecule, the codon-
bounded surface is specific for a unique sRNA molecule.   After
the first AA—sRNA is bound, a second AA—sRNA precursor
becomes bound by an adjacent cavity whose specificity is likewise determined by binding to the adjacent mRNA codon.
A peptide bond is then formed enzymatically between the two
amino acids to yield a dipeptide (two amino acids linked by a
peptide bond) terminated by an sRNA molecule, the adaptor
molecule of the latter amino acid.   This process of amino acid
addition then repeats over and over, adding one amino acid at a
time, to form a complete chain (Figure 11–9).   In these events
the following steps should be emphasized:

1. The growing carboxyl end is always terminated by an
sRNA molecule that fits into a cavity (growing protein binding
site) of the larger subunit.   The binding of this terminal sRNA
molecule provides the main force that holds the growing polypeptide chain to the ribosome.

2. A peptide bond is formed immediately after the sRNA

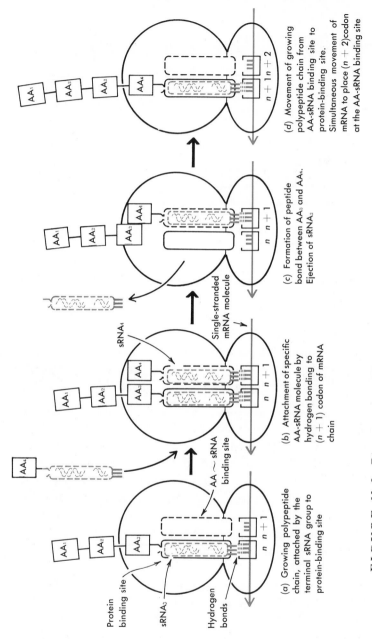

FIGURE 11-9 *Diagrammatic representation of the stepwise growth of a polypeptide chain.*

Protein binding site

sRNA₃

Hydrogen bonds

AA ~ sRNA binding site

sRNA₁

Single-stranded mRNA molecule

(a) Growing polypeptide chain, attached by the terminal sRNA group to protein-binding site

(b) Attachment of specific AA-sRNA molecule by hydrogen bonding to (n + 1) codon of mRNA chain

(c) Formation of peptide bond between AA₃ and AA₄. Ejection of sRNA₃

(d) Movement of growing polypeptide chain from AA-sRNA binding site to protein-binding site. Simultaneous movement of mRNA to place (n + 2) codon at the AA-sRNA binding site adaptor is released from the carboxyl terminal amino acid; the amino acid carboxyl group to which the sRNA adaptor has been attached is used to form the peptide bond.

3. Very soon after peptide bond formation (if not simultaneously with it), the released sRNA molecule is ejected from the protein binding site. The new terminal sRNA molecule (the adaptor component of the amino acid that has just joined the chain) then most likely moves into the protein-binding site.

4. At the same time the mRNA template (bound to the smaller ribosome subunit) moves to place codon $n + 1$ in the position previously occupied by codon n.

5. After the polypeptide chain has grown to full length, the terminal sRNA must be split off, thereby creating a free terminal COO^- group. Until this happens, the newly formed chain remains tightly bound to the larger of the two ribosomal subunits. The enzymatic basis for the release phenomenon is not yet known.

6. After the completed polypeptide is released, the now free ribosome attaches to a new starting point on an mRNA molecule.

TWO DIFFERENT ENZYMES ARE NEEDED TO FORM THE PEPTIDE BOND

Because the amino acid carboxyl groups are "activated" by their attachment to their sRNA adaptor, it was initially guessed that perhaps only one specific enzyme would be needed for making the peptide bond. Furthermore, there was no reason to suspect that energy would need to be added in the polymerization reaction. These hunches, however, were wrong. At least two separate enzymes are somehow involved in the process. And the energy-rich molecule GTP (analogous to ATP, with adenine replaced by guanine) is required. As yet, not even a general outline either of how GTP works or of why at least two enzymes are required has been worked out. Despite these uncertainties, however, it is possible to draw parallels between the making of the peptide bond of protein and the formation of the inter-nucleotide bonds of nucleic acids. In both cases, the same en-

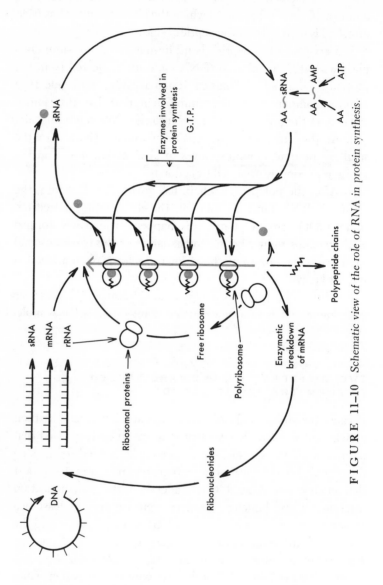

FIGURE 11-10 *Schematic view of the role of RNA in protein synthesis.*

zyme(s) is (are) always used no matter which specific amino acids (or nucleotides) are to be polymerized. Moreover, the ordering of both acids and nucleotides is achieved by prior binding of the precursors to macromolecular templates.

MUCH MORE MUST BE LEARNED ABOUT RIBOSOMES

It is very likely that the broad general outlines of protein synthesis are now established. Each of the key features shown in Figure 11–10 has been established by a variety of experiments. Nonetheless, much new information must be obtained before we can honestly state that protein synthesis is understood at the molecular level. At the heart of our uncertainty is the role of the ribosome. Though a few physical parameters such as MW and RNA content have been accurately established, almost nothing is known about the exact structures of rRNAs or ribosomal proteins, or how they combine with sRNA or mRNA. Since ribosomes cannot yet be crystallized, x-ray diffraction analysis is not possible, so that now, high-resolution EM photographs provide the best opportunity for probing their structure. EM analysis, however, cannot show details at the atomic level. We must thus be prepared for a long wait and much hard work before we understand why such a complicated structure is necessary for protein synthesis.

SUMMARY

Amino acids do not attach directly to RNA templates. They first combine with specific adaptor molecules to form AA~adaptor molecules. It is the adaptor component that has a strong chemical affinity for RNA nucleotides. All the adaptor molecules are soluble RNA molecules (sRNA) of MW~25,000. A given sRNA molecule is specific both for a given amino acid and for a specific group of three template nucleotides (a codon). The amino acids are covalently attached through their carboxyl groups to the ends of sRNA molecules. This covalent bond is a high-energy bond. Adapted amino acids are thus "activated." There is a specific activating enzyme (amino-acyl synthetase) for each amino acid, and so it is an enzyme molecule that recognizes the amino acid. The over-all accuracy of protein synthesis can thus be no greater than the accuracy with which the activating enzymes can selectively recognize the various amino acids.

After activation, the AA—sRNA molecules diffuse to the ribosomes, spherical particles on which the peptide bonds form. Ribosomes have molecular weights of about 3×10^6 and consist of about one-half protein and one-half RNA. Their RNA component (rRNA) does not contain genetic information. The template itself is a third form of RNA, messenger RNA (mRNA). Messenger RNA attaches to ribosomes and moves across the ribosomes to bring successive codons into position to select the correct AA—sRNA precursors.

Protein chains always grow in a stepwise fashion, beginning at the amino terminal end. A given mRNA molecule generally works simultaneously on many ribosomes (a polyribosome). Thus at a given moment many codons of the same template molecule are "at work." The stepwise growth from the amino terminal end leaves the growing end always terminated by an sRNA molecule. This sRNA molecule is held in a cavity on the ribosome, thereby binding the growing chain to the ribosome. Neither the mechanism of mRNA movement over the ribosomes nor the detailed enzymatic basis of peptide bond formation is yet understood.

REFERENCES

Crick, F. H. C., "On Protein Synthesis," *Symp. Soc. Exptl. Biol.*, **12**, pp. 138–163 (1958). A presentation of the ideas that led the author to propose the adaptor hypothesis.

Vogel, H. J., V. Bryson, and J. Lampen (eds.), *Informational Macromolecules*, Academic, New York, 1963. A collection of papers about polynucleotides, protein synthesis, and the genetic code.

Watson, J. D., "The Involvement of RNA in the Synthesis of Proteins," *Science*, **140**, 17–26 (1963). A history of work between 1953 and 1962 that has established how RNA participates in protein synthesis.

Spirin, A. S., *Macromolecular Structure of Ribonucleic Acids*,

Reinhold, New York, 1964. A discussion of current ideas about the structure of RNA and how it is organized within ribosomes.

Rich, A., "Polyribosomes," *Sci. Am.*, December, 1963, pp. 44–53. A description of how hemoglobin is synthesized on polyribosomes.

Spielgelman, S., and M. Hayashi, "The Present Status of the Transfer of Genetic Information and Its Control," *Cold Spring Harbor Symp. Quant. Biol.*, **28**, 161–181 (1963). A lucid presentation of some of the authors' experiments which support the central dogma (DNA→RNA→protein).

12

THE
REPLICATION
OF VIRUSES

WE HAVE SEEN THAT IN THE TRANSFER
of genetic information from DNA to
amino acid sequences the RNA intermediate is chemically almost identical
to DNA. It is, in fact, so similar that
the natural question arises why we
need to have DNA as the genetic substance. Would it not be simpler if the
genes were RNA? Then an intermediate would not be necessary for protein
synthesis. At present we cannot answer this question. RNA not only has
the potential for storing genetic information in the form of its sequence of
bases but is also, in special cases, a
genetic molecule capable of self-
replication.

All these special cases involve viruses
whose chromosomal components are
RNA molecules. Until now, no evidence for self-replicating RNA within
normal cells (i.e., lacking viruses) has
been found. As emphasized earlier,
most, if not all, RNA in uninfected
cells is made on DNA templates. The
existence of RNA viruses thus does not
negate the idea that RNA is not normally a template for more RNA molecules and that it instead functions in
the ordering of amino acids during protein synthesis. It does, however, immediately open this question: Does
RNA self-replication also involve base
pairing and the formation of complementary double helices? Before we
look into this problem, some more details about the general principles of viral structure and multiplication must
be examined.

342

THE CORE AND COATING OF VIRUSES

Both the size and structural complexity of viruses show great variation. Some have molecular weights as small as several million, whereas others approach the size of very small bacteria. However, all viruses differ fundamentally from cells, which have both DNA and RNA, in that viruses contain only one type of nucleic acid, which may be either DNA or RNA. The genetic nucleic acid component is always present in the center of the virus particle, surrounded by a protective coat (shell). Some of the shells are quite complex; they contain several layers and are built up from a number of different proteins, as well as from lipid and carbohydrate molecules (Figures 12–1, 12–2, 12–3). In other cases, for example in tobacco mosaic virus (TMV)— a virus that multiplies in tobacco plants—or in the small RNA bacterial viruses F2 and R17, the shell contains only one type of protein and no lipid or carbohydrate.

All shells contain many copies of the protein component(s), often arranged either with helical symmetry or with cubical (or quasi-cubical) symmetry. Thus the TMV shell has about 2150 identical protein molecules (MW = 17,000) helically arranged around a central RNA molecule containing approximately 6000 nucleotides (Figure 12–4). In F2 (or R17) there are 180 identical proteins (MW $\sim$ 14,000) cubically arranged about an inner RNA molecule with 3000 nucleotides.

The use of a large number of identical protein molecules in the construction of the protective shell is an obligatory feature of the structures of all viruses. This follows from their limited nucleic acid content, which in turn places an absolute restriction on the maximal number of amino acids in the proteins coded by the viral chromosome. For example, the $\sim$6000 nucleotides in a TMV-RNA chain can code for $\sim$2000 amino acids, corresponding to a protein molecular weight of about 2.5×10^5. This is very much smaller than the molecular weight of TMV's protein shell (3.5×10^7). Thus, even if the entire TMV-RNA chain coded for its coat protein (which it does not), approximately 150 identical protein molecules would be needed. This use of a large number of identical protein subunits is why the simpler viruses, which contain only one type of protein molecule in their coat, have either helical or cubical (or quasi-cubical) symmetry. Only these two types of symmetry permit the identical protein subunits to be packed together in a regular (or quasi-regular) fashion and thus to have virtually identical (except for their contacts with the nucleic acid core) chemical environments.

FIGURE 12–1   The morphology of Herpes, a large DNA-containing virus which multiplies in animal cells. (a) A schematic view of its general structure showing the DNA-containing core embedded in a regular shell (capsid), and an outer envelope. (b) An electron micrograph showing the 1000-A diameter capsid surrounded by a 1500-A envelope. (c) A high-resolution electron micrograph of the capsid. It contains 162 subunits (capsomeres) arranged about fivefold, threefold, and twofold axes of symmetry. [(b) and (c) reproduced from Wildy et al., Virology, 12, 204 (1960), with permission.]

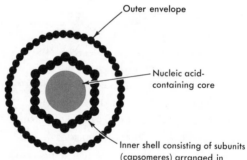

(a)

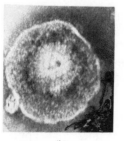

(b)

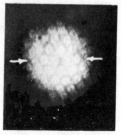

(c)

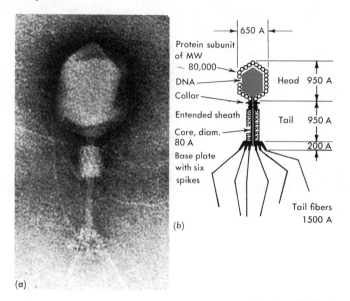

FIGURE 12–2 *The structure of the T-even (2, 4, and 6) phage particle. (a) An electron micrograph of T2 [reproduced from R. W. Horne et al., J. Mol. Biol., 1, 281 (1959), with permission]. (b) A schematic drawing showing detailed features revealed by electron microscopy.*

NUCLEIC ACID: THE GENETIC COMPONENT OF ALL VIRUSES

Viruses afford some of the best demonstrations that genetic specificity is carried by nucleic acid molecules. Many viral nucleic acids are easily isolated from their protein shell and prepared in highly purified form. When they are added to host cells, new infective virus particles are produced; each is identical to those from which the nucleic acid was isolated (Figure 12–5). These very important experiments definitively show that the viral nucleic acid carries the genetic specificity to code both for its own replication and for the amino acid sequences in its specific coat proteins.

This is true not only for the DNA viruses, but also for viruses containing RNA. In fact, the first demonstration of infectious viral nucleic acid was made by using RNA isolated from TMV.

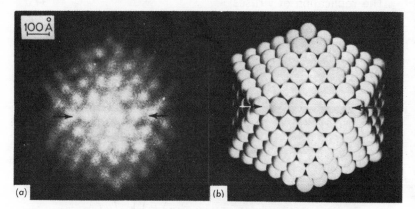

FIGURE 12–3   Adenovirus structure. These DNA-containing viruses,
which multiply in animal cells, have very regular
structures. (a) A particle at high magnification. 252
capsomeres are used to construct the outer shell.
(b) A model of an icosahedron in the same orientation. [Reproduced from R. W. Horne et al., J. Mol.
Biol.; 1, 86 (1959), with permission.]

Before this demonstration, doubts had persisted whether the
RNA component of TMV was really genetic. This uncertainty existed because the large majority of TMV particles are
not ordinarily infectious. Usually fewer than one in a million
particles enters the tobacco leaf and serves as parent for progeny
particles. It could thus be argued that perhaps this rare particle contained DNA. However, the isolation of infectious
TMV-RNA dispelled this uncertainty and clearly showed that
sequences of nucleotide bases in RNA, like those in DNA,
carry genetic messages.

VIRAL NUCLEIC ACID MAY BE EITHER
SINGLE– OR DOUBLE–STRANDED

The nucleic acid of most viruses has the form of its cellular
counterparts. Thus all the best known DNA viruses, such as
smallpox (or its harmless relative Vaccinia), polyoma, and the
T2, T4, and T6 group of bacterial viruses, have the double-
helical structure. Correspondingly the RNA of TMV, influenza

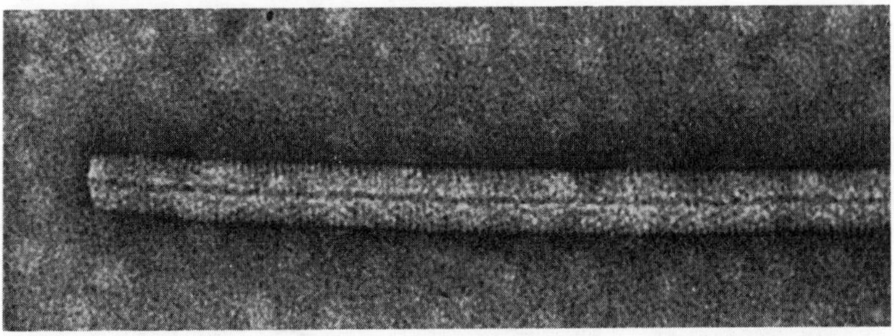

FIGURE 12-4   A high-resolution electron micrograph of one end of a TMV particle. The diameter is approximately 180 A, whereas the length of a complete particle is 3000 A. The particle is covered with a dark stain which penetrates the hollow central core. [Photograph reproduced from J. T. Finch, J. Mol. Biol., 8, 872 (1964), with permission.]

virus, poliomyelitis virus, and the bacterial virus F2 is single-stranded. There are, however, several groups of bacterial viruses in which the DNA is single-stranded and there is at least one group of RNA viruses (the Reo viruses) in which the RNA assumes a complementary double-helical form.

Fundamentally, it does not matter whether the genetic message is initially present as a single strand or as the double helix; for the single strand can be quickly used to form a complementary replica soon after it enters a suitable host cell. The really important fact is that the genetic information is present as a sequence of nucleotide bases.

VIRAL NUCLEIC ACID AND PROTEIN SYNTHESES OCCUR INDEPENDENTLY

Exactly what happens after a viral nucleic acid molecule enters a susceptible host cell depends upon the specific viral system. Particularly important is whether the virus contains DNA or RNA. If the genetic component is DNA, then during viral replication the DNA serves as a template both for its own replication and for the viral specific RNA necessary for the synthesis of its specific proteins. On the contrary, if RNA is the

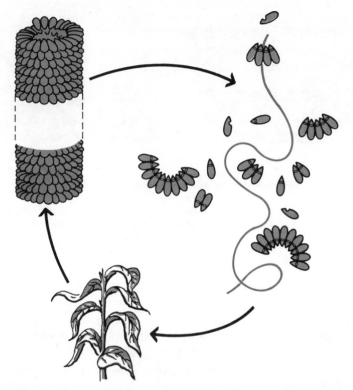

FIGURE 12-5 Proof that RNA is the genetic component of TMV. The rod-shaped TMV particles can easily be separated into their protein and RNA components, which can then be separately tested for their ability to initiate virus infection. Only the RNA molecules have this ability. The virus particles produced by infecting with pure RNA are identical to those resulting from infection with intact virus.

genetic component, the RNA molecules have two template roles, the first to make more RNA molecules and the second to make the viral specific proteins. In both cases, however, the end result of virus infection is the same: the production of many new copies of both the viral nucleic acids and of the coat proteins. The new progeny molecules then spontaneously aggregate to form mature virus particles. For many viruses (if not all) no enzymes are necessary for maturation, since there are usually no covalent bonds binding the nucleic acid core to the coat proteins. Only weak secondary bonds (salt linkages, van der Waals forces, and hydrogen bonds) are involved. This last point is shown clearly with TMV. Here the rod-shaped particles can be gently broken down and their free RNA and coat protein components separated. When they are again mixed together, new infectious particles, identical to the original rods, quickly form (Figure 12–6). We thus see that the essential aspects of virus multiplication are known once we understand the principles by which viral nucleic acid and protein components are individually synthesized.

FIGURE 12–6   *Formation of a TMV particle from its protein subunits and its RNA molecule.   (Redrawn from H. Fraenkel-Conrat, Design and Function at the Threshold of Life: The Viruses, Academic, New York, 1962, Figure 18.)*

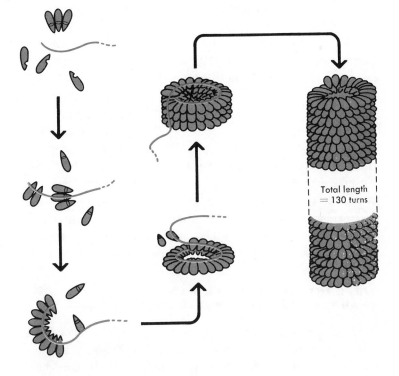

Total length
= 130 turns

SYNTHESIS OF VIRAL SPECIFIC PROTEINS

Viral specific proteins are synthesized in the same way as normal cellular proteins. The viral specific messenger RNA molecules attach to host ribosomes forming polyribosomes to which the AA ~ sRNA precursors are attracted. No example is known where the infecting virus particle carries the genetic information to synthesize rRNA or sRNA chains. Thus the synthesis of all viral specific proteins is accomplished using host cell sRNA and ribosomes.

VIRAL NUCLEIC ACIDS CODE FOR BOTH ENZYMES AND COAT PROTEINS

The viral nucleic acid genetic component must code the amino acids sequences in the protein(s) that make(s) up the protective coat. These coat proteins are never found in normal uninfected cells and are completely specific to a given virus. In addition, the synthesis of one or many additional new enzymes usually occurs to permit successful viral multiplication. For example, some process must ensure the release of newly produced virus particles from their host cell. This is clearly a nontrivial problem in the case of bacterial viruses multiplying in bacteria with rigid cell walls. Since these walls do not spontaneously disintegrate, they could effectively inactivate progeny particles by preventing their release and transfer to new host cells. To take care of this problem, many phages have a gene that codes for the amino acid sequence of lysozyme, a cell-wall-destroying enzyme. This enzyme begins to be synthesized when the coat proteins appear, and causes the rupture of the cell wall at about the time virus maturation is complete.

VIRAL INFECTION OFTEN RADICALLY CHANGES HOST CELL METABOLISM

Sometimes the synthesis of viral specific nucleic acids and proteins goes hand in hand with normal cell synthesis. The chromosomes of the host cell often continue to function throughout a large fraction of the viral life cycle. In many cases, however, soon after infection, most of the cellular metabolism is directed toward the synthesis of new molecules connected exclusively with the appearance of new virus particles. In the most extreme cases, all DNA and RNA synthesis on the host chromosomes ceases, the preexisting RNA templates are degraded, and all subsequent protein synthesis occurs on new RNA templates constructed by the viral nucleic acid.

The extent to which a virus is able to control its host's synthetic facilities varies greatly, depending both on the nature of the infecting virus and on the type of host cell. In general, the larger the viral nucleic acid content, the larger the number of viral genes directed toward stopping host cell functions unnecessary for the production of new viral particles. How these viral specific genes redirect cellular metabolism is only beginning to be understood. For example, during T2 multiplication, the host *E. coli* chromosome is enzymatically broken down, most likely by an enzyme coded for by T2 DNA. In contrast, the viral chromosome is not enzymatically altered, most likely because it contains an unusual base (see below) not found in *E. coli* DNA. This differential destruction of the host chromosome, however, is not the sole, if even major, cause of the metabolic dominance of the viral chromosome. Long before evidence can be detected of host chromosome breakdown, it has ceased to serve as a template for *E. coli* mRNA. A search is now on to find still another enzyme specifically affecting the functioning of *E. coli* DNA.

REPLICATION OF DOUBLE-HELICAL VIRAL DNA

The synthesis of double-helical viral DNA is accomplished by the same basic mechanism that forms the DNA of cellular chromosomes. In both cases there occurs strand separation followed by attraction of complementary bases. Likewise, the zipping up of the polynucleotide backbone of viral DNA is often catalyzed by the host enzyme DNA polymerase. Viral DNA thus does not necessarily have to code for the enzymes involved in its replication. There are many examples, however, where DNA viruses carry information for the amino acid sequences of enzymes connected with the synthesis of their precursor nucleotides. One of the most striking cases involves T2 multiplication (Figure 12–7). No cytosine is present in its DNA, a fact that initially suggested that T2 DNA might be very different from normal DNA. Instead there is always present the closely related base 5-OH-methylcytosine, which, like cytosine, forms base pairs with guanine. The 3-D structure of T2 DNA is thus basically the same as that of normal double-helical DNA (Figure 12–8).

FIGURE 12–7   *Chemical details of the life cycle of the double-stranded DNA virus T2.*

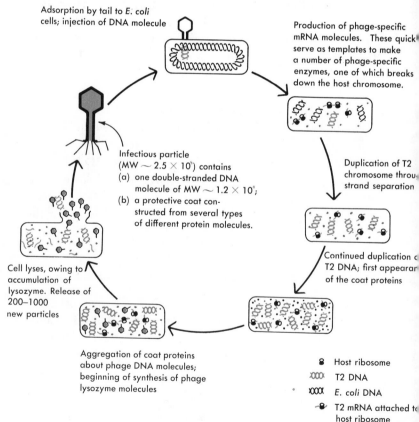

Adsorption by tail to *E. coli* cells; injection of DNA molecule

Production of phage-specific mRNA molecules. These quick serve as templates to make a number of phage-specific enzymes, one of which breaks down the host chromosome.

Infectious particle (MW ～ 2.5 × 10⁸) contains
(a) one double-stranded DNA molecule of MW ～ 1.2 × 10⁸;
(b) a protective coat constructed from several types of different protein molecules.

Duplication of T2 chromosome throu strand separation

Continued duplication of T2 DNA; first appearar of the coat proteins

Cell lyses, owing to accumulation of lysozyme. Release of 200–1000 new particles

Aggregation of coat proteins about phage DNA molecules; beginning of synthesis of phage lysozyme molecules

🙼 Host ribosome
)OOO(T2 DNA
°)OOO(*E. coli* DNA
🙼 T2 mRNA attached to host ribosome
∴ Phage-specific enzym
∵ Phage-coat proteins

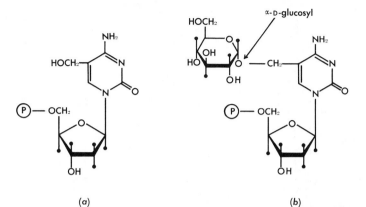

(a)   (b)

F I G U R E   12–8   *Phages of the T-even group do not contain cytosine in their DNA. Instead they contain the related base 5-OH-methylcytosine (a), which base pairs exactly like cytosine. One or more glucose residues are attached to some of their 5-CH₂OH groups. (b) shows this base with one glucose molecule attached. The biological significance of these unusual bases has not yet been clearly established. One speculative hypothesis asserts that their function is to protect T-even DNA from a phage specific enzyme which only breaks down unmodified DNA. This hypothesis would explain how the E. coli DNA is selectively broken down during viral synthesis.*

No 5-OH-methylcytosine is found in uninfected *E. coli* cells, and so the specificity of the several new enzymes required for its biosynthesis must be coded for by the T2 DNA. In addition, the rate of DNA synthesis in T2-infected cells is several times faster than in normal cells. This faster rate is achieved by having other T2 genes code for many of the enzymes involved in normal nucleotide metabolism, as well as for DNA polymerase itself (Figure 12–9).

Host cell RNA polymerase must be used to catalyze the formation of some, if not all, of the RNA templates for these enzymes. A special RNA polymerase of viral specificity cannot be necessary for all viral protein template synthesis; for, like all other DNA-coded enzymes, it would itself have to be made on an RNA template.

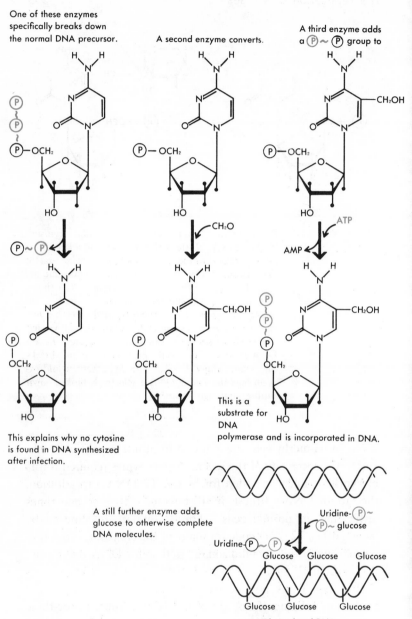

One of these enzymes specifically breaks down the normal DNA precursor.

A second enzyme converts.

A third enzyme adds a (P) ~ (P) group to

This explains why no cytosine is found in DNA synthesized after infection.

This is a substrate for DNA polymerase and is incorporated in DNA.

A still further enzyme adds glucose to otherwise complete DNA molecules.

Uridine-(P)~ (P)~ glucose

Uridine-(P)~(P)
Glucose   Glucose   Glucose

Glucose   Glucose   Glucose

Glucosylated DNA

FIGURE 12–9   The biochemical mechanism that brings about the synthesis of DNA lacking cytosine and containing instead 5-OH-methylcytosine and its glucose derivatives. Immediately after infection, a number of specific enzymes are synthesized. These are coded for by the viral DNA, and each has a specific role in ensuring the successful multiplication of the virus.

REPLICATION OF SINGLE-STRANDED DNA VIRUSES

Two classes of bacterial viruses containing single-stranded DNA are now known. One of them includes the small spherical phage ϕx174 mentioned in Chapter 9. The other class is comprised of very long (8000 A), thin (80-A diameter) phages (e.g., Fl, Fd, M13) which grow only on male bacteria. As yet there is no explanation why these viruses contain single-stranded DNA. It is clear, however, that each virus population contains only one nucleotide sequence, not a mixture of two complementary sequences. The strand present in the infectious virus particles is called the "+" (plus) strand. Immediately after entry of the "+" strand into a host cell, it serves as a template for the formation (by DNA polymerase) of a complementary "−" (minus) strand, thereby forming a double helix (Figure 12–10). The double helix [often called the replicative form (RF)] is then replicated in the conventional manner using host cell DNA polymerase to form many new double-helical copies. Up to this stage, no synthesis of new enzymes of viral specificity may be required. At least one new enzyme, however, may be needed for the subsequent formation of the single-stranded "+" form found in the mature virus. Some specific device is needed to ensure that only one of the two potential replicas is produced.

VIRAL RNA SELF-REPLICATION: REQUIREMENTS FOR A NEW VIRAL SPECIFIC ENZYME

Cellular RNA molecules never serve as templates for the formation of new RNA strands. The replication of RNA viruses thus demands the participation of a completely new enzyme capable of forming new RNA strands upon parental RNA templates. This enzyme, called RNA *synthetase*, is formed after the viral RNA enters the cell, and single strands attach to host ribosomes. Like both DNA polymerase and RNA polymerase, RNA synthetase catalyzes the formation of a complementary strand upon a single-stranded template. The fundamental mechanism for the copying of all nucleic acid base

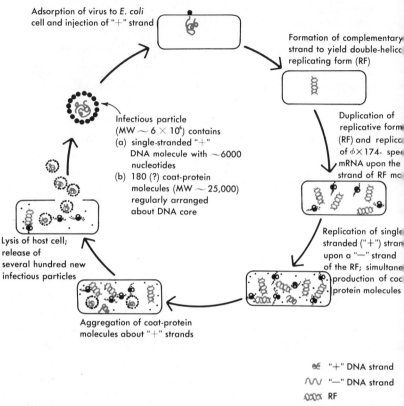

Adsorption of virus to E. coli cell and injection of "+" strand

Formation of complementary strand to yield double-helical replicating form (RF)

Infectious particle (MW ~ 6 × 10⁶) contains
(a) single-stranded "+" DNA molecule with ~6000 nucleotides
(b) 180 (?) coat-protein molecules (MW ~ 25,000) regularly arranged about DNA core

Duplication of replicative form (RF) and replica of φX174- spec mRNA upon the strand of RF mo

Lysis of host cell; release of several hundred new infectious particles

Replication of single stranded ("+") stran upon a "—" strand of the RF; simultane production of coc protein molecules

Aggregation of coat-protein molecules about "+" strands

$\mathfrak{G}$ "+" DNA strand
$\sim$ "—" DNA strand
$\alpha\alpha\alpha$ RF
$\sim$ φ×174 mRNA
$\mathfrak{G}$ Host ribosome
$\because$ Coat-protein molec

FIGURE 12–10   *The life cycle of the single-stranded DNA virus φx174.*

sequences is thus the same.   Pairing of complementary bases is always used to achieve accurate replication of specific nucleotide sequences.

Soon after their formation, complementary RNA double helices (Figure 12–11) serve as templates for new strands, some of which become part of progeny particles, while others are used as templates for specific protein formation (Figure 12–12). Exactly how this happens depends upon whether the mature virus contains single- or double-stranded RNA.   In both cases,

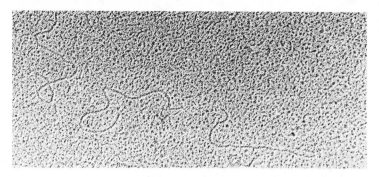

FIGURE 12–11   *An electron micrograph (by P. H. Hofschneider of Munich) of three double-helical replicative forms of the single-stranded RNA virus M13. Each molecule is approximately 1 μ in length. [Reproduced from P. H. Hofschneider, J. Mol. Biol., 10, 559 (1964), with permission.]*

however, only one of the two complementary strands is used to make the protein template (i.e., mRNA). A close parallel thus exists between the formation of mRNA in both DNA and RNA viral systems.

During the reproduction of single-stranded RNA viruses, the strand having the template function is the same strand found in the mature particles (i.e., "+"). This is not surprising, since it and not its complement ("−") must code for the RNA synthetase molecules necessary to initiate viral RNA replication. The device that ensures the selective copying of the "+" RNA strands is not yet understood. It would not be surprising, however, if the device were similar to that used to ensure that only one of the two DNA strands is copied during cellular RNA synthesis.

A LOWER SIZE LIMIT EXISTS FOR DIVIDING CELLS

A lower size limit exists for a cell even if it is growing in an external environment containing essentially all its required small molecules. It must be large enough to contain a functional semipermeable membrane, a protein-synthesizing apparatus, and

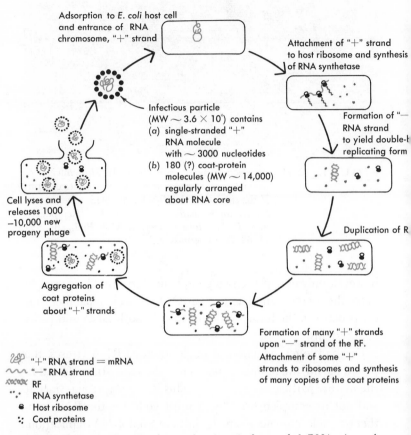

Adsorption to E. coli host cell
and entrance of RNA
chromosome, "+" strand

Attachment of "+" strand
to host ribosome and synthesis
of RNA synthetase

Infectious particle
(MW ∼ 3.6 × 10⁶) contains
(a) single-stranded "+"
RNA molecule
with ∼ 3000 nucleotides
(b) 180 (?) coat-protein
molecules (MW ∼ 14,000)
regularly arranged
about RNA core

Formation of "—
RNA strand
to yield double-[
replicating form

Cell lyses and
releases 1000
–10,000 new
progeny phage

Duplication of R

Aggregation of
coat proteins
about "+" strands

Formation of many "+" strands
upon "—" strand of the RF.
Attachment of some "+"
strands to ribosomes and synthesis
of many copies of the coat proteins

"+" RNA strand = mRNA
"—" RNA strand
RF
RNA synthetase
Host ribosome
Coat proteins

FIGURE 12–12   The life cycle of a single-stranded RNA virus of
the F2 (R17, M13, etc.) family.

sufficient genetic material to code for the various enzymes required to make its necessary proteins and nucleic acid components. In addition, its chromosomes must carry the information
for the enzymes needed to make the small molecules that cannot
be transported across the semipermeable cell membrane. For
example, even though all the amino acids and purine and pyrimidine bases can be supplied to most cells as food, phosphorylated compounds such as ATP usually cannot be supplied.
Their biosynthesis must normally take place in cells, and hence
genes must exist for the enzymes needed to build them up from
their smaller purine and pyrimidine building blocks.

It is not yet possible to say exactly what the lower size limit for a cell is. The amount of DNA in Rickettsiae is still not accurately known, but a conservative guess is that one Rickettsiae chromosome contains 10 to 20 per cent as much DNA as an *E. coli* chromosome. Its gene content is thus probably between 200 and 400. There are reports of still smaller cells, but such statements must be viewed with much caution because, if taken at face value, they imply that as few as 100 different proteins can maintain the living state.

THE LOWER SIZE LIMIT OF A VIRUS IS VERY MUCH SMALLER

In contrast, we have not been surprised to find that the chromosomes of many viruses are relatively small and code for only a few proteins. In the extreme case, we suspect that DNA viruses can exist using host enzymes for all their necessary synthesis, and carrying only the genetic instructions needed to order the amino acids in their shell proteins. If we make an intensive search for very small DNA viruses, we may find one containing only one type of shell protein, in which all the nucleic acid codes for this protein. Most viruses, however, are genetically much more complex, both because their protective shells are made up from several different types of proteins, and because their interactions with the host cell are relatively subtle requiring the employment of many enzymes to successfully manipulate the host cell in favor of viral products.

THE SIMPLEST KNOWN VIRUSES CONTAIN THREE TO FIVE GENES

The smallest well-characterized viruses are the RNA bacterial viruses of the F2 group that reproduce in *E. coli*. The F2 nucleic acid chain contains only about 3000 nucleotides and so can code for just 1000 amino acids. Of these, slightly over 100 are located in the polypeptide chain used to construct the F2 protein shell. Probably at least one-third of the remaining 900 amino acids are found in the F2-specific RNA synthetase, which would leave approximately 600 amino acids to make the one to three additional proteins that we suspect will be required for F2 reproduction. One of these may be a specific lysozyme, for some device is needed to release the 2000 to 20,000 progeny particles produced during the average growth cycle in an *E. coli* cell.

Even smaller RNA-containing virus particles are found in tobacco cells infected with a tobacco necrosis virus. Its nucleic acid chain contains only about 1000 nucleotides, just enough to code for one average size protein. These particular particles, however, are never found alone but are made only when susceptible cells are simultaneously infected with a different, larger (6000-nucleotide) RNA virus. This situation suggests that the RNA of the very small virus is replicated by using viral specific enzymes (in particular RNA synthetase) coded for by the RNA of the larger particle.

The smallest known DNA virus is polyoma, a virus that multiplies in mouse cells. It depends upon the host cell for the synthesis of virtually all its precursors, so it is not surprising that growth of the virus occurs in the nucleus, the site of normal cell DNA synthesis. Polyoma DNA is a double helix with an MW of 3×10^6, corresponding to 5000 nucleotide pairs. It can code for only several proteins, one of which must be the protein that forms the protective coat. The functions of its other genes are not yet known; most likely one or more are involved in directing the metabolism of the nuclei of the infected cells toward viral synthesis. No viral enzymes, however, should be necessary for replicating polyoma DNA. The basic structure of polyoma DNA is identical to its host's DNA, and replication can, therefore, occur by using host DNA polymerase and normal cellular nucleotide precursors.

MORE COMPLEX VIRUSES HAVE MORE GENETIC MATERIAL THAN SIMPLE ONES

This point is best seen by examining how the large bacterial virus T4 multiplies in *E. coli* cells. Structurally it is very complex and contains many different proteins in its protective coat. Already over 30 genes have been implicated in the synthesis of these pro-

teins (Figure 7–19). In addition, at least 15 more are involved
in the synthesis of its nucleotide precursors—in particular to
seeing that 5-OH-cytosine and its glucose derivatives are used in
place of cytosine to make its DNA. Many other genes are probably involved in quickly blocking normal host macromolecular
synthesis. Thus T4 multiplication, a process initially thought
to require perhaps but a few genes, is now thought to require
the function of about 100 genes.

SUMMARY

All known viruses contain a nucleic acid core (either DNA or
RNA) surrounded by a protective shell that always contains
protein and, in some of the more complicated particles, also
lipids and/or carbohydrates. The viral DNA may be either single-stranded or double-stranded. Likewise, both single- and
double-stranded RNA viruses exist. The presence of nucleic
acid is not surprising, since a genetic component must be present.
What is surprising at first glance is that RNA is the genetic
component of many viruses (for example, tobacco mosaic virus
and influenza). This means that viral RNA molecules serve as
templates for their own formation.

After the viral nucleic acid enters a host cell, synthesis of both
viral specific nucleic acid and the specific components found in
the viral protective coat occurs. These components then specifically aggregate to form new infectious viruses identical with the
infecting parental particle. The selective synthesis of virus components in a host cell is often aided by prior synthesis of viral
specific enzymes involved in nucleic acid metabolism. For example, the duplication of single-stranded RNA needs the presence of RNA synthetase. This enzyme converts the infecting
single-stranded RNA molecule into a double-stranded molecule. It now appears likely that the basic rules involved in the
duplication of RNA molecules are the same as the rules for
DNA. In all cases, new polynucleotide strands are made by
the formation of complementary copies using DNA-like base
pairs.

REFERENCES

Crick, F. H. C., and J. D. Watson, "Virus Structure: General Principles," *Ciba Found. Symp. Nature Viruses*, 1957, pp. 5–13. An early statement explaining the structural consequences of the limited nucleic acid content of viruses.

Fraenkel-Conrat, H., *Design and Function at the Threshold of Life: The Viruses*, Academic, New York, 1962. A paperback introduction to some simple ideas about TMV.

Klug, A., and D. L. D. Caspar, "The Structure of Small Viruses," *Advan. Virus Res.*, 7, 225–325 (1960). A beautiful exposition of the principles of virus construction, with special emphasis on TMV.

Stent, G. S., *Molecular Biology of Bacterial Viruses*, Freeman, San Francisco, 1963. Among other good features, it contains a very clear discussion of the role played by viral specific enzymes.

Ochoa, S., C. Weissmann, P. Borst, R. H. Burdon, and M. A. Billeter, "Replication of Viral RNA," *Federation Proc.*, 23, 1285 (1964). An exposition of how RNA viruses may reproduce.

13

THE GENETIC

CODE

EVEN WHEN THE GENERAL OUTLINE OF how RNA participates in protein synthesis had been established (1960), there was little optimism that we would soon know details of the genetic code itself. At that time we believed that identification of the codons for a given amino acid would require exact knowledge of both the nucleotide sequences of a gene and the corresponding amino acid order in its protein product. As mentioned earlier, the elucidation of amino acid sequences, though a laborious objective, is now a very practical one. On the other hand, the current methods for determining DNA (or for that matter RNA) sequences are still very primitive, so that virtually no natural mRNA base sequence information exists at present. Fortunately, this pessimism was unnecessary: In 1961, just one year after the discovery of mRNA, the use of artificial messenger RNAs partially cracked the genetic code with the unambiguous demonstration of a codon for the amino acid phenylalanine. To explain how this discovery was made, we must first describe some details of how biochemists study protein synthesis in cell-free systems.

ADDITION OF mRNA STIMULATES IN VITRO PROTEIN SYNTHESIS

The need for three RNA forms (sRNA, rRNA, and mRNA) for protein synthesis was demonstrated largely by experiments using cell-free extracts prepared from cells actively engaged in protein synthesis. In these experiments carefully disrupted cells were fractionated to see which cell components were necessary for incorporation of amino acids into proteins. All these experiments utilized radioactively labeled (H^3, C^{14}, or S^{35}) amino acids because in vitro protein

FIGURE 13–1   *Experimental details of in vitro studies of protein synthesis.*

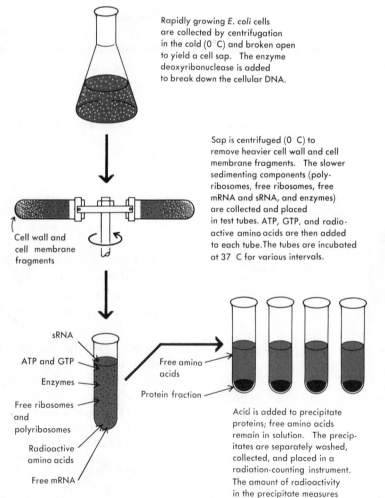

Rapidly growing *E. coli* cells are collected by centrifugation in the cold (0 C) and broken open to yield a cell sap. The enzyme deoxyribonuclease is added to break down the cellular DNA.

Sap is centrifuged (0 C) to remove heavier cell wall and cell membrane fragments. The slower sedimenting components (poly-ribosomes, free ribosomes, free mRNA and srNA, and enzymes) are collected and placed in test tubes. ATP, GTP, and radio-active amino acids are then added to each tube. The tubes are incubated at 37 C for various intervals.

Cell wall and cell membrane fragments

srRNA

ATP and GTP

Enzymes

Free ribosomes and polyribosomes

Radioactive amino acids

Free mRNA

Free amino acids

Protein fraction

Acid is added to precipitate proteins; free amino acids remain in solution. The precip-itates are separately washed, collected, and placed in a radiation-counting instrument. The amount of radioactivity in the precipitate measures the amount of amino acids incorporated (protein synthesis).

synthesis is still very inefficient, i.e., there is no detectable net synthesis. Only by using labeled precursors can the incorporation of precursors into proteins be convincingly demonstrated (Figure 13–1).

A typical time course of the in vitro incorporation of radioactive amino acids into proteins is illustrated by the graph of Figure 13–2. It shows that synthesis in an *E. coli* extract proceeds linearly for several minutes and then gradually stops. During this interval there is a corresponding loss of mRNA, owing to the action of degradative enzymes present in the extract. This suggests that the major cause of the inefficiency of cell-free protein synthesis is loss of the template component. The correctness of this supposition is shown by adding new mRNA to extracts that have just stopped making protein. Such an addition causes an immediate resumption of synthesis. mRNA-depleted extracts are very valuable in testing mRNA activity. Because they contain very little functional mRNA, they can be used to detect small amounts of template activity in externally added mRNA.

FIGURE 13–2   *Effect of addition of mRNA on the in vitro incorporation of amino acids into protein by an E. coli cell extract (37°C).*

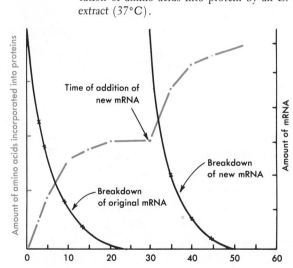

VIRAL RNA IS mRNA

In Chapter 12 we indicated that in many viruses the genetic component is single-stranded RNA. When these viruses infect a cell, their infecting RNA molecule must first act as a template for the synthesis of the specific proteins needed to initiate the life cycle of the virus. Among these necessary proteins is the RNA-replicating enzyme RNA synthetase. It is thus impossible for the infecting single-stranded molecule to act as a template for its complementary strand until it has *first* acted as a template for some protein synthesis. This means that the infecting viral RNA must itself be able to attach to its host's ribosomes and direct the synthesis of viral specific proteins (that is, that it must act as mRNA). This point is neatly shown with cell-free systems. For example, the addition of TMV RNA to an mRNA-depleted E. *coli* extract immediately stimulates the incorporation of amino acids into proteins.

SPECIFIC PROTEIN CAN BE MADE IN CELL–FREE SYSTEMS

Even with addition of excess mRNA, there is still only a small amount of amino acid incorporation into polypeptide chains in our in vitro systems. This means that we do not yet know the conditions that permit normal in vivo synthesis. Doubts were initially raised about whether, in fact, the newly made proteins had structures at all similar to those of natural proteins. Fortunately, the use of specific viral RNA showed that these doubts were unfounded and that the genetic code can be accurately read in cell-free systems. In these experiments, the RNA isolated from the bacterial virus F2 was added to preincubated E. *coli* extracts. It acted as a template and promoted the incorporation of amino acids into protein. Some complete polypeptide chains were made and released from the ribosomes. These newly made protein products were then compared with the F2 coat protein, which has a MW of 14,000. Some of the in vitro products were found to have identical amino acid sequences with the in vivo synthesized coat protein, thus demonstrating that, under cell-

free conditions, mRNA molecules can select the appropriate
AA~sRNA precursors.

Recently, there have also been many attempts to observe the
cell-free synthesis of a variety of other proteins. Although
hemoglobin has been made successfully in cell-free extracts of
immature red blood cells (reticulocytes), attempts to make the
proteins normally synthesized by other cells have generally
failed, most likely because the mRNA templates have not been
held intact under cell-free conditions. It should eventually be
possible, however, to control this undesired breakdown. Then
the cell-free synthesis of a variety of proteins may be achieved.

STIMULATION OF AMINO ACID INCORPORATION BY SYNTHETIC mRNA

The above experiments with viral RNA, while telling us that
reading specificity is preserved in cell-free systems, by themselves
say nothing about the exact form of the genetic code. They
cannot tell us which three-letter words (out of the possible 64)
(Table 13–1) code for any particular amino acid. To obtain
such data, use was made of synthetic polyribonucleotides, whose

TABLE 13–1   *The 64 possible three-letter codons*

AAA	AAG	AAC	AAU
AGA	AGG	AGC	AGU
ACA	ACG	ACC	ACU
AUA	AUG	AUC	AUU
GAA	GAC	GAC	GAU
GGA	GGG	GGC	GGU
GCA	GCG	GCC	GCU
GUA	GUG	GUC	GUU
CAA	CAG	CAC	CAU
CGA	CGG	CGC	CGU
CCA	CCG	CCC	CCU
CUA	CUG	CUC	CUU
UAA	UAG	UAC	UAU
UGA	UGG	UGC	UGU
UCA	UCG	UCC	UCU
UUA	UUG	UUC	UUU

formation involves the enzyme polynucleotide phosphorylase. This enzyme, found in all bacteria, catalyzes the reaction

RNA $+$ (P) $\rightleftharpoons$ ribonucleoside $-$ (P) $\sim$ (P)   (13–1)

Under normal cell metabolite concentrations, the equilibrium conditions favor RNA degradation to nucleoside diphosphates, so that the main cellular function of polynucleotide phosphorylase may be to control mRNA lifetime (see Chapter 14). By use of high initial nucleoside diphosphate concentrations, however, this enzyme can be made to catalyze the formation of the internucleotide 3′–5′ phosphodiester bond (Figure 13–3) and thus make synthetic RNA molecules. Since it is not a biosynthetic enzyme, no template RNA is involved in the RNA synthesis; the base composition of the synthetic product depends entirely upon the initial concentration of the various ribonucleoside diphosphates in the reaction mixture. For example, when only adenosine diphosphate is used, the resulting RNA contains only adenylic acid, and thus is called polyadenylic acid or poly A. It is likewise possible to make poly U, poly C, and poly G. Addition of two or more different diphosphates produces mixed copolymers such as poly AU, poly AC, poly CU, and poly AGCU. In all these mixed polymers, the base sequences are approximately random, with the nearest-neighbor

F I G U R E   13–3   *Synthesis (degradation) of RNA molecules using the enzyme polynucleotide phosphorylase.*

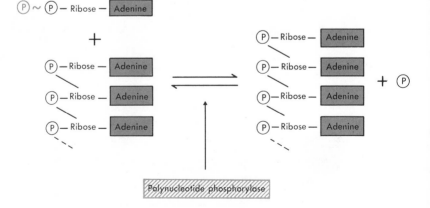

frequencies determined solely by the relative concentrations of the initial reactants. For example, poly AU molecules with two times as much A as U are formed in sequences like (UAAUAU AAAUAAUAAAAUAUU . . .).

Almost all these synthetic polymers will attach to ribosomes and function as templates. Some polymers are not efficient templates. This does not necessarily mean that they lack functional base sequences (codons). Instead they may be inactive because most of their bases are hydrogen-bonded, so that they cannot attach to the ribosomes.

POLY U CODES FOR POLYPHENYLALANINE

Poly U was the first synthetic polyribonucleotide discovered to have mRNA activity. None of its bases are normally hydrogen bonded in solution, and it binds well to free ribosomes. It selects phenylalanine sRNA molecules exclusively, thereby forming a polypeptide chain containing only phenylalanine (polyphenylalanine). Thus we know that a codon for phenylalanine is composed of a group of three uridylic acid residues (UUU) (the group number 3 comes from the genetic experiments described in Chapter 9). Similarly, we are able tentatively to assign (CCC) as a proline codon and (AAA) as a lysine codon on the basis of analogous experiments with poly C and poly A. Unfortunately, the guanine residues in poly G firmly hydrogen bond to each other and form multistranded triple helices that do not bond to ribosomes. Thus this type of experiment cannot tell us whether (GGG) is a functional codon.

MIXED COPOLYMERS ALLOW
ADDITIONAL CODON ASSIGNMENTS

Poly AC molecules can contain eight different codons (CCC), (CCA), (CAC), (ACC), (CAA), (ACA), (AAC), and (AAA), whose proportions depend on the copolymer A/C ratio. When CA copolymers attach to ribosomes, they cause the incorporation of asparagine, glutamine, histidine, and threonine, in addition to the proline expected from (CCC) codons and the lysine expected from (AAA) codons. The proportions of these amino acids incorporated into polypeptide products depend on the A/C ratio. Thus, since an AC copolymer containing much more A than C promotes the incorporation of

T A B L E   13–2   *Amino acid incorporation into proteins*[a]

Amino acid	Observed amino acid incorpora- tion	Tentative codon assign- ments	Calculated triplet frequency				Sum of cal- culated triplet fre- quencies
			3A	2A1C	1A2C	3C	
Poly AC (5:1)							
Asparagine	24	2A 1C		20			20
Glutamine	24	2A 1C		20			20
Histidine	6	1A 2C			4.0		4
Lysine	100	3A	100				100
Proline	7	1A 2C, 3C			4.0	0.8	4.8
Threonine	26	2A 1C, 1A 2C		20	4.0		24
Poly AC (1:5)							
Asparagine	5	2A 1C		3.3			3.3
Glutamine	5	2A 1C		3.3			3.3
Histidine	23	1A 2C			16.7		16.7
Lysine	1	3A	0.7				0.7
Proline	100	1A 2C, 3C			16.7	83.3	100
Threonine	21	2A 1C, 1A, 2C		3.3	16.7		20

[a] The amino acid incorporation into proteins was observed after adding random copolymers of A and C to a cell-free extract similar to that described in Figure 13–1. The incorporation is given as a percentage of the maximal incorporation of a single amino acid. These values were then used to make tentative codon assignments, which were then used to calculate the frequencies with which three nucleotides would have positions in the same codon. In these calculations the sum of the frequencies of the triplets coding for the maximally incorporated amino acid was set at 100. Lysine, the maximally incorporated amino acid when A is in excess, is believed to be coded for by 3 A's. The relative frequencies of these codons is a function of the probability that a particular nucleotide will occur in a given position of a codon. For example, when the A/C ratio is 5:1, the ratio of AAA/AAC = $5 \times 5 \times 5:5 \times 5 \times 1 = 125:25$. We thus assign to the 3A codon a frequency of 100 and to the 2A and 1C coden a frequency of 25:125 = 20.

many more asparagine than histidine residues, we conclude that asparagine is coded by two A's and one C and histidine is coded by two C's and one A (Table 13-2). Similar experiments with other copolymers have allowed a number of additional assignments. These experiments, however, cannot reveal the order of the different nucleotides within a codon. There is no way of knowing from random copolymers whether the histidine codon containing two C's and one A is ordered (CCA), (CAC), or (ACC). Moreover, because of the difficulty of interpreting small amounts of incorporation, a few of the assignments made in this way are likely to be wrong. For example, the experiments with AU (1:5) suggested that lysine is coded by two A's and one U as well as by (AAA). More recent experiments, however (see below), strongly hint that U is absent from all lysine codons.

ORDERING CODONS BY sRNA BINDING

A direct way of ordering the nucleotides within some of the codons was developed in 1964. It utilizes the fact that, in the absence of protein synthesis, specific sRNA molecules bind to ribosome-mRNA complexes. For example, when poly U is mixed with ribosomes, only phenylalanine sRNA will attach. Correspondingly, the attachment of poly C to ribosomes promotes the binding of proline sRNA. Most important, this specific binding does not demand the presence of long mRNA molecules. In fact, the binding of a *trinucleotide* to a ribosome is sufficient. The addition of the trinucleotide UUU results in phenylalanine sRNA attachment, whereas lysine sRNA specifically binds to ribosomes if AAA is added. The discovery of the trinucleotide effect immediately opened the possibility of relatively easily determining the order of nucleotides within many codons. Before this discovery, it seemed obvious that the order could not be determined unless organic chemists could synthesize long polynucleotides with regular repeating sequences. Now, however, the possession of trinucleotides of known sequence is sufficient to order many codons. For example, the trinucleotide $^{5'}GUU^{3'}$ promotes valine sRNA attachment,

TABLE 13–3   *Binding of specific sRNA molecules to trinucleotide-ribosome complexes*

Trinucleotide		sRNA bound
⁵'UUU³'	UUC	Phenylalanine
UCU	UCU	Serine
CCU	CCC	Proline
CUU	CUC	Leucine
GUU		Valine
UGU		Cysteine
AAA		Lysine
GAA		Glutamic acid

⁵'UGU³' stimulates cysteine sRNA binding, and ⁵'UUG³' causes leucine sRNA binding. A massive effort is currently being made to quickly synthesize all 64 possible trinucleotides with the hope of definitively assigning the order of the majority of codons. In Table 13–3 are listed all the codons determined as of March, 1965, in this way. It now seems likely, however, that all the correct combinations cannot be determined this way. Some of the trinucleotides bind much less efficiently than UUU or UUG, thereby making it impossible to know whether they code for a specific amino acid.

CODON ASSIGNMENT FROM REGULAR COPOLYMERS

At the same time as the trinucleotide technique became available, methods were developed using a combination of organic chemical and enzymatic techniques to prepare synthetic polyribonucleotides with known repeating sequences. These regular copolymers direct the incorporation of specific amino acids into polypeptides. For example, the repeating sequence CUCUCUCU . . . is the messenger for a regular polypeptide in which leucine and serine alternate. UGUGUG . . . similarly promotes the synthesis of a polypeptide containing two amino acids, cysteine and valine. These observations together with several additional results shown in Table 13–4 reveal several new codon orders beyond those so far obtained from

TABLE 13-4 *Assignment of codon orders using regular co-polymers*

Copolymer	Amino acids incorporated	Codon assignments
CUC|UCU|CUC . . .	Leucine	$^{5'}$CUC$^{3'}$
	Serine	UCU
UGU|GUG|UGU . . .	Cysteine	UGU
	Valine	GUG
ACA|CAC|ACA . . .	Threonine	ACA
	Histidine	CAC

sRNA binding to trinucleotide-ribosome complexes. Since new regular copolymers will soon be available, it seems likely that most of the essential features of the genetic code will be available to us by the end of 1965. Now, using the above data together with the amino acid replacements (see below) found in mutant proteins, it is possible to make tentative assignments of the order of over half the possible codons (Table 13-5).

THE CODE IS DEGENERATE

Many amino acids are selected by more than one codon (degeneracy). For example, both (UUU) and (UUC) code for phenylalanine, while serine is coded by both (UCU) and (UCC). Now there are strong hints that degenerate codons have common nucleotides. The present data suggest that, when the first two nucleotides are identical, the third nucleotide can be either cytosine or uracil and still code for the same amino acid. It is not yet clear whether adenine and guanine are likewise interchangeable, although there are weak hints against this possibility. All degeneracy, however, does not seem to be based on equivalence of the first two nucleotides. Leucine, for example, seems to be coded by (UUA), (UUG), as well as by (CUU) and (CUC).

It is not yet known whether the equivalence of U and C in the third position implies that a given sRNA molecule can attach to more than one mRNA codon. We do not know whether

TABLE 13-5   *The genetic code as of May, 1965*[a]

First position (5' end)	Second position				Third position (3' end)
	U	C	A	G	
U	Phe	Ser	Tyr	Cys	U
	Phe	Ser	Tyr	Cys	C
	Leu	Ser	Nonsense Try		A
	Leu	Ser	Nonsense	Try	G
C	Leu	Pro	His	Arg	U
	Leu	Pro	His	Arg	C
	Leu	Pro	GluN	Arg	A
	Leu	Pro	GluN	Arg	G
A	Ileu	Thr	AspN	Ser	U
	Ileu	Thr	AspN	Ser	C
	Ileu Meth	Thr	Lys	Arg	A
	Meth	Thr	Lys	Arg	G
G	Val	Ala	Asp	Gly	U
	Val	Ala	Asp	Gly	C
	Val	Ala	Glu	Gly	A
	Val	Ala	Glu	Gly	G

[a] The nucleotide order within nonunderlined codons is firmly established. Codons underlined are given on a tentative basis.

there are separate phenylalanine sRNA molecules for the (UUU) and (UUC) codons, or if a single sRNA molecule can attach to both codons. It seems likely, however, when the first and second positions are different, that a distinct sRNA is involved. For example, leucine sRNA (Figure 13-4) can be separated into at least two components; one selectively binds to UUA codons, while the other binds to CUU (CUC?) codons.

NONSENSE VERSUS MISSENSE MUTATIONS

The replacement of a codon specific for a given amino acid by another codon specific for another amino acid is called a *missense mutation*. On the other hand, the change to a codon that does not correspond to any amino acid is called a *nonsense mutation*. The existence of extensive degeneracy means that most mutations are likely to cause missense rather than nonsense. Missense mutations produce proteins changed in only one location, and so the altered proteins which they produce frequently possess some of the biological activity of the original

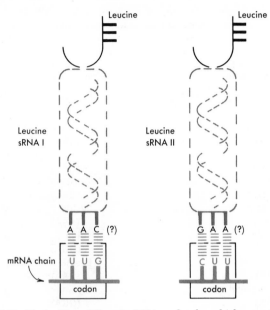

FIGURE 13–4 *Two different sRNA molecules which accept leucine residues. Each recognizes a different code word.*

proteins. The abnormal hemoglobins (see Chapter 4) are the result of missense mutations.

Table 13–6 shows that the amino acid replacement data obtained from these changed hemoglobin molecules support the idea that most mutations result from the substitution of a single nucleotide. A companion replacement series (Table 13–7) obtained from mutant TMV protein molecules points to the same conclusion. Moreover, the fact that only specific changes are observed over and over (e.g., glycine to aspartic acid) also supports the hypothesis that these altered proteins arise from single nucleotide changes. If most observed mutations reflected changes in each of several adjacent nucleotides, a larger variety of amino acid switches would be observed.

There is also firm evidence for the existence of nonsense mutations that stop the reading of the mRNA message. Chain growth stops when these codons are reached, and so when they occur in the middle of a genetic message, incomplete polypeptides are released from the ribosomes. There is growing evi-

TABLE 13–6   Examples of possible codon changes underlying some amino acid replacements in the mutant hemoglobins

Amino acid in normal hemoglobin		Amino acid in mutant hemoglobin	
Lysine (AAA)	⟶	Glutamic acid (GAA)	A → G
Glutamic acid (GAA)	⟶	Glutamine (CAA)	G → C
Glycine (GGU)	⟶	Aspartic acid (GAU)	G → A
Histidine (CAU)	⟶	Tyrosine (UAU)	C → U
Asparagine (AAU)	⟶	Lysine (AAA)	U → A
Glutamic acid (GAA)	⟶	Valine (GUA)	A → U
Glutamic acid (GAA)	⟶	Lysine (AAA)	G → A
Glutamic acid (GAA)	⟶	Glycine (GGA)	A → G

dence that both UAA and UAG are nonsense codons. Whether other nonsense codons exist is not yet known. We also do not know (see below) whether nonsense codons are involved in the normal release of completed chains.

CODE SIGNALS MUST BE GIVEN TO START AND STOP CHAIN GROWTH

The information to start or stop chain growth must itself be carried in mRNA molecules. The chain does not automatically start at one end of the mRNA molecule and continue until the other end is reached. The fact that many mRNA chains code for more than one polypeptide chain demands that chains begin and end at points along the length of the mRNA (Figure 13–5). Some device must terminate chain growth at a fixed internal spot and cause the release of the finished chain from its terminal sRNA connection to the ribosome. Correspondingly, a signal

T A B L E 13–7 *Amino acid replacements induced by nitrous acid treatment of TMV*[a]

Proline (CCC)	⟶	Serine (UCC)	C → U
Proline (CCC)	⟶	Leucine (CUC)	C → U
Isoleucine (AUU)	⟶	Valine (GUU)	A → G
Isoleucine (AUA)	⟶	Methionine (AUG)	A → G
Leucine (CUU)	⟶	Phenylalanine (UUU)	C → U
Glutamic acid (GAA)	⟶	Glycine (GGA)	A → G
Threonine (ACA)	⟶	Isoleucine (AUA)	C → U
Threonine (ACG)	⟶	Methionine (AUG)	C → U
Serine (UCU)	⟶	Phenylalanine (UUU)	C → U
Serine (UCC)	⟶	Leucine (UUG)	C → U
Aspartic acid (GAC)	⟶	Glycine (GGC)	A → G

[a] All the observed changes can be fitted both with possible codon assignments and with the postulated mutagenic action of nitrous acid (C → U, A → G).

must often tell a free ribosome to initiate chain growth at the middle of an mRNA chain. No solid knowledge now exists as to whether there are specific three-letter codons for the normal starting and stopping of chains. But the fact that mutations to nonsense codons cause premature chain release argues that a specific nucleotide sequence(s) is (are) the cause of the normal release of completed polypeptide chains. This viewpoint is supported by the fact that there is no release of polyphenylalanine molecules coded for by poly U templates, which contain only the codon for phenylalanine (UUU).

On the other hand, the fact that a variety of synthetic polymers (poly U, C, A, etc.) can initiate chain growth seems to argue that chain initiation does not always require—if it ever requires—a special codon. The validity of this argument, however, rests on the belief that the *accuracy* with which the mRNA message is read is as high in vitro as in vivo. Even a very rare misreading might be sufficient to allow chain initiation to occur.

READING MISTAKES CAN OCCUR IN CELL-FREE PROTEIN SYNTHESIS

We know, in fact, that under certain conditions reading mistakes can be very frequent in cell-free systems. Soon after the discovery that poly U is the template for polyphenylalanine, the apparent paradox arose that in the absence of phenylalanine, poly U templates directed the synthesis of polyleucine. This meant that the (UUU) codon was selecting leucine-specific sRNA molecules. At first the possibility was considered that a fundamental ambiguity in the (UUU) codon might exist. Now, however, it is clear that the anomalous leucine incorporation was due to the use of excessive amounts of Mg^{2+} in the incorporation experiments. When the Mg^{2+} levels are lowered, poly U-directed leucine incorporation becomes much less frequent. The result is important, as it underlines the necessity of using normal physiological conditions in experiments with cell-free systems if we want to extrapolate the events occurring within a normal cell.

SUPPRESSOR GENES UPSET THE READING OF THE GENETIC CODE

Mistakes in reading the genetic code also occur in living cells. These mistakes underlie the phenomenon of suppressor genes. Their existence was for many years very puzzling and seemingly paradoxical. Numerous examples were known where the effects of harmful mutations were reversed by a second genetic change. Some of these subsequent mutations were very easy to understand, being simple *reverse* (or back) mutations which change an altered nucleotide sequence back to its original arrangement. Much more difficult to understand were other mutations occurring at different locations on the chromosome which suppress

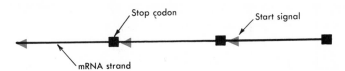

FIGURE 13-5   Schematic picture of how code signals along an
mRNA molecule may be used to initiate or stop the
synthesis of a polypeptide chain. This mRNA molecule codes for three different polypeptide chains.

the change due to a mutation at site A by producing an additional genetic change at site B. Such *suppressor mutations*
fall into two main categories: those due to nucleotide changes
within the same gene as the original mutation but at a different
site on this gene (intragenic suppression), and those occurring
in another gene (intergenic suppression). Those genes which
cause suppression of mutations in other genes are called *suppressor genes*.

Now we realize that these two types of suppression both work
by causing the production of good (or partially good) copies of
the protein made inactive by the original harmful mutation.
For example, if the first mutation caused the making of inactive
copies of one of the enzymes involved in making arginine, then
the suppressor mutation allows the synthesis of arginine by re-
storing the synthesis of some good copies of this same enzyme.
However, the mechanisms by which intergenic and intragenic
suppressor mutations cause the resumption of the synthesis of
good proteins are completely different.

Those mutations which can be reversed through additional
changes in the same gene often involve insertions or deletions of
single nucleotides. These shift the reading frame (see Chapter
9) so that all the codons following the insertion (or deletion)
are completely misread. Intragenic suppression may occur
when a second mutation deletes (or inserts) a new nucleotide
near the original change and thus restores the original codon
arrangement beyond the second change (Figure 13-6). Even
though there are still scrambled codons between the two
changes, there is a good probability, because of degeneracy, that

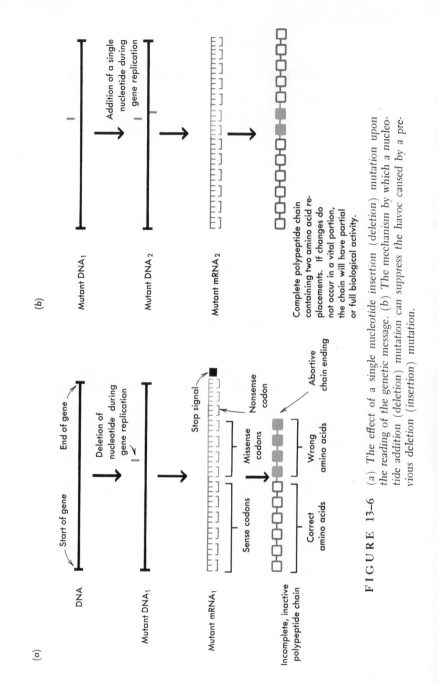

FIGURE 13-6 (a) The effect of a single nucleotide insertion (deletion) mutation upon the reading of the genetic message. (b) The mechanism by which a nucleotide addition (deletion) mutation can suppress the havoc caused by a previous deletion (insertion) mutation.

the scrambled codons all code for some amino acid. If so, full-length, *often-functional* proteins may be produced.

Intragenic suppressors can also result from a second missense mutation. In these cases, the original loss of enzymatic activity is due to an altered 3-D configuration resulting from the presence of a wrong amino acid. A second missense mutation in the same gene brings back biological activity if it somehow restores the original configuration around the functional part of the molecule. An example of this type of suppression in the tryptophan synthetase system was shown in Chapter 8 (Figure 8–13).

SPECIFIC CODONS ARE MISREAD BY SPECIFIC SUPPRESSOR GENES

Suppressor genes do not act by changing the nucleotide sequences of the mutant DNA. Instead, they change the way in which the mRNA templates are read. There are a number of different suppressor genes in *E. coli.* Since each causes the misreading of specific codons, they can reverse the effects of only a small fraction of the single nucleotide changes within a given gene. For example, if we collect a large number of mutations blocking the synthesis of the enzyme β-galactosidase (see Chapter 14), only several per cent of these mutations will be suppressed by a given suppressor gene a. These few mutations would be due to changes to codons whose reading is specifically affected by gene a. Similarly, a completely different small fraction of β-galactosidase mutations can be suppressed by suppressor gene b.

One suppressor gene suppresses the nonsense codon (UAG) by inserting the amino acid serine into the chains at the sites where their growth is otherwise stopped. Thus the mutant mRNA templates by being misread are able to serve as the templates for full-length active proteins. Other suppressor genes cause mistakes in the reading of codons corresponding to specific amino acids. For example, instead of an mRNA codon always selecting the correct amino acid x, it sometimes inserts amino acid y. Thus when a specific suppressor gene is present,

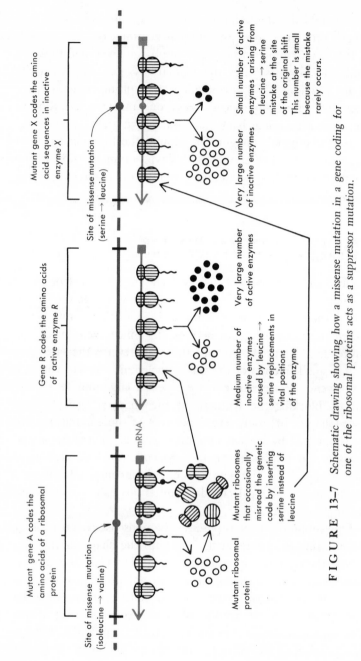

Mutant gene A codes the amino acids of a ribosomal protein

Gene R codes the amino acids of active enzyme R

Mutant gene X codes the amino acid sequences in inactive enzyme X

Site of missense mutation (isoleucine → valine)

Site of missense mutation (serine → leucine)

mRNA

Mutant ribosomal protein

Mutant ribosomes that occasionally misread the genetic code by inserting serine instead of leucine

Medium number of inactive enzymes caused by leucine → serine replacements in vital positions of the enzyme

Very large number of active enzymes

Very large number of inactive enzymes

Small number of active enzymes arising from a leucine → serine mistake at the site of the original shift. This number is small because the mistake rarely occurs.

FIGURE 13-7 *Schematic drawing showing how a missense mutation in a gene coding for one of the ribosomal proteins acts as a suppressor mutation.*

382

a missense codon in a mutant mRNA template will sometimes insert a "sense" amino acid. If this happens often enough, sufficient copies of the functional protein will be produced to permit normal growth of the host cell (Figure 13–7). At other times, the limited amount of good proteins produced by misreading is not sufficient for normal growth, giving rise to the frequent observation that suppressed mutants often grow slowly.

It is generally observed that a given suppressor gene can suppress mutations in a number of different genes. This fact is easily understood by the misreading concept. For example, the ability to synthesize both arginine and tryptophan in certain double mutants unable to make either amino acid can be restored by a single change in a suppressor gene. We merely need to postulate that both these growth requirements are caused by the same specific changes to missense or nonsense.

SUPPRESSOR GENES ALSO MISREAD GOOD GENES

We thus see that suppressor genes do not specifically misread mRNA templates made on mutant genes. In fact, they affect the synthesis of essentially all proteins. Thus most suppressor mistakes occur in the copying of good mRNA templates, thereby hindering the synthesis of sound proteins. These changes, however, are not generally very harmful to the growing cell, since many more good copies of each protein than bad ones are produced. There is, however, no advantage in a normal cell harboring suppressor mutations which cause it to produce even a small fraction of bad proteins. Thus suppressors tend to be selected against in evolution, unless there is simultaneously present a harmful mutation whose effect they must compensate for.

Exactly how these suppressor genes work at the molecular level is just beginning to be investigated. One obvious way is by a change in either a specific activating enzyme or a specific sRNA which results in the occasional linking of the wrong amino acid to a given sRNA. This type of explanation has just received strong support from the observation that an *E. coli* strain carrying a suppressor gene specific for the nonsense codon

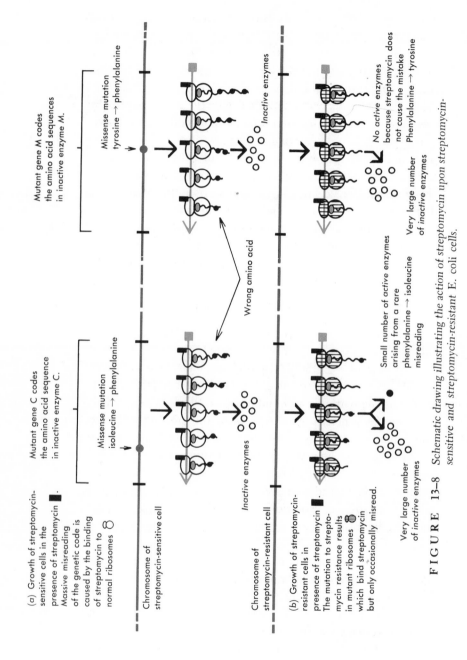

(a) Growth of streptomycin-sensitive cells in the presence of streptomycin ▪. Massive misreading of the genetic code is caused by the binding of streptomycin to normal ribosomes ⦶

Chromosome of streptomycin-sensitive cell

Mutant gene C codes the amino acid sequence in inactive enzyme C.

Missense mutation isoleucine → phenylalanine

Inactive enzymes

Wrong amino acid

Chromosome of streptomycin-resistant cell

(b) Growth of streptomycin-resistant cells in presence of streptomycin ▪. The mutation to streptomycin resistance results in mutant ribosomes ⊛ which bind streptomycin but only occasionally misread.

Very large number of inactive enzymes

Small number of active enzymes arising from a rare phenylalanine → isoleucine misreading

Mutant gene M codes the amino acid sequences in inactive enzyme M.

Missense mutation tyrosine → phenylalanine

Inactive enzymes

No active enzymes because streptomycin does not cause the mistake Phenylalanine → tyrosine

Very large number of inactive enzymes

FIGURE 13–8   Schematic drawing illustrating the action of streptomycin upon streptomycin-sensitive and streptomycin-resistant E. coli cells.

(UAG) possesses a unique sRNA component not found in strains lacking this suppressor gene. This unique sRNA component can suppress a nonsense mutation which blocks in vitro synthesis of the coat protein of the RNA phage R17. This point was shown using an in vitro system where normal R17 RNA promoted the synthesis of normal coat protein. When mutant RNA containing nonsense codon was used, no coat protein was produced, unless purified sRNA from the correct suppressor strain was added.

The possibility also exists that many codon misreadings result from structural changes in the ribosomes. This hypothesis is supported by the finding of a suppressor strain having altered ribosomes. The most likely interpretation of this coincidence is that an amino acid change in one of the ribosomal proteins so distorts the ribosome structure that the disturbed template-ribosome complex is no longer able to choose unambiguously the correct sRNA molecule (Figure 13–7).

STREPTOMYCIN ALSO CAUSES MISREADING

The belief that distorted ribosomes may misread the genetic code is strongly supported by recent experiments showing that the addition of the antibiotic streptomycin to either in vitro systems or living cells promotes mistakes in the translation of the genetic code. It does this by combining with the ribosomes, and thereby disturbing the normal mRNA-sRNA-ribosome interactions. The extent of the misreadings depends upon whether the streptomycin is added to streptomycin-sensitive or streptomycin-resistant cells. Addition of streptomycin to sensitive cells results in large-scale misreadings. The mutation to streptomycin-resistance alters the ribosomes in such a way that misreadings occur much less commonly. They are, nonetheless, frequent enough to suppress a number of mutations by causing the synthesis of a small number of active enzyme molecules (Figure 13–8).

It now appears that the streptomycin does not cause indiscriminate misreading. When poly U is used as a template with sensitive ribosomes, the most frequent error is the replacement of phenylalanine (UUU) by isoleucine (AUU). This hints that the presence of streptomycin normally disturbs the position of only one out of three nucleotides in the (UUU) codon (Figure 13–9).

Thus it is now possible to make a general prediction about what the normal function of suppressor genes is. A gene becomes a suppressor gene by mutation. Before this mutation occurs, the gene is a normal, active gene, which codes for a specific sRNA, for one of the ribosomal proteins, or for one of the enzymes involved in protein synthesis. It has so evolved that its product has the optimal configuration for accurate reading of the genetic code. (We suspect that under optimal cell conditions the errors that occur in protein synthesis are largely due to the inherent chemical limitation of the specificity of enzymes; see the discussion in Chapter 11 of how enzymes recognize amino acids.) If a mutation changes such a gene so that its altered product increases the misreading level, this gene becomes a suppressor gene. Only when an increased mistake level is necessary for cellular existence do its mutant products have a selective advantage over their normal counterparts.

THE CODE IS LARGELY, IF NOT ENTIRELY, UNIVERSAL

Poly U stimulates polyphenylalanine incorporation in cell-free extracts from a variety of different organisms ranging from bacteria to higher mammals. Likewise, poly C promotes proline incorporation and poly A causes lysine incorporation in all extracts tested regardless of their cellular source. Such indications of the universality of the code among contemporary organisms hint that the genetic code has remained constant over a long evolutionary period. But until all the codons in one organism have been unambiguously worked out, this point will be neither rigorously proved nor disproved. Invariability in most of the code is expected. Consider what a mutation which changed the genetic code would result in. Such a mutation might, for example, alter the sequence of the serine-specific sRNA molecules of the class that corresponds to (UCU), thereby causing them to

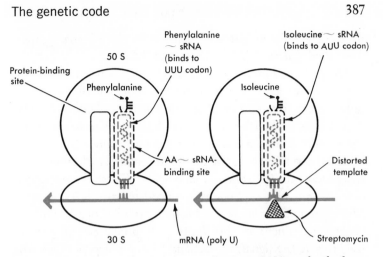

FIGURE 13–9 *Selection of an isoleucine~sRNA molecule by a ribosome–poly U–streptomycin complex. Here the streptomycin-induced misreading involves an isoleucine~sRNA molecule which normally attaches to the (AUU) codon.*

attach to (UUU) sequences instead. This would be a lethal mutation in haploid cells containing only one gene directing the production of each type of sRNA: No normal serine-specific sRNA of that class would be produced, and serine would not be inserted into many of its normal positions. Even if there were more than one gene for each sRNA type (e.g., in a diploid cell), this type of mutation would still be lethal, since it would cause the simultaneous replacement of many phenylalanine residues by serine in most cell proteins.

SUMMARY

The most direct way to study the genetic code is to examine protein synthesis in cell-free extracts. The most useful in vitro systems employ cell extracts that have been depleted of their original messenger component. Addition of new mRNA to these extracts results in the production of new proteins whose amino acid sequences are determined by the externally added mRNA. For example, the introduction of phage F2 RNA pro-

duces new proteins virtually identical to the F2 coat protein. Thus viral genetic RNA also acts as mRNA.

The first (and probably most important) step in cracking the genetic code occurred when the synthetic polyribonucleotide poly U was found to code specifically for polyphenylalanine. A codon for phenylalanine is thus (UUU). Use of other synthetic polyribonucleotides, homogeneous (poly C, etc.) and mixed (poly AU, etc.), has produced a number of other codon assignments for the various amino acids. So far the nucleotide order within over 50 codons has been tentatively established. Many amino acids are coded for by more than one codon (degeneracy). There are also hints that specific codons may be used to give the signals to start and to stop polypeptide growth. Certain mutations (intergenic suppressor mutations) appear to increase the frequency of mistakes in reading the genetic code. As a result of this increase of the mistake level, a mutant gene may occasionally produce a normal product.

The genetic code appears to be essentially the same in all organisms. This is not surprising: Variations in it from organism to organism would mean that the code had evolved by mutation, and it is almost impossible to imagine a mutation that is not lethal which would change the letters in a codon.

REFERENCES

Nirenberg, M. W., and J. H. Matthaei, "The Dependence of Cell-Free Protein Synthesis in E. coli upon Naturally Occurring or Synthetic Polyribonucleotides," Proc. Natl. Acad. Sci., U.S., 47, 1588 (1961). This is the classic paper which demonstrated that poly U codes for polyphenylalanine.

Nirenberg, M. W., O. W. Jones, P. Leder, B. F. C. Clark, W. S. Sly, and S. Pestka, "On the Coding of Genetic Information," Cold Spring Harbor Symp. Quant. Biol., 28, 549 (1963). This article illustrates how copolymers have helped to demonstrate the nucleotides that code for a specific amino acid.

Speyer, J. E., P. Lengyel, C. Basilio, A. J. Wahba, R. S. Gardner, and S. Ochoa, "Synthetic Polynucleotides and the Amino Acid Code," Cold Spring Harbor Symp. Quant. Biol., 28, 559 (1963). Another demonstration of how codon composition has been established through the use of copolymers.

Crick, F. H. C., "The Recent Excitement in the Coding Problem," in J. N. Davidson and W. E. Cohn (eds.), *Progress in Nucleic Acid Research*, Academic, New York, 1963, Vol. 1, p. 164. A superb analysis of the state of the coding problem as of late 1962.

Leder, P., and M. W. Nirenberg, "RNA Code Words and Protein Synthesis II: Nucleotide Sequence of a Valine RNA Code Word," *Proc. Natl. Acad. Sci., U.S.*, **52**, 420 (1964). An elegant paper that establishes the order of nucleotides within a codon for valine.

Davis, J., W. Gilbert, and L. Gorini, "Streptomycin, Suppression, and the Code," *Proc. Natl. Acad. Sci., U.S.*, **51**, 883 (1964). Here are the experimental details of the first in vitro demonstrations that streptomycin causes misreading of the genetic code.

Nishimura, S., D. S. Jones, and H. G. Khorana, "The in vitro Synthesis of a Co-polypeptide Containing Two Amino Acids in Alternating Sequence Dependent upon a DNA-like Polymer Containing Two Nucleotides in Alternating Sequence," *J. Mol. Biol.*, 1965, in press. Another classic paper on the genetic code. Here is found an unambiguous demonstration that each codon contains three nucleotides.

14

REGULATION

OF PROTEIN

SYNTHESIS

AND

FUNCTION

THE WORKING OUT OF THE GENERAL
features of the participation of nucleic
acid molecules in protein synthesis provides a solid base from which we can
examine how the rate of synthesis of
the various protein molecules is controlled. Within a given cell a great
variation exists in the number of molecules of its different proteins; thus devices to ensure the selective synthesis
of those proteins needed in large numbers must exist. Until recently this
problem was approached chiefly with
ignorance, speculation, and hope.
Now, however, we realize that the rate
of the synthesis of a protein is itself
partially under internal genetic control and partially determined by the
external chemical environment. To
show how these factors can interact,
we shall focus attention on microbial
systems, since they have been the basis
of most of the important concepts up
to now.

ALL PROTEINS ARE NOT
PRODUCED IN THE SAME
NUMBERS

Earlier we estimated from its length
that the E. coli chromosome codes for
between 2000 and 4000 different polypeptide chains. Exactly how many
different proteins are simultaneously
present in a given cell is not yet known.
Based upon the probable number of
enzymes needed to make the various

390

necessary metabolites, general estimates argue for the presence of at least 600 to 800 different enzymes in a cell growing with glucose as its sole carbon source. Some of these enzymes, particularly those connected with the first steps in glucose degradation and with the reactions which make the common amino acids and nucleotides, are present in relatively large amounts. Also required in large amounts are the enzymes needed to produce the energy-rich bonds in ATP. In contrast, other enzymes, particularly those involved in making the much smaller amounts of the necessary coenzymes, are present in trace quantities. There must also be relatively large amounts of the various structural proteins used to construct the cell wall, the cell membrane, and the ribosomes.

VARIATIONS IN THE AMOUNTS OF DIFFERENT E. COLI PROTEINS

Precise values for the number of protein molecules normally present within a bacterial cell are known for only a few proteins. The best-studied case is the E. coli enzyme β-galactosidase (MW $= 5 \times 10^5$), which splits the sugar lactose into its glucose and galactose moieties (Figure 14–1). This is a very important enzyme, because lactose cannot be used as either a carbon or energy source unless it is first broken down to the simpler sugars galactose and glucose. E. coli cells growing with lactose as their exclusive carbon source generally contain about 3×10^3 molecules of β-galactosidase, which represents about 3 per cent of the total protein. This is the maximum quantity that can be synthesized if just one gene coding for the β-galactosidase amino acid sequence is present on each E. coli chromosome. If this gene is present in two copies, 6 per cent of the total protein produced by the cell can be β-galactosidase. There exist, in fact, superproducing mutant strains, probably containing many copies of this gene, that can synthesize almost 15 per cent of their protein as β-galactosidase. This supersynthesis, however, is achieved only at the expense of making too little of other necessary proteins. Cells making excessively large amounts of β-galactosidase grow poorly and tend to be replaced by mutants that have a balanced protein synthesis.

Good data also exist for the amounts of the structural proteins of the ribosomes. There are approximately 30 of these proteins (average MW ∼ 30,000) that collectively comprise about 10 per cent of the total protein in rapidly growing cells. Thus the average ribosomal protein represents 0.3 per cent of the total *E. coli* protein. No similar quantitative data have yet been obtained for the enzymes required in the biosynthesis of the coenzymes. In some cases we expect that only very few molecules will be present. This point, however, will be hard to establish, since the isolation of even one of these enzymes in the amounts necessary for a molecular weight determination will require very large amounts of cells.

FIGURE 14–1   *The sugar lactose can be hydrolytically cleaved to galactose and glucose by the enzyme β-galactosidase. Mutants that fail to make this protein cannot utilize lactose as a carbon source.*

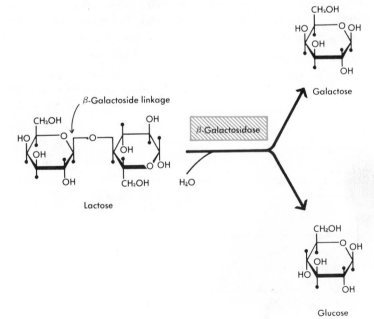

Great variation can exist between the amount of a protein present when it is needed and when the environmental conditions are such that it would serve no useful function. For example, there are approximately 3000 β-galactosidase molecules in each normal *E. coli* cell growing in the presence of β-galactosides, such as lactose, and less than one-one-thousandth of this number in cells growing upon other carbon sources. Substrates like lactose, whose introduction into a growth medium specifically increases the amount of an enzyme, are known as *inducers*; their corresponding enzymes are called *inducible enzymes*. An entirely different form of response is shown by many enzymes involved in cellular biosynthesis. For example, *E. coli* cells growing in a medium without any amino acids contain all the enzymes necessary for the biosynthesis of the 20 necessary amino acids. When, on the other hand, the growth medium contains these amino acids, their corresponding biosynthetic enzymes are almost entirely missing. Biosynthetic enzymes whose amount is reduced by the presence of their *end products* (e.g., histidine is the end product of the histidine biosynthetic enzymes) are called *repressible* enzymes. Those end-product metabolites whose introduction into a growth medium specifically decreases the amount of a specific enzyme are known as *corepressors*. The inductive and repressive responses are equally useful to bacteria: When enzymes are needed to transform a specific food molecule or to synthesize a necessary cell constituent, they are present; when they are unnecessary, they are effectively absent.

Adaptation is not, however, an all-or-nothing response, for under conditions of intermediate need, there may be an intermediate enzyme level (Figure 14–2). Similar variation can exist in the quantities of structural proteins. This is best shown by the variation in the number of the ribosomes themselves. When bacteria are growing at their maximum rate, ribosomes amount to 25 to 30 per cent of the cell mass. If, however, their

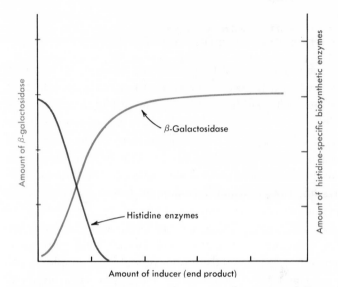

FIGURE 14-2   *Variation in the amount of enzyme per cell as a function of the amount of inducer (end product) present in the growth medium.*

growth rate is cut down by unfavorable nutritional conditions, the bacteria need fewer ribosomes to maintain their slower rate of protein synthesis, and the ribosome content can drop to as little as 20 per cent of its maximum value.

VARIATION IN PROTEIN AMOUNT CAN REFLECT THE NUMBER OF SPECIFIC mRNA MOLECULES

In actively dividing bacteria, most individual protein molecules, once synthesized, are quite stable. Variation in the amount of proteins thus generally reflects rates of synthesis, not relative stability. This variation in the rate of synthesis is in turn partially related to differences in the number of available mRNA templates. The number of β-galactosidase templates in cells actively making β-galactosidase, for example, greatly exceeds the number found in cells not engaged in synthesizing this enzyme. Now our best estimate is that during maximal β-galactosidase synthesis, 30 to 50 β-galactosidase mRNA molecules are present in each cell.   In contrast, when no enzyme is being made, the average cell contains fewer than one mRNA molecule specific for β-galactosidase synthesis.

REPRESSORS CONTROL THE RATE
OF MUCH mRNA SYNTHESIS

The decision whether to make the mRNA molecules that code for the inducible and repressible enzymes is controlled by a special group of molecules called *repressors*.   Each repressor blocks the synthesis of unique proteins.   Exactly how they act is now being intensively studied; the most plausible current hypothesis is that repressors work by combining with specific sites on DNA, thereby blocking the transcription of the corresponding mRNA molecules.   Supporting this hypothesis is the finding that the number of a specific mRNA molecule varies with the presence or absence of its corresponding repressor.   Alternatively, it is possible to believe that repressors do not control the synthesis of specific mRNA molecules, but rather in some way control their average lifetime.   As we shall mention later, there is great variation in the lifetime of mRNA molecules, so it is possible that a repressor might act by combining with an mRNA molecule, hence preventing its attachment to a ribosome and thereby increasing the probability of its enzymatic breakdown.

Repressors, like the proteins whose formation they repress, are coded by chromosomal DNA; the genes that code for them are called *regulatory genes*.   A number of mutant regulatory genes, unable to code for functional repressors, have been isolated.   Cells containing inactive regulatory genes produce their respective proteins independent of need (Figure 14–3).   These mutants are called *constitutive mutants*, since those proteins produced in fixed amounts independent of need are called *constitutive proteins*.

Some of these mutations in regulatory genes can be suppressed by the occurrence of suppressor mutations in other genes.   That is, the presence of a suppressor gene can restore the synthesis of functional repressors.   This suggests that mistakes in the reading of the mRNA message change the structure of repressors, which

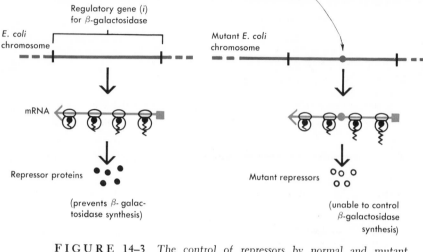

FIGURE 14–3   *The control of repressors by normal and mutant genes. The identification of the repressor as a protein is still circumstantial.*

in turn hints that some, if not all, repressors are protein molecules. It is not yet possible to directly check this identification, since until now, no one has been able to isolate a chemically pure repressor. We can only test for the presence of repressors by their ability to block the in vivo synthesis of specific proteins. We shall not be able to assay their presence outside of cells until we can use cell-free systems in the routine synthesis of their respective enzymes. Unfortunately, as mentioned in Chapter 13, most of the proteins synthesized in cell-free systems have no biological activity.

COREPRESSORS AND INDUCERS DETERMINE THE FUNCTIONAL STATE OF REPRESSORS

Repressors, however, are not always able to prevent specific mRNA synthesis (functioning?). If they were, they would always inhibit the synthesis of their specific proteins. Instead, all repressor molecules can exist in both an active and an inactive form, depending on whether they are combined with highly specific small molecules, the *inducers* and the *corepressors*. The attachment of an inducer inactivates the repressor. For example, when combined with a β-galactoside* (inducer), the β-galactosidase repressor does not block the synthesis (functioning?) of β-galactosidase mRNA. Thus the addition of β-galactosides to growing cells permits β-galactosidase synthesis by decreasing the concentration of active β-galactosidase repressors. In contrast, the binding of a corepressor changes an inactive repressor into an active repressor. For example, the addition of amino acids to cells growing in their absence increases the number of the active form of the repressors controlling the synthesis of the enzymes involved in amino acid biosynthesis. This quickly shuts off synthesis (functioning?) of their specific mRNA molecules (Figure 14–4).

No covalent bond is thought to be formed between repressors and their specific inducers or corepressors. Instead there is a portion of each repressor molecule which is complementary in shape to a specific portion of its inducer (corepressor). This allows weak secondary bonds (hydrogen bonds, salt linkages, or van der Waals forces) to hold together a repressor and an inducer (corepressor). Since these bonds are weak, they are rapidly made and broken. This is a very desirable feature, since it allows the repressor state (active or inactive) to adjust quickly to the physiological need. For example, the synthesis (functioning?) of β-galactosidase mRNA ceases almost immediately after the removal of lactose.

REPRESSORS CAN CONTROL
MORE THAN ONE PROTEIN

In some cases, repressors may control the synthesis of only one protein. Often, however, a single repressor affects the synthesis of several enzymes. The *E. coli* β-galactosidase repressor, for example, controls at least two enzymes: β-galactosidase itself,

---

* Now there are suspicions that lactose itself is not the true inducer of β-galactosidase synthesis. Instead some lactose molecules are first transformed into a related compound, which in turn attaches to the repressor.

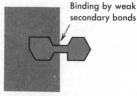

Binding by weak
secondary bonds

(a) *Active β-galactosidase repressor* + *β-Galactoside (inducer)* ⇌ *Inactive repressor-inducer complex*

(prevents β-galactosidase
synthesis)

(unable to control
β-galactosidase synthesis)

Binding by weak
secondary bonds

(b) *Inactive* histidine repressor + Histidine (corepressor) ⇌ *Active* repressor-corepressor
complex

(unable to control synthesis
of enzymes
for histidine synthesis)

(controls rate of synthesis
of enzymes
for histidine synthesis)

FIGURE 14–4   *Schematic drawing illustrating the opposite effects
of corepressors and inducers upon the activity of repressors. We see here that, depending upon whether
the enzymes are inducible or repressible, the free repressors are either active or inactive.*

and galactoside permease, an enzyme that controls the rate
of entry of β-galactosides into the bacteria. When active
β-galactoside permease is absent, *E. coli* cells are unable to
concentrate β-galactosides within themselves.* Since both

* There is a possibility that in fact three genes are controlled by the
β-galactosidase repressor. It is certain that permeability to β-galactosides
is under its control and that the permeaseless mutations map very close,
if not adjacent, to the gene coding for β-galactosidase. There is also
evidence that the enzyme galactoside acetylase is controlled by this same
repressor and that the mutations that specifically cause the absence of the
acetylase protein also occur in roughly the same chromosomal region as
the permeaseless mutants. Furthermore, since many mutations that cause
the loss of the permease function also cause the loss of the acetylase

β-galactosidase and β-galactoside permease are ordinarily needed to metabolize β-galactosides, their *coordinated synthesis* is clearly desirable. Coordinated synthesis is brought about by having the two enzymes coded by adjacent genes, thereby allowing a single mRNA molecule to carry both genetic messages (Figure 14-5). An even larger number of genes (10) are coordinately repressed by the repressor of the amino acid histidine. Here again this is achieved by having a single mRNA molecule carry the messages of all these genes.

The collections of adjacent nucleotides that code for single mRNA molecules and that are under the control of a single repressor, are called *operons*. Some operons thus contain one gene, others two, and still others several genes. At first it was thought that repressors were specific for single operons. Recently, however, a case has been found that is most simply interpreted by assuming that a specific repressor can act on three different operons: The genes responsible for *E. coli* arginine biosynthesis have been found distributed among three unlinked operons. Nonetheless, there is evidence that one regulatory gene controls the level of enzymes belonging to all the operons.

OPERATORS CONTROL THE FUNCTIONING OF OPERONS

The functioning of an operon is under the direct control of a specific chromosomal region, the *operator*. The operator is always located adjacent to the genes whose transcription (functioning?) it controls, so there is a specific operator for each operon. Operators have essentially negative functions: If a functional operator is absent, the corresponding repressor cannot inhibit the synthesis (functioning?) of the specific

---

protein, there has been a tendency to believe that the acetylase enzyme, in some still to be discovered fashion, is the enzyme that controls permeability. But now this argument is weakened by the finding of some permeaseless mutants that still have acetylase activity. It thus appears that further genetic and biochemical analyses must be done to establish the true relation between the permease and acetylase functions.

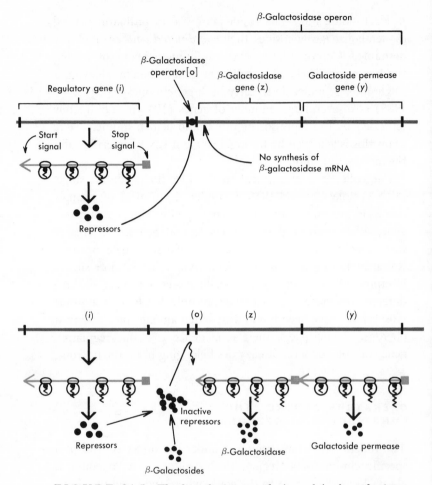

FIGURE 14–5   The hypothesis currently favored for how the interaction of repressor, corepressor, and operator controls
the synthesis of the E. coli proteins β-galactosidase
and β-galactoside permease.   In this and in subsequent illustrations we show repressors combining with
DNA.   This point has not yet been proved, and the
alternative hypothesis exists that repressors act by
combining with mRNA, thereby preventing its attachment to ribosomes, and so allowing its rapid
enzymatic breakdown to nucleotides.   It is important
to note that, under both sets of hypotheses, a specific
repressor decreases the amount of a specific mRNA
molecule.

mRNA, and as a result there is constitutive synthesis of its corresponding protein product. We do not yet possess any evidence whether the interactions of repressors and operators is direct or indirect. Presently, the most plausible hypothesis of operator function postulates that the operators are sites on the DNA molecules to which the active repressor molecules bind. Under this hypothesis, when the active repressor is bound to the operator, the synthesis of the specific mRNA of the adjacent operon is blocked. Alternatively, if repressors combine with specific sites on mRNA molecules then the operator must code for these binding sites.

The existence of operators was first revealed by genetic analysis. The structure of the operator can mutate to an inactive form preventing the working of repressors. When this happens, constitutive enzyme synthesis results. These mutants are therefore called O^c (constitutive) mutants. O^c mutations can easily be distinguished from mutations in the repressor genes by measuring enzyme synthesis in special, partially diploid cells containing two copies of the relevant chromosomal regions. Cells containing one nonfunctional and one functional repressor gene are still repressible, since good repressor molecules can act on both operators (Figure 14–6). In contrast, cells containing only one bad operator will always be constitutive no matter what the condition of the repressor gene (Figure 14–7).

mRNA SYNTHESIS MAY BEGIN NEAR THE OPERATOR

Nothing is known about how RNA polymerase molecules start and stop mRNA synthesis at fixed sites along the DNA molecule. This information must be directly coded in some way by nucleotide sequences in the DNA itself. It now seems simplest to imagine that synthesis begins at the end of the operon adjacent to its operator. This suspicion is derived from genetic mapping of the β-galactosidase operator mutations: They are all situated very close to one end of the β-galactosidase gene. In fact, they are so closely linked to this end that it was first suspected that the operator region might overlap with nucleo-

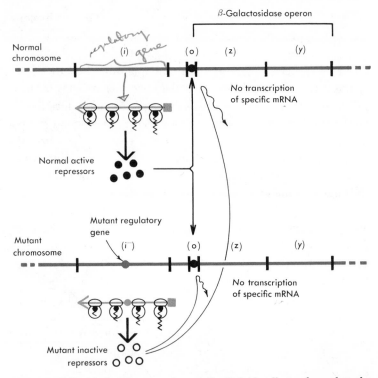

FIGURE 14-6   *The use of partially diploid cells to show that the presence of functional repressors is dominant over the presence of inactive repressors. No significant amounts of β-galactosidase molecules will be produced in these cells in the absence of externally added β-galactosides. (Here, as in Figure 14–5, we illustrate the possibility that repressors prevent mRNA transcription.)*

tides coding for terminal amino acids in the β-galactosidase molecule. Now, however, it appears likely that no overlap exists.

UNEQUAL PRODUCTION OF PROTEINS CODED BY A SINGLE mRNA MOLECULE

Variation in the number of molecules of different proteins arises also from the fact that the proteins coded by a single mRNA molecule need not be produced in similar numbers. This point is demonstrated by the study of the lactose operon proteins:

(a) Haploid cell containing mutant operator (o^c)

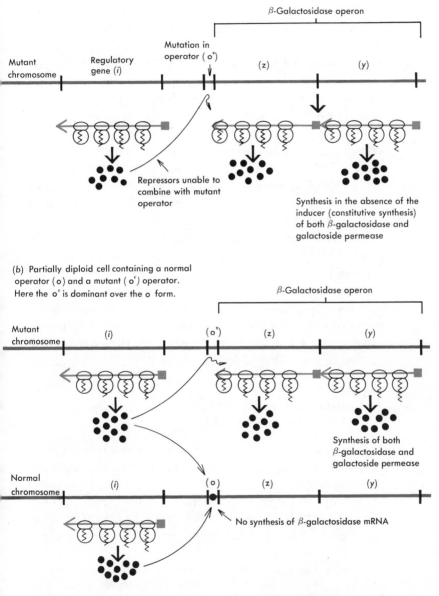

β-Galactosidase operon

Mutant chromosome

Regulatory gene (i)

Mutation in operator (o^c)

(z)

(y)

Repressors unable to combine with mutant operator

Synthesis in the absence of the inducer (constitutive synthesis) of both β-galactosidase and galactoside permease

(b) Partially diploid cell containing a normal operator (o) and a mutant (o^c) operator. Here the o^c is dominant over the o form.

β-Galactosidase operon

Mutant chromosome

(i)   (o^c)   (z)   (y)

Synthesis of both β-galactosidase and galactoside permease

Normal chromosome

(i)   (o)   (z)   (y)

No synthesis of β-galactosidase mRNA

FIGURE 14–7   The control of specific mRNA synthesis by normal and mutant operators. Here again we assume that the repressors prevent mRNA transcription.

Many more copies of β-galactosidase than of galactoside permease are synthesized.* This may mean that ribosomes attach to the different starting points along a given mRNA molecule at different rates, depending upon the starting nucleotide sequence. Another possible explanation is that the rate at which a given mRNA sequence is read is influenced by its specific codon content. In any case, however, it seems reasonable that mechanisms may exist that permit differential reading rates along single mRNA molecules. Although the coordinated appearance of related enzymes is obviously of great advantage to a cell, there is no reason why equal numbers should be produced. An equal number would be useful only if the specific catalytic activity rates (turnover numbers) of related proteins were equal. In general, however, there are great variations in individual turnover numbers.

The same argument holds for RNA virus messenger molecules. During virus reproduction, very many more copies are made of the coat protein(s) than of the viral specific enzymes. Since it would make no sense to produce all the viral specific proteins in equal amounts, there has evolved some control mechanism to bring about selective reading. It is not now known whether the regulation in viral systems is the same as that controlling the reading of normal cellular RNA.

BACTERIAL mRNA IS OFTEN METABOLICALLY UNSTABLE

When corepressor (inducer) molecules are added to or removed from growing bacteria, the rate of synthesis of the respective proteins is altered rapidly. This rapid adaptation to a changing environment is possible not only because growth requires continual synthesis of new mRNA molecules, but even more significantly, because many bacterial mRNA molecules are

---

* What was measured in this experiment was the amount of acetylase activity. Even if the acetylase and permease functions are controlled by two different genes, the argument here is not affected, since what we wish to demonstrate is that two proteins controlled by the same mRNA template are made in different numbers.

metabolically unstable. ⌈The average lifetime of many *E. coli* mRNA molecules at 37°C is about 2 minutes, after which they are enzymatically broken down.⌉ The resulting free nucleotides are then phosphorylated to the high-energy triphosphate level and reutilized in the synthesis of new mRNA molecules.

There is thus virtually complete replacement of the templates for many proteins every several minutes. For example, within several minutes after addition of suitable β-galactosides, *E. coli* cells synthesize β-galactosidase at the maximum rate possible for that particular inducer level. If on the contrary all mRNA molecules were metabolically stable, the maximum synthetic rate would not be reached until cell growth had effectively diluted out previously made mRNA molecules. Correspondingly, the existence of unstable β-galactosidase mRNA also means that, once β-galactosides are removed, synthesis of β-galactosidase quickly halts and does not resume until it is again necessary (Figure 14–8).

It now seems as if the average lifetimes of mRNA molecules of varied specificity may differ greatly. If true, this means that the mRNA lifetime is itself genetically determined, that is, the nucleotide sequence (perhaps at one end) of a mRNA molecule determines the chance of enzymatic digestion. The enzymatic mechanism by which individual mRNA molecules are broken down has not yet been clarified. There are suggestions that mRNA molecules are stable so long as they are bound to ribosomes. Perhaps after the mRNA molecules finish moving across the ribosomes, there is a choice as to whether the free end attaches to a new ribosome or to a degradative enzyme which then breaks it down.

MANY STABLE RNA MOLECULES CAN EXIST IN DIFFERENTIATED CELLS

It has begun to appear more and more likely that much of the mRNA of the highly differentiated cells of higher animals is metabolically stable. Immature reticulocytes (red blood cells) provide a good example. These cells produce virtually no RNA while they are synthesizing their principal protein, hemoglobin.

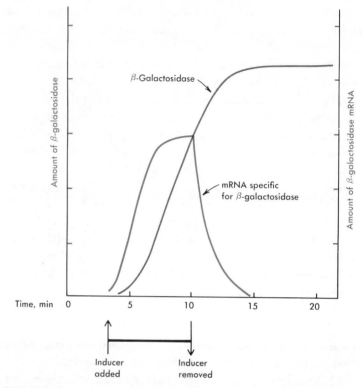

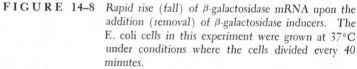

FIGURE 14-8 *Rapid rise (fall) of β-galactosidase mRNA upon the addition (removal) of β-galactosidase inducers. The E. coli cells in this experiment were grown at 37°C under conditions where the cells divided every 40 minutes.*

If their mRNA molecules were rapidly made and broken down, it would be possible to detect incorporation of RNA precursors into RNA; none is detected. This stability has an obvious advantage, particularly since the very constant environment of red blood cells, as contrasted with the highly fluctuating growth conditions of bacteria, makes great flexibility unnecessary. Red blood cells are designed to synthesize largely (>90 per cent) hemoglobin. There is no reason to break down hemoglobin mRNA chains only to resynthesize them. Similarly, most of the mRNA found in the cytoplasm of the adult liver makes plasma protein to be released into the circulatory system. Correspondingly, most, although not all, cytoplasmic mRNA in liver cells is stable. In contrast, there appears to be a fairly rapid breakdown of the mRNA located in the nucleus. These mRNA molecules may have the task of synthesizing the new proteins needed to respond to sudden shifts in liver metabolism.

SOME PROTEINS MAY NOT BE UNDER CONTROL OF REPRESSORS

There are a variety of proteins within the cell whose amount does not seem to be influenced by the external environment. As an example, in *E. coli* the amounts of the enzymes controlling the degradation of glucose do not radically change when glucose is either removed from or added to the growth medium. Thus the glucose degradative enzymes seem to be *constitutive enzymes* whose rate of synthesis is controlled by neither inducers nor corepressors. We do not yet understand why this is so, since there should be a selective advantage to the cells that can change the amounts of these enzymes. We must of course consider that further experiments may demonstrate an inducer or corepressor. On the other hand, it now seems wiser to pose the more general question: Must all genes belong to operons or is it possible that the amounts of proteins can be controlled in other ways?

The constitutive synthesis of a very large amount of an enzyme is easy to imagine. This is in fact what we observe when mutations produce an inactive repressor or operator. This is an important observation, since it tells us per se that repressors and operators are not required for the synthesis (functioning?) of mRNA molecules. When the loss of a repressor or operator occurs, the resulting constitutive synthesis of single proteins may occur at the same rate as occurs under optimal conditions of induction or repression. The amount of constitutive synthesis is a reflection of four factors: (1) the rate at which a specific mRNA molecule can be made in the absence of repressors or operators; (2) the rate at which ribosomes attach to the starting point of the mRNA template; (3) the rate at which a message itself is read; and (4) the lifetime of the particular template.

Unfortunately, we now understand absolutely nothing about the factors controlling any of these rates, so that it is at present impossible to assess the absolute or even relative importance of any of them. Nonetheless, the knowledge that so many factors might influence the rate of constitutive synthesis points to the idea that the synthesis of the many proteins needed only in small amounts might be regulated without the involvement of repressors or operators.

REPRESSOR SYNTHESIS MUST ALSO BE REGULATED

At a given time there are only about 1000 mRNA molecules in a single E. coli cell. A guess at the minimal number of operons influenced by corepressors (inducers) is 100 to 200. It is thus hard to imagine that there are more than 1 or 2 mRNA molecules specific for each repressor. A larger number of mRNA molecules coding for repressors (regulatory mRNA) would greatly restrict the amount of mRNA coding for necessary structural and enzymatic proteins. We conclude that the synthesis of regulatory mRNA is probably carefully controlled. It cannot be done, however, by an entirely new group of repressors; that would mean that an infinite number of different repressors would be required to repress each other's synthesis. Thus, either a repressor itself can repress its own synthesis, or repressors are constitutively synthesized. There is no clearcut reason at this time to favor one hypothesis over the other, since even within cells we cannot easily measure the amount of a repressor that is present.

REGULATION OF PROTEIN FUNCTION BY FEEDBACK INHIBITION

The catalytic activity of many proteins is affected by their binding to specific small molecules. In this way, the activity of enzymes may be blocked when they are not needed. Consider, for example, what happens when an E. coli cell growing on minimal glucose medium is suddenly supplied with the amino acid isoleucine. Immediately the synthesis (functioning?) of the mRNA molecules needed to code for the specific enzymes utilized in isoleucine biosynthesis ceases. Without a further control mechanism, pre-existing enzymes could cause continued isoleucine production, now unnecessary because of the extracellular supply. Wasteful synthesis, however, almost never occurs, because high levels of isoleucine block the activity of the enzyme involved in the first step of its biosynthesis starting from threonine (Figure 14-9). This inhibition is due to the binding of isoleucine to the enzyme threonine deaminase. Thus bound, this enzyme is unable to convert threonine to α-ketobutyrate. Because the association between the enzyme and isoleucine is weak and reversible, relatively high isoleucine concentrations

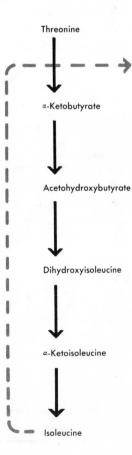

FIGURE 14-9 *The pathway of isoleucine biosynthesis starting from threonine. The dotted colored line shows that isoleucine inhibits the enzyme (threonine deaminase) which transforms threonine into α-ketobutyrate.*

must exist before most of the enzyme molecules are inactivated. This very specific inhibition is called *feedback (end-product) inhibition,* because accumulation of a product prevents its further formation. Only the first step in a metabolic chain is blocked. With the first reaction blocked, there is no accumulation of unwanted intermediates, so that inhibition of the remaining enzymes would serve no end.

The final enzymatic step in the synthesis of an end-product feedback inhibitor is often separated by several intermediate metabolic steps from the substrate (or from the product) of the enzyme involved in the first step of its biosynthesis (Figure 14–10). The structure of the inhibitor may thus only loosely

FIGURE 14–10   *Schematic diagram showing how feedback inhibition controls the biosynthesis of pyrimidines in E. coli.*

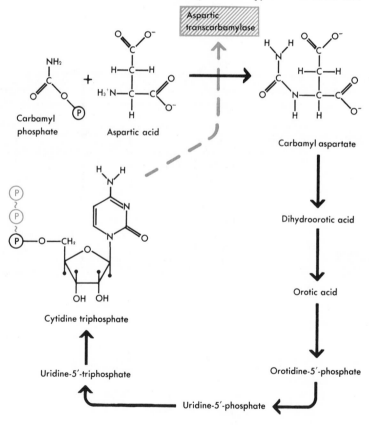

resemble that of the substrate of the inhibited enzyme, so that one would not expect an end-product inhibitor to combine with the enzymatically active site (region that binds the substrate) of the enzyme it inactivates. Instead, there is the suspicion that it reversibly combines in some cases with a second site on the enzyme and yet causes the enzyme activity to be blocked, perhaps by causing a change in the precise enzyme shape (allosteric transformation) and thus preventing the enzyme from combining with its substrate (Figure 14-11). Such proteins, whose shapes are changed by the binding of specific small molecules at sites other than the active site are called *allosteric proteins*, and, correspondingly, those small molecules that bring about allosteric transformations are called *allosteric effectors*. There are now only scant data on the chemical forces binding specific

FIGURE 14-11   *Schematic view of how the binding of an end-product inhibitor inhibits an enzyme by causing an allosteric transformation.*

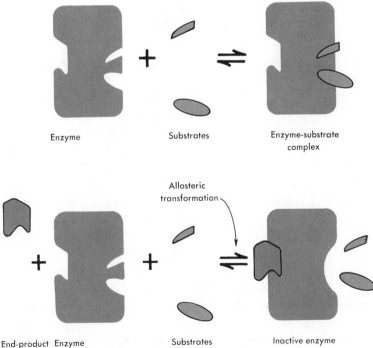

Enzyme   Substrates   Enzyme-substrate
                                                  complex

Allosteric
transformation

End-product Enzyme   Substrates   Inactive enzyme
inhibitor

feedback inhibitors to proteins. As in the postulated repressor-corepressor union, the binding is believed to depend upon weak secondary forces (hydrogen bonds, salt linkages, and van der Waals forces), and not to involve any covalent bonds. Hence feedback inhibition can be quickly reversed once the end-product concentration is again reduced to a low level.

SUMMARY

Cells have control mechanisms to ensure that proteins are synthesized in the required amounts. Only very recently have we begun to understand their molecular basis. Most of our knowledge is limited to bacterial cells, in particular to E. coli. Bacteria contain many enzymes whose rate of synthesis depends on the availability of external food molecules. These external molecules (corepressors or inducers) control the rate of protein synthesis by controlling the synthesis (functioning?) of the specific mRNA templates. Corepressors (inducers) act by binding to specific molecules, the repressors. Repressors exist in an active state when they have combined with a corepressor and in an inactive state when they have combined with an inducer. Active repressors may act by combining with specific regions of the DNA (operators). Alternatively they may block mRNA synthesis (functioning?). The length of DNA controlled by a specific repressor, the operon, often comprises several genes with related metabolic functions (e.g., the production of successive enzymes in the synthesis of an amino acid or nucleotide). A still-undiscovered mechanism brings about the differential synthesis of different proteins coded by the same mRNA molecules; some of the proteins are made much more frequently than others.

Cells that have metabolically unstable mRNA molecules can quickly shift their spectrum of protein synthesis in response to a radical change in their surrounding environment (e.g., food supply). This is true especially for bacteria. In many other cells, particularly those which always make the same types of proteins (e.g., red blood cells), most mRNA molecules appear metabolically stable.

The suspicion exists that the rate of synthesis of many protein molecules is not controlled by repressors and inducers (constitutive synthesis). If this is indeed the case, devices must exist that permit proteins to be synthesized at different fixed rates. Some of these rates must be high, others very low. Nothing is yet known about what controls the synthesis of the repressors. Of particular importance is the question of whether they are synthesized at fixed rates. This is an important problem, since repressors may themselves be proteins.

Control over cell metabolism is also quickly effected by end-product inhibition of enzyme function. An end-product metabolite can reversibly combine with the first enzyme involved in its specific biosynthetic pathway. This combination transforms the enzyme into an inactive form. Now there is a suspicion that the end-product inhibitor does not combine with the enzymatically active site but binds to a second site on the enzyme, causing a change in the enzyme shape. Proteins whose shapes and activities are changed by combination with other molecules are called allosteric proteins.

REFERENCES

Jacob, F., and J. Monod, "Genetic Regulatory Mechanisms in the Synthesis of Proteins," *J. Mol. Biol.*, **3**, 318 (1961). A beautiful review that ties together the concept of messenger-RNA with the problem of the control of protein synthesis.

Martin, R. G., and B. N. Ames, "Biochemical Aspects of Genetics: The Operon," *Ann. Rev. Biochem.*, **33**, 235 (1964). Here is found a review of the recent evidence on which the operon concept is based.

Monod, J., J. P. Changeux, and F. Jacob. "Allosteric Proteins and Cellular Control Systems," *J. Mol. Biol.*, **6**, 306–329 (1963). A comprehensive review of the problem of allostery.

Gerhart, J. C., and A. B. Pardee, "The Effect of the Feedback Inhibitor, CTP, on Subunit Interactions in Aspartate Transcarbamylase," *Cold Spring Harbor Symp. Quant. Biol.*, **28**, 491 (1963). A summary of an enzyme system, the study of which was important in developing the concept of allostery.

15

CELL DIFFEREN- TIATION AND THE PROBLEM OF ANTIBODY SYNTHESIS

THE CAREFUL READER WILL HAVE NO-ticed that many statements in the preceding chapter were qualified; our understanding of how bacterial cells control the synthesis of specific proteins is less complete than our general knowledge about the mechanism of protein synthesis, and much less complete than our understanding of the structure of DNA. Thus although we can state unambiguously that the genetic information of cellular chromosomes resides in the nucleotide sequences of DNA molecules, we can state only tentatively that repressors are proteins. In addition, we can say nothing at the molecular level about how repressors control the number of specific mRNA molecules. These uncertainties do not seriously annoy us, however, since there is every reason to believe that within the next several years our speculations will harden into facts.

We must not, however, be mesmerized by our past successes into asserting uncritically that our achievements at the molecular level with bacteria can automatically be extended to the cells of higher plants and animals; we must remember that bacteria and viruses were chosen because of their simplicity, that higher plants and animals are exceedingly complex objects, and that much wisdom must be exercised in deciding which of the genetic processes of higher organisms can be investigated profitably at the molecular level within the next ten to twenty years. In particular, we should ask if we have sufficient background at this time to attack embryology at the molecular level.

AMOUNT OF DNA PER CELL INCREASES ABOUT A THOUSANDFOLD FROM E. COLI TO MAMMALS

Before experts climb a high mountain, they carefully measure its height and try to anticipate how difficult the ascent will be. Likewise, it would be most useful to know how much more complex the mammalian cell is than the *E. coli* cell, genetically speaking. One obvious approach is to determine how much DNA is present per mammalian cell; the answer is approximately 1000 times that in *E. coli*. This number gives us an *upper limit* of the number of different genes, since there is no reason to believe that protein size (and hence gene size) increases from the lower to the higher forms of life. It may be, therefore, that a mammalian cell is capable of synthesizing over a million different proteins. Thus the task of relating a given mutant character to a specific mutant protein will be much more formidable than the corresponding job with bacteria. In some cases, however, the amount of DNA may be quite misleading; there are groups of amphibians that contain 50 times more DNA in their cells than is present in mammalian cells. Here there is no obvious reason to believe that greater boilogical complexity is involved, for it is possible that each of these amphibian genes is present in very many identical copies.

We must then be cautious about relating DNA content directly to the number of different proteins that may be synthesized by a given cell. Nonetheless, mere morphological examination with the electron microscope tells us that a much larger variety of subcellular structures exist in the mammalian cell than in *E. coli*, and so we must expect a correspondingly larger number of structural proteins and enzymes to be necessary for their construction and function. It would be surprising, in any case, if the mammalian cell were not at least 100 times more complex genetically than *E. coli*; in fact we should be prepared to face a thousandfold difference in complexity.

THE HEART OF EMBRYOLOGY IS
THE PROBLEM OF CELL DIFFERENTIATION

The mechanisms by which fertilized eggs develop into multicellular organisms have been a continuous source of mystery to biologists. A fundamental component of embryological development is the process of cell growth and division, which produces large numbers of progeny cells. *Cell differentiation,* however, is at the heart of the matter, since higher plants and animals are constructed from a large variety of different cell types (e.g., nerve cells, muscle cells, thyroid cells, blood cells, etc.).

Differentiation occurs as the fertilized egg divides to form a large number of progeny cells. In some organisms, specialization begins with the first few cell divisions after fertilization. In other organisms a large number of divisions occur before any progeny cell is fixed in its fate. Irrespective of the exact time that differentiation occurs, however, it always results in the transformation of the parental cell into a large number of morphologically different progeny cell types.

Differentiation can be examined from three viewpoints. First, what are the external forces acting upon the original undifferentiated cell which might initiate a chain of events resulting in two progeny cells of different constitution? Sometimes the existence of asymmetrically acting external forces is easy to perceive. For example, gravity forces the yolk of a fertilized amphibian egg to the bottom. Thus, after the first few cell divisions, some of the progeny cells have more yolk than others.

The second way to analyze differentiation is to ask, What are the molecular differences between differentiated cells? Are they extreme, or do the morphological differences arise from the presence of only a few unique proteins in abnormally large numbers? Now all our evidence indicates the opposite conclusion: Each type of differentiated cell contains many types of molecules peculiar to that cell type. Thus a complete description of differentiation at the molecular level would necessarily be a most formidable task.

Third, we must ask whether the various changes which bring

about differentiation are irreversible, and, if so, how they are perpetuated at the molecular level. This is the most difficult question that embryology faces, and hence much effort and ingenuity have gone toward seeking biological systems in which a straightforward attack can be made.

Since differentiation is the basis of all multicellular life, its eventual elucidation is now a prime goal of modern biology. Until very recently, it was largely studied as an isolated subject, apart from modern genetic or biochemical ideas. Now, however, it is clear that the morphological tools of the classical embryologist cannot give satisfying answers. Instead, as in genetics, the fundamental answers must lie at the molecular level. The parallel with modern genetics may, in fact, be very close, since embryologists now believe that many of the basic control mechanisms that fix a cell's potential chemical reactions act at the level of the gene. Thus the recent advances which have made aspects of biochemistry and genetics indistinguishable may hopefully encompass the exciting aspects of embryology in the near future.

DIFFERENTIATION IS USUALLY IRREVERSIBLE

At present it is possible to isolate a large variety of differentiated cells and grow them outside living organisms under laboratory conditions. Some of these cells can be grown, like bacteria, under well-defined nutrient conditions. This technique allows us to ask, for example, whether a nerve cell continues to look like a nerve cell when growing outside its normal cellular environment: The answer is yes. Something has happened that has permanently destroyed the cell's capacity to synthesize proteins other than those found in nerve cells.

DIFFERENTIATION IS NOT DUE TO CHROMOSOME GAIN OR LOSS

Because differentiation is irreversible, an obvious hypothesis by which we can explain its occurrence is that during differentiation only a fraction of the genes of the fertilized egg are passed on to a nerve cell, etc. This sort of scheme, however, appears to be completely wrong. As far as we can tell, all cells of an organism, with the obvious exception of the haploid sex cells, contain the same chromosomal complement. All cell divisions are preceded by regular mitotic division of chromosomes, so that daughter cells all receive identical chromosome groups. We cannot say, however, that no permanent changes have occurred at the level of individual genes. The question remains whether it is possible to mutate specific genes selectively, thereby making them become nonfunctional (or functional). Our problem now is to devise methods that can test this possibility. Unfortunately, this task seems very difficult at present.

MULTICELLULAR ORGANISMS MUST HAVE DEVICES TO CONTROL WHEN GENES ACT

Irrespective of the molecular mechanism (i.e., whether a chemical change in the gene itself is involved), there is now very good evidence that, in multicellular organisms, as in bacteria, all genes in a cell do not function at the same time. Something must dictate that a muscle cell, for example, selectively synthesize the various proteins used to construct muscle fiber, and so forth.

Thus, the understanding of embryology will, in one sense, be the understanding of how genes selectively function. Moreover, we must ask not only what causes two progeny cells to synthesize different proteins, but also what makes them *continue* to synthesize exclusively the same group of proteins. With the problem phrased in this way, it is clear that *no one* will ever be able to work out *all* the chemical details that accompany embryological development of any higher plant or animal. For even a modest approach to a comprehensive understanding, we would have to look at the behavior of hundreds of different proteins. Nonetheless, common sense tells us that, as in bacteria, there may exist some general principles governing the selective occurrence of specific proteins. For example, differentiation conceivably may occur at the chromosome level by devices that control the amount of specific mRNA synthesis.

GENES OF HIGHER ORGANISMS DIFFER IN THE RATES AT WHICH THEY PRODUCE THEIR SPECIFIC mRNA PRODUCTS

In fact, there is now excellent evidence for differential rates of RNA synthesis by a single chromosome. Some of this evidence comes from the study of the giant chromosomes of the flies *Drosophila* and *Chironomous*. These chromosomes are easy to observe, because each consists of a collection of about 1000 identical chromosomes, neatly stuck sidewise to each other in lateral register. Where the genes are closely stuck to each other, they are probably in a nonfunctional state, since autoradiographic experiments using radioactive precursors of RNA suggest that very little RNA is synthesized in these regular regions. However, there are regions along these *Drosophila* chromosomes at which a much more disorganized arrangement of the individual chromosomes occurs (Figure 15–1). These regions, which are called "puffs," are sites of intense RNA synthesis (Figure 15–2) and so are clearly active genes. Most important, the locations of puffs do not remain constant during embryological development. Instead, some genes appear to function only at specific stages of development.

There is also cytological evidence for differential rates of functioning of homologous chromosomes in mammalian cells. Recently, the unexpected discovery was made that in female mammals the two identical *x* chromosomes look quite different. One always appears highly condensed (hinting that it does not function), whereas the other is extended. This suggestion is confirmed by biochemical analysis, which shows that in the *x* chromosomes of a given cell only one gene from each pair is active. Surprisingly, the inert chromosome varies from one cell to another; so female tissue is in reality a mosaic containing mixtures of two different cell types. Though the molecular basis for this bizarre condition is still unknown (it appears to be restricted to the *x* chromosomes), it is quite important in showing that there are devices that can specifically block the functioning of an entire chromosome.

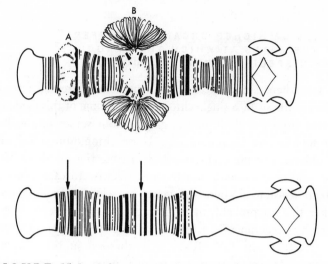

FIGURE 15-1   A diagrammatic view of part of a giant insect chromosome (from the salivary gland of Chironomous)
at two different stages in development. The two
puffs (A and B) observed in stage one are not visible
at a later stage. The origin of the puffs A and B can
be traced to single bands in the unexpanded phase.
[Redrawn from W. Beermann, Chromosoma, 5 (2);
Table 1 (1952), with permission.]

Thus a growing number of embryologists are beginning to ask
whether the functioning of some genes in mammals and higher
plants is controlled by repressors similar to those postulated to
exist in bacteria. The dilemma exists, however, that most of the
characters which embryologists study are hopelessly complex
from the chemical viewpoint (consider the eye); only a few can
be related to the occurrence of well-defined chemical reactions.
For example, although nerve cells are easy to identify on morphological grounds, almost nothing is known about their structure on the molecular level, and not one protein molecule in
nervous tissue has been well characterized. Although our famil-
iarity with several muscle proteins is more complete, our primitive knowledge of their detailed chemistry is likely to make the
analysis of precise gene-protein relationships a most tricky
endeavor.

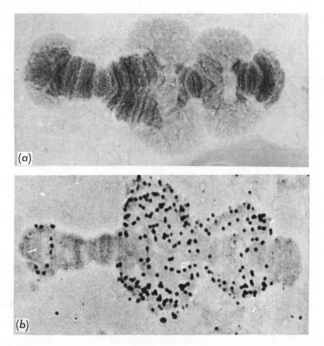

FIGURE 15-2 An autoradiograph (courtesy of W. Beermann) of a giant chromosome from an insect injected with radioactive uridine. Most of the RNA synthesis, as demonstrated by incorporation of radioactive uridine, occurs at the puffs. (a) Chromosome 4 from the salivary gland of Chironomous tentans with three large puffs. (b) Autoradiograph of the same chromosome with the same three puffs after a half-hour pulse of tritiated uridine.

NECESSITY OF FINDING A MODEL SYSTEM FOR STUDYING DIFFERENTIATION

We must ask whether any of the embryologists' systems for studying differentiation are appropriate for a serious attack at the present time. To begin with, let us emphasize the fact that merely cataloging obvious protein and nucleic acid differences between the various differentiated cells is unlikely to yield any fundamental answer. We already know from classical morphology that there are differences. Instead, incisive answers are likely to come only from more meaningful questions. Two of the more important goals are, first, the identification of the external factors (embryonic inducers), which cause the directed transformations of many undifferentiated cells. For example, the differentiation of many nerve cells depends upon an external factor received from nearby cells. A second important goal is to discover how the inducer changes the undifferentiated cell. In particular, we wish to understand the chain of events that relates inducers to the functioning of specific genes.

These problems are likely to be solved only when undifferentiated cells growing in tissue cultures can be specifically transformed by the addition of their embryonic inducers. Even though there exist many claims that in vitro differentiation has been obtained, careful examination of the experiments reveals that they are usually overinterpreted. For example, undifferentiated chicken cells can often be transformed into nerve cells by the addition of a distinct chemical compound. At first sight, this is a most spectacular result. Unfortunately, there is no single distinct compound that induces a nerve cell, but rather a large variety of seemingly unrelated molecules, all of which have the same result. Under certain concentration conditions, even NaCl is an inducer. Most embryologists suspect that all currently known chemicals which induce in vitro act unspecifically and that the true specific embryonic inducers have not yet been observed.

ANTIBODY SYNTHESIS MAY PRESENT A SYSTEM FOR STUDYING CELL DIFFERENTIATION

The colossal magnitude of the task of attempting to understand the molecular basis of complex differentiation problems such as the origin of nerve cells has led many biologists to look for cell systems other than those studied by the classical embryologist— cell systems in which a precise signal is given to start the synthesis of a particular protein. To date, perhaps the most interesting case of this sort is the synthesis of specific *antibody* molecules.

Antibody synthesis is a defense response found in higher vertebrates that helps combat the harmful effects of pathogenic microorganisms. Antibodies accomplish this task by combining with the microorganisms to form complexes that are then destroyed by phagocytosis (digestion by certain scavenger white blood cells, e.g., macrophages) (Figure 15–3). For example, the introduction of a virus into the circulatory system of a higher vertebrate stimulates production of specific antibodies that combine specifically with the virus particles to prevent their further multiplication. An individual is *immune* to a virus as long as the corresponding antibodies are present in his circulatory system (the study of antibodies and their interaction is

FIGURE 15–3 *Diagrammatic view of the sequence of events between the injection of an antigen and the appearance of circulating antibodies.*

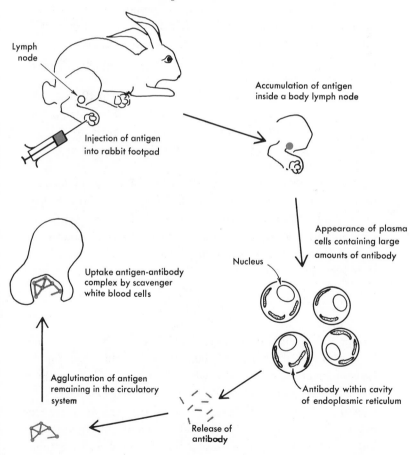

Lymph
node

Injection of antigen
into rabbit footpad

Accumulation of antigen
inside a body lymph node

Uptake antigen-antibody
complex by scavenger
white blood cells

Nucleus

Appearance of plasma
cells containing large
amounts of antibody

Agglutination of antigen
remaining in the circulatory
system

Release of
antibody

Antibody within cavity
of endoplasmic reticulum

called *immunology*). Those objects which stimulate antibody synthesis (e.g., a virus particle) are called *antigens*.

An object is potentially antigenic when it possesses an arrangement of atoms at its surface that differs from the surface configuration of any normal host component. The immunological defense system is thus based on the ability of an organism to distinguish between its own molecules and foreign ones. Antibodies are produced against a virus not because the system realizes that the virus will produce a disease, but rather because it recognizes that the virus is a foreign object and hence must be eliminated from the circulatory system.

This immediately raises the question, What are the requirements for an object to have antigenic properties? One major requirement is that an antigen either be a macromolecule or be built up from macromolecules (e.g., a virus particle). Most proteins and some polysaccharides and nucleic acids are antigens. Small molecules by themselves can seldom induce specific circulating antibodies. The lack of response to small molecules is not based on lack of specificity. Many small molecules, nonantigenic by themselves, when coupled covalently to a larger molecule (e.g., to a protein), change the antigenic properties of the large molecule.

It seems unlikely that the entire surface of a large molecule is necessary for its antigenicity. Most probably, the immunological system responds to specific groups of atoms (antigenic determinants) located at a number of sites about a molecular surface (Figure 15–4). A given protein molecule is thus likely to induce the formation of several types of antibodies, whereas objects the size of bacteria possess a very large number of different antigenic determinants.

At present, we are still very uncertain exactly how many unique antigenic determinants exist. The number is certainly large, perhaps larger than 10,000. We make this guess on the basis of experiments that test whether antibodies induced by a given protein ever accidentally combine with a completely unrelated protein. Most strikingly, cross reactions almost never occur. If there were as few as 1000 different antibodies, there should now be numerous examples of unexpected cross reactions.

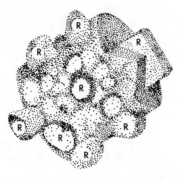

FIGURE 15-4 Diagrammatic view of an antigen. The symbol R represents a single determinant of immunological specificity and is the actual group that combines with an antibody molecule. (Redrawn from J. E. Cushing and D. H. Campbell, Principles of Immunology, McGraw-Hill, New York, 1957, p. 37, with permission.)

ANTIBODIES ARE ALWAYS PROTEINS

All antibodies are proteins. The selective synthesis of a specific antibody thus represents the selective synthesis of a specific protein molecule. Within a given species, most antibodies have approximately the same size. In man, most antibodies sediment in the ultracentrifuge at a speed of 7 S (Svedbergs). This class of antibodies is called the 7-S antibody. They have a molecular weight of about 160,000. Four polypeptide chains are present in each molecule. They fall in two pairs: two heavy chains, each of MW about 60,000, and two light chains, each with a MW of about 20,000. In a given molecule, the two heavy chains are identical, as are the two light chains. The four chains are held together by several covalent S-S bonds and probably also by weaker secondary bonds (Figure 15-5). The chains are so arranged that each antibody molecule contains two sites at opposite ends of the molecule which combine with antigens. Since neither the precise amino acid sequences nor even a rough outline of antibody chain arrangement is known, we do not know at the molecular level exactly how antibodies bind to antigens. Nonetheless, it is clear that antigens and antibodies must

Antigen   Antibody   Antigen

FIGURE 15–5   A current model for the structure of the 7-S antibody and how it combines with an antigen (redrawn
from G. J. V. Nossal, Sci. Am., Dec. 1964, p. 114,
with permission). The two heavy and two light
chains are bonded to each other by S-S bonds.

possess complementary surfaces that permit secondary bonds to
hold them together. There is no evidence of any covalent bond
formation.

The existence of two identical binding sites permits a single
antibody molecule to link together two similar antigens; this
feature is of great advantage in allowing antibodies to defeat an
infection by a microorganism. This is because all microorganisms contain a large number of identical antigenic determinants. Thus in the presence of specific antibodies, a
microorganism becomes linked to a large number of similar
microorganisms through antibody bridges (Figure 15–6).
These aggregates then tend to be taken up and destroyed by
scavenger white blood cells.

ANTIBODY SPECIFICITY RESIDES IN AMINO ACID SEQUENCE

There are two completely different hypotheses about what
distinguishes one antibody molecule from another. One theory
stems from the fact that the gross molecular structure of all
antibodies is similar. This resemblance provides a basis for
believing that the amino acid sequences of all antibody molecules are the same, and for postulating that the essential
difference between different antibodies resides in the precise
three-dimensional structure: the folding of the identical chains.
If this were true, the antigen would determine which antibody
should be formed by combining with a newly synthesized
antibody chain before it has folded to the final three-dimen-

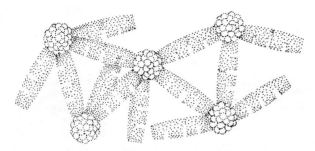

FIGURE 15–6   A diagrammatic view of how antigens and antibodies combine to form large aggregates. (Redrawn from J. E. Cushing and D. H. Campbell, Principles of Immunology, McGraw-Hill, New York, 1957, p. 30, with permission.)

sional form. The interaction would allow part of the antibody molecule to fold around the antigen, automatically creating a complementary shape between the two molecules. Because, according to this scheme and most variants of it, the antigen directly determines the shape of the antibody, such models are called *instructive theories* of antibody formation (Figure 15–7).

Now, however, instructive theories are in disfavor. Instead, there is a growing tendency to believe that there are not only three-dimensional differences, but also differences in primary structure (amino acid sequences) between different antibodies. One of the most compelling types of evidence comes from experiments in which the three-dimensional structure is temporarily destroyed (denatured) and allowed to reform in the absence of antigen: The antibody molecules resume their specificity! There is also a growing body of direct chemical evidence, based on analysis of amino acid sequences of purified antibodies. Here definite differences seem to exist, suggesting that antibodies have two distinct regions: one common to all antibodies, which accounts for the impression that all antibodies are chemically very similar, and one whose amino acid sequence (and, hence, three-dimensional form) differs from one antibody to another.

The existence of distinct amino acid sequences for each specific antibody immediately raises the question of whether

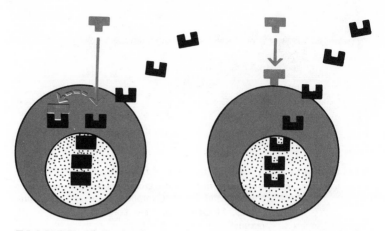

FIGURE 15-7 A schematic comparison of the instructive and selective theories of antibody formation. Under the instructive theory, an antigen enters a plasma cell and forms a template on which a complementary antibody is laid down. Selective theories propose that mere contact of a given antigen with a potential antibody-producing cell signals the cell nucleus to produce mRNA chains specific for a complementary antibody. (Redrawn from G. J. V. Nossal, Sci. Am., December 1964, p. 112, with permission.)

there is a distinct gene for each antibody. Since a given antibody-producing animal can produce a very large number of antibodies, this raises the possibility that a very large number of genes might code for the amino acid sequences of antibodies. For many years this possibility has seemed repugnant to many immunologists, aware of the immense number of different antigenic determinants. Now, however, the dilemma can no longer be avoided. Since the amino acid sequences are different, there must exist corresponding differences in their mRNA templates, and thus in the relevant DNA regions.

We are also faced with the problem that, if different genes exist, what is the control mechanism by which the presence of an antigen tells the gene controlling a corresponding antibody to function? In some way the presence of an antigen must cause the selective synthesis of unique amino acid sequences (the selective theory of antibody formation).

LIGHT AND HEAVY CHAINS BOTH INFLUENCE THE SPECIFICITY OF ANTIBODIES

The region of the antibody that combines with an antigenic determinant includes parts of both light and heavy chains. At first it was suspected that most of the specificity was due to variations in the amino acid sequences of the heavy chains, but now it has been realized that in most cases the amino acid sequence of the light chain is also involved. There is growing evidence that both the light and heavy chains have two distinct sections, one at the COO^- end, where the amino acid sequence is common for all antibodies, the other at the NH_2 terminal end, where the amino acid sequence differs from one light (heavy) chain to another.

The discovery that both the light and heavy chains are specific mitigates the dilemma, posed in the preceding section about the great number of genes needed to code for different antibodies. Since each antibody must be coded for by two genes (one for the light chain, the other for the heavy chain), the number of possible antibodies may be the number of different light chains multiplied by the number of different heavy chains. Thus a million different antibodies may be formed by only two thousand genes, coding for a thousand different light chains and a thousand different heavy chains.

PLASMA CELL SITE OF ANTIBODY SYNTHESIS

It is obvious that, before we can seriously test the selective theories, we must know which types of cells produce antibodies. For a long time it has been known that the spleen and the lymph nodes are sites of antibody synthesis. At first it was thought that a scavenger white blood cell, the macrophage, produced antibody. Now, however, it is clear that another type of white blood cell, the plasma cell, is the main if not sole site of antibody production. When an antigen is injected into an animal, there appears within several days an increased number of immature plasma cells, called *plasmablasts*. These new cells arise from the division of a still-undiscovered precursor cell (perhaps a small lymphocyte) as a result of the injection of the antigen. Each plasmablast exists but a short time before dividing to form new progeny cells. The progeny cells are not, however, morphologically identical to their parents. Each successive division cycle results in cells having a more pronounced cytoplasm filled with an increasing number of ribosomes. By the fifth day after the antigen is injected, the cycle of successive cell division has produced adult plasma cells, which are by then rapidly turning out antibody molecules (Figure 15–8).

Thus the injection of an antigen into the bloodstream has two separate effects. One is the transformation of the inert ribosome-poor plasma cell precursors into the ribosome-rich plasma cells capable of rapid protein synthesis (Figure 15–9). This development is common to all antibody synthesis. The second effect of the antigen is probably far more specific; it is most likely the production of the specific messenger-RNA molecules, which code for the unique amino acid sequences of the specific antibody molecules.

A GIVEN PLASMA CELL USUALLY PRODUCES ONE TYPE OF ANTIBODY MOLECULE

When a number of different antigens are injected simultaneously into an animal, the question naturally arises whether a given plasma cell produces antibodies against all the foreign antigens or, instead, produces only one type of antibody. According to instructive theories, we might expect that many different types of antigen would enter a single plasma cell, and so each cell should produce a variety of antibodies. The experimental answer, however, seems to be the opposite. When the antibodies produced in a single cell are examined (this can be done by isolating single plasma cells after they have begun to produce antibody), it has been found that most cells can produce only one specific antibody. Thus almost every antibody-producing plasma cell represents a most highly specialized factory, devoting much of its protein synthesis to the production of only one product.

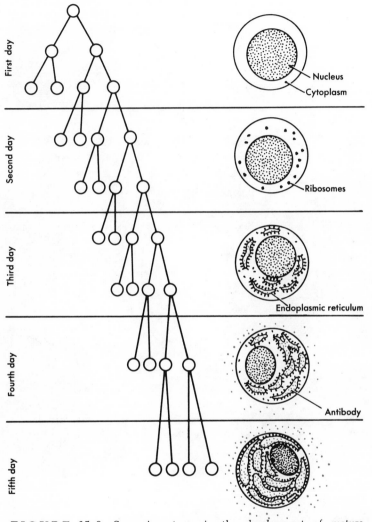

FIGURE 15-8 Successive stages in the development of mature plasma cells. At least 8 cell generations and 5 days of growth are required before the appearance of cells producing a great deal of antibody. The most noticeable feature of the mature cells is the extensive endoplasmic reticulum whose internal cavity is filled with antibody molecules. (Redrawn from G. J. V. Nossal, Sci. Am., Dec. 1964, p. 109, with permission.)

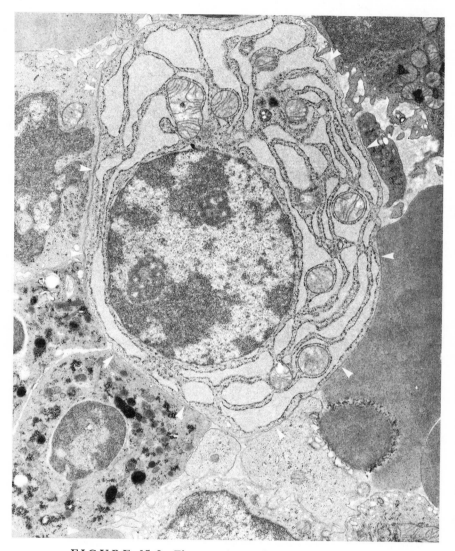

FIGURE 15-9   Electron micrograph of a plasma cell from the spleen of a guinea pig (courtesy of K. R. Porter, Biological Laboratories, Harvard). The cell margins are indicated by white arrows. The cavity of endoplasmic reticulum is greatly distended by the presence of large amounts of antibody molecules. Ribosomes are visible as black dots attached to the endoplasmic reticulum. The objects around the edges are other types of white blood cells.

SECOND INJECTION OF ANTIGEN INCREASES THE NUMBER OF ANTIBODY–PRODUCING CELLS

Several days after a single injection of an antigen, the number of plasma cells which are producing the corresponding antigen is relatively small. For still unclear reasons, only a small number of the plasmablast precursors become transformed into antibody-producing plasma cells. When, however, the first injection is followed some weeks later by a second injection, a much larger number of antibody-producing plasma cells is found. Correspondingly, very many more antibody molecules are made and released. This is the reason that immunization is usually carried out by repeated injections of the same antigen.

The above results hint that a first antigen injection may transform some of the *unspecific precursor cells* into *transformed precursor cells* which, when subjected to a second contact with the same antigen, multiply to produce plasma cells with the corresponding antibody. Some inactive plasmablasts may thus possess immunological memory. In some very precise way, they seem to know that they have previously had contact with a specific antigen.

ANTIBODY–PRODUCING CELLS NEED NOT CONTAIN ANTIGENS

We might guess that both immunological memory and the production of specific antibodies are based upon contact with specific antigen molecules. Now, however, there is sound evidence that very little if any specific antigen is present inside an antibody-producing plasma cell. Such evidence arises from experiments in which a highly radioactive antigen is injected into an animal. Some days later, thin sections of antibody-producing regions are examined by autoradiographic techniques to find out where the antigens have gone. Much of the labeled antigen is found inside the scavenger macrophage cells, which have no direct connection with antibody synthesis. In contrast, most plasma cells seem to contain not even a single antigen molecule, and only a few antigens can be seen in the plasmablasts. This observation, if confirmed, clearly rules out any instructional theory. Each antibody-producing cell is simultaneously making thousands of antibodies. Given the instructional model, we would expect that thousands of antigens would be found in each cell, perhaps bound to the ribosomal sites of protein synthesis. Thus this observation strongly supports the idea that the antigen either directly or indirectly *selects* the synthesis of a specific mRNA molecule.

It remains unclear, however, whether the antigen need be present to ensure the massive synthesis of the mRNA template. The fact that the precursor plasmablasts contain only a few antigen molecules hints that antigen need not be present, but the question must still be considered open. If no antigen is present, then we must consider the possibility that the genetic apparatus of any given antibody-producing cell has itself been transformed.

THEORY OF CLONAL SELECTION

The fact that the presence of an antigen leads to a great increase in the number of cells which produce that specific antibody has suggested to some immunologists that the sole function of the antigen is to stimulate specific cell division. This *clonal selection theory* (a clone is a group of cells all descended from a common ancestor) presumes that the antigen need provide no information other than the fact that it is present. This theory assumes that there *preexists*, prior to the appearance of the antigen, a large variety of different plasma cell precursors, each class endowed with the capacity to form only one (or sometimes two) specific types of antibody. The antigen then acts to select the appropriate class by causing its selective division. Some of the newly divided precursors give rise after several cell generations to mature plasma cells. Others may continue to divide without producing antibody. These would be the cells responsible for immunological memory.

These speculations bring us again to the problem raised earlier of whether there exists a separate gene for each of the different light and heavy antibody chains. Certainly the total pop-

ulation of plasma cells within a single animal must contain a
large number of different antibody genes. This fact, however,
does not help us with the crucial point of whether every plasma
cell possesses each gene. In fact, it is possible to distinguish two
broad categories of hypotheses about genes coding for antibodies.
One set of categories is the above-mentioned possibility that
each haploid chromosome contains a large number of antibody
genes. If this is the case, then a given plasma cell must be restricted (at random?) to the production of only one type of
antibody. How this might happen is not at all obvious.

The alternative set assumes that, in the fertilized egg, each
haploid chromosome set contains only one, or at most a few,
genes for the light and heavy chains, Under this set of
schemes, during the many cell divisions following fertilization,
these antibody genes are randomly modified to produce a large
number of different antibody genes, each present in only a
very small fraction of the total population of plasma cell precursors. These cells are then triggered to divide and produce
their specific antibody whenever they come into contact with
the appropriate antigen.

There are a variety of ways by which a small number of antibody genes could give rise to a very large number of antibody
genes. One way presupposes that the genes for the light and
heavy chains are much more mutable than other genes. This
is hard to imagine, not only because other genes must not be
mutated, but also because the high mutability must be restricted
to approximately one-half the "light" gene and one-half of the
"heavy" gene. Otherwise, we should not find that all light
(heavy) chains have identical amino acid sequences in the
COO^- terminal halves. Another way to generate a large number
of different genes is for each cell to possess several different
genes for the light (and heavy) chain. Each of the genes
would have identical nucleotides in one half (the COO^- end)
and quite different sequences in the other half (the NH_3^+
end). Crossing over (mitotic recombination) between these
related genes would then produce new nucleotide sequences,
each coding for a new set of amino acid sequences. Now there
is no clear way to decide between recombination hypotheses

and those based upon mutation. However, when the amino acid sequences for a number of distinct antibodies become available, it may be apparent that regularities in amino acid sequences exist that favor recombination models over those based on random mutations.

IMMUNOLOGICAL TOLERANCE

Up to now, we have avoided mentioning a very important characteristic of the immunological response. How does an antibody-forming system know that a molecular surface is present on a *foreign* molecule? How is it able to avoid making antibodies against its own proteins and nucleic acids? This lack of responsiveness has nothing to do with the inherent anti- genicity of the molecules. For example, almost any human protein, if injected into a rabbit, will induce the formation of specific antibodies. Likewise, rabbit proteins are antigenic in humans. These facts lead to the conclusion that an immuno- logical system learns how to recognize native molecules. Such a learning process occurs very early in life, before the development of an active immune response to foreign proteins. If a foreign antigen is injected into a newly born animal before it possesses an antibody-forming system, then, in adult life, the animal is unable to form antibodies against the early injected foreign antigen. The foreign antigen is recognized as though it were a host protein. This lack of immunological responsiveness to all those antigens present when the antibody-forming system was being developed is called *immunological tolerance*.

It would indeed be surprising if the seemingly opposite behaviors of specific tolerance and specific antibody response were in fact completely unrelated. One hypothetical way to relate the two responses rests on the fact that a cell making large amounts of antibody is usually unable to multiply and thus lives for only several days. Perhaps if the theory of clonal selection is correct, then very early in life there exist only a few cells genet- ically competent to form antibodies against a specific antigen. Immunological tolerence might result if at this early time the attachment of an antigen, instead of somehow causing a significant antibody response, resulted in immediate cell death.

INABILITY TO INDUCE ANTIBODIES IN VITRO

It is obvious to even the most enthusiastic immunologist that neither the formation of a specific antibody nor the development of immunological tolerence as a result of the injection of a specific antigen is understood either at the cellular or at the molecular level. This fact leads to the immediate question: Why not study the induction of antibodies with isolated cells outside the intact animal? Such a procedure would automatically enable us not only to identify unambiguously the precursors to the plasmablast intermediates, but, even more importantly, to tell whether they were already differentiated as to which antibody they would produce. Unfortunately, up to now, all attempts at antibody induction at the level of single cells have met with complete failure. Only when the precursor cells are in an intact animal do the antigens work. Nonetheless, the goal is being actively pursued, since science is full of examples where processes previously thought to occur only in living organisms where subsequently demonstrated outside the intact organism.

Much progress would also be made if antibodies themselves could be synthesized in a cell-free system containing only ribosomes, mRNA, sRNA, and the necessary enzymes and precursors. Here again, all efforts have led to no success. These failures, however, parallel similar failures with cell-free protein synthesis in even more intensively studied bacterial systems. Thus, when achieved, cell-free antibody synthesis may help to create a better understanding of the detailed steps in protein synthesis.

At the present moment, the only direction in which the immunologist can move at the molecular level with some prospects of obvious success is the study of the antibody itself. Our knowledge of detailed antibody structure is still incomplete, and much more work is required to understand antibody structure at the level at which we now look at myoglobin or hemoglobin. Here, however, even though the detailed protein structure information may in itself be quite interesting, there is no reason to believe that it will necessarily yield information relating to the primary problem of how the antigen induces the synthesis of a specific antibody. We thus see that the molecular biologists who have decided to concentrate on antibody synthesis as a means of understanding cell differentiation have chosen a problem that, upon close examination, seems even more complicated than embryological differentiation seen from afar. Even so, there is no reason to believe that the really fundamental embryological problems, when properly posed, will prove any easier to solve.

SUMMARY

Virtually nothing is known about the molecular basis of the control of protein synthesis in the cells of the multicellular higher organisms. In particular, little information exists as to mechanisms that bring about cell differentiation. Once a cell has become differentiated, all its descendants produce a specific group of unique proteins. There are hints that this selective protein synthesis, like that of microbial cells, is sometimes based on the selective synthesis of unique types of RNA. Thus differentiated cells must have mechanisms that control the rate at which specific DNA regions are read. A major difficulty that now hinders basic understanding is our current inability to study differentiation outside an intact organism. Though embryonic differentiation can be made to occur in tissue culture, it has not yet been possible to isolate the specific external factors that normally induce a cell to differentiate in a given direction.

Thus there is a great need to find a "simple" system in which cells become irreversibly differentiated to produce a well-defined protein in response to the addition of a specific, well-understood, external molecule. One system, initially thought to be "simple," is the synthesis of specific antibodies as a result of the injection of specific foreign objects. Those objects that induce the synthesis of specific antibodies are called antigens. Many macromolecules, including most proteins and some carbohydrates and nucleic acids, are antigens. Antibodies are proteins with a MW of about 160,000. Antibodies inactivate antigens by combining with them to form complexes that are engulfed by scavenger white blood cells. It was originally thought that an antigen induced the formation of a specific antibody by combining with a nascent antibody before it acquired its final three-dimensional shape. According to this hypothesis, the antibody would fold around the antigenic surface, thereby forming a region complementary in shape to the antigen's specific surface (instructive theories). Now, however, it is generally thought that each specific antibody possesses a unique sequence of amino acids which folds in a unique three-dimensional shape. The function of the antigen is thus to select the synthesis of the specific mRNA templates that code for the desired amino acid sequence (selective theories).

The site of antibody synthesis is the plasma cell. It is a highly differentiated cell that arises (from small lymphocytes?) by means of intermediate plasmablast cells. Most plasma cells can make only one type of antibody. Little if any antigen is present in antibody-producing cells. This fact suggests that each plasma cell is hereditarily restricted to the production of only one (two) type(s) of antibody. The number of plasma cells producing a given antibody increases with repeated antigen injections. This hints that the presence of an antigen stimulates the division of cells capable of giving rise to the plasma cells which produce the corresponding antibody (theory of clonal selection). This theory assumes the preexistence, prior to the injection of an antigen, of a very large variety of cells differentiated with respect to the antibody their progeny can produce.

Since antibodies are formed only against foreign proteins, an animal's immunological system must be able to recognize its own proteins. This learning process occurs early in life, before circulating antibodies exist. If a foreign protein is injected into a newborn animal, the animal in later life is unable to form antibodies against the foreign protein (immunological tolerance).

REFERENCES

Sussman, M., *Growth and Development*, 2nd ed., Prentice-Hall, Englewood Cliffs, N.J., 1964. A brief paperback introduction to embryology that nicely ties in the problems of the classical embryologist with the ideas of modern genetics.

Ebert, J., *Interacting Systems in Development*, Holt, New York, 1965. An excellent, quite detailed paperback introduction to embryology with emphasis on the desirability of explanations on the molecular level.

Brachet, J., *Biochemical Cytology*, Academic, New York, 1957. A 1956 survey of the biochemical facts relevant to the problems of cytologists and embryologists.

Beermann, W., and O. Clever, "Chromosome Puffs," *Sci. Am.*, April, 1964, pp. 50–58. A beautifully illustrated discussion of the functioning of the giant chromosomes of insects.

Cushing, J. E., and D. H. Campbell, *Principles of Immunology*, McGraw-Hill, New York, 1957. A textbook discussion, at the college level, of classical immunological ideas.

Landsteiner, K., *The Specificity of Serological Reactions*, rev. ed., Dover, New York, 1964. A paperback reprint of a scientific classic, last revised in 1943. Still a beautiful introduction to immunology.

Edelman, G. M., and J. A. Gally, "A Model for the 7S Antibody Molecule," *Proc. Natl. Acad. Sci. U.S.*, **51**, 846 (1964). A recent summary of facts about the structure of antibodies.

Lederberg, J., "Genes and Antibodies," *Science*, **129**, 1649 (1959). The problems of antibody synthesis as seen in 1959 by an inquisitive geneticist.

Burnet, F. M., *The Integrity of the Body: A Discussion of Modern Immunological Ideas*, Harvard University Press, Cambridge, 1962. A speculative imaginative discussion, with emphasis on the author's clonal selection hypothesis.

Nossal, G. J. V., "How Cells Make Antibodies," *Sci. Am.*, December, 1964, pp. 106–115. A clear summary of the immunological dilemmas as of late 1964.

16

A GENETICIST'S VIEW OF CANCER

IN THE PREVIOUS CHAPTER, IT BECAME glaringly obvious that the problems of understanding the genetic basis of cell differentiation at the molecular level may be exceedingly difficult to solve. Only today are we beginning to gain some confidence that we are close to understanding the essential molecular features upon which the life of even the simplest bacterial cell depends. The jump to an attempt to understand the much more complex vertebrate cell with its thousandfold greater amount of DNA has only begun. Though we can now grow some of these cells in tissue culture, we are always painfully aware that the normal environment of a cell from a multicellular organism is the intact organism, and that when we remove a cell from its normal cellular companions, we may so alter it that it is unable to function in the way that interests us. The case of the induction of specific antibody systems is most relevant. At first, antibody formation appears to be a case of irreversible differentiation, which should be much simpler to study than other examples of cell specialization. But so far we have been unable to study antibody formation outside the intact animal, and therefore a scientific attack at the molecular level cannot yet be effectively undertaken.

Thus it might be thought that, if it is still very difficult to attack the molecular basis of normal differentiation, it should be even harder to understand failures in cell heredity which produce abnormal cells unable to integrate into organized multicellular complexes. That is, if we are still a colossally long way from understanding a healthy animal cell at the molecular level, have we any chance of gaining an insight into the diseased cell? Are we likely to understand soon the majority of diseases at a molecular level? Fortunately, we already know that at least a few diseases can be so understood. The abnormal hemoglobin molecules (see Chapter 8) which cause various blood diseases (anemias) are a case in point. Here we are able to understand their molecular bases (but not yet cure them!), because we had prior, very detailed knowledge about the structure of normal hemoglobin. *Our chance to understand a disease depends greatly upon whether it is based upon abnormalities in molecules with which we are already familiar.*

From this viewpoint, we can look at the problem of cancer. The term *cancer* encompasses a large variety of different diseases, all characterized by the property that cells grow when they should not. We are thus dealing with the problem of *the control of cell division,* and so we must ask what tells a normal cell in a multicellular organism to stop dividing. This is a problem which does not exist at the bacterial level, for bacteria separate from each other soon after cell division has occurred. Our studies of bacterial cells therefore provide no direct hints. The problem must thus be attacked directly at the level of the mammalian cell. Here, unfortunately, despite much intelligently conceived effort, we are still essentially in the dark as to the molecular factors which ensure that cells cease to grow and divide at the correct time. Hence many intelligent biochemists hold the view that now is not the time to work seriously on the biochemistry of cancerous cells. They argue that, even though cancer cells are the cause of enormous human suffering, nonetheless it does not make sense to put a disproportionate share of our scientific effort into trying to meet an unripe intellectual challenge. They compare the current situation with the desire to understand the nature of solar energy at the time of Newton.

I suspect, however, that this pessimism may not be justified and that an understanding of at least some aspects of uncontrolled cell growth may soon be achieved at the molecular level. Such optimism arises from some recent, spectacular results on the induction of tumors by viruses. Before we state the arguments, however, it may be well to try to define the problem more exactly.

CANCERS CAN ARISE IN ALMOST ALL DIFFERENTIATED CELLS

There are many distinct types of uncontrolled growth (cancer). Each appears to arise by an inheritable change in a specific cell. Almost all types of differentiated cells can be transformed into cancer (malignant) cells. Thus, liver cells, skin cells, nerve cells, kidney cells, blood cells, bone cells, etc., can all become cancer cells. In general, cancer cells exhibit many morphological and functional characteristics common to their normal precursors. For example, cancer cells arising in the thyroid gland often produce the hormone thyroxin, which is specifically synthesized by normal thyroid cells.

Contiguous masses of cancer cells are called tumors. There is great variation in the rate at which tumors grow. Some grow relatively slowly, whereas others grow rapidly and, if not removed by surgery or radiation treatment, inevitably kill their host. Great differences also exist in the affinity of the various types of cancer cells for other cells. Some cancer cells tend to remain at the location where they arise. The tumors they produce are often not harmful, because they can usually be easily removed. Others quickly spread through an organism and invade a variety of normal tissues. Invasive cancers, after they have spread, usually cannot be completely removed by surgery or other treatment and so almost always lead to death unless detected soon after their origin.

CANCER CELLS GROW WHEN THEY SHOULD NOT

We cannot distinguish a cancer cell from a normal cell by the fact that the tumor cell is constantly dividing while the normal one divides only rarely. In fact, tumors most often arise in cells normally undergoing frequent division. In mature animals, many normal cells are in the process of constant growth and cell division. This is particularly true of the cells exposed to the external environment. For example, the epithelial cells of the skin and those lining the various cavities of the digestive system are constantly forming new cells to replace the large number of cells that die each day. Likewise, the various types of blood cells have relatively short lives and must be replaced by the division of preexisting precursor cells. On the other hand, organs such as the liver and the brain have cells which seldom divide in a mature adult. In addition to those two types, there are other cells, normally quiescent, which after the appearance of a specific hormone suddenly begin to divide and continue to do so as long as the hormone is present.

The difference between a cancer cell and a normal cell is thus often not an all-or-none matter, but is a question of the frequency of division. Either the cancer cell may divide more rapidly than a normal cell, or, if the normal cell requires the stimulus of a specific hormone, then the cancer cell may not need this stimulus, or may require less hormone before commencing division. Thus the only useful distinction is that the cancer cell is less subject to the normal control devices which tell a cell not to divide.

CONTACT INHIBITION

There is now growing evidence that, when two normal animal cells touch one another, a signal is often generated which stops both cells from further cell movement and in some cases from further cell division. This phenomenon of *contact inhibition* is revealed by noticing how isolated mouse cells grow on a solid glass surface. Normal cells have a great affinity for solid surfaces and stick to the glass rather than float freely in the nutrient medium. As long as there are relatively few cells about, division proceeds regularly about once every 24 hours. The division rate often slows down when the cells have formed a confluent monolayer. It is as if these cells are able to divide as long as they are not in close contact with several other cells. In contrast, when a variety of cancer cells (but not all) are observed, growth does not cease when a monolayer has formed. Instead, the cancer cells pile on top of each other, forming masses of cells several layers thick (Figure 16–1). The basis of these phenomena is still very unclear. It may be related to a greater stickiness of the normal cells. When they touch each other, they often remain fixed, whereas many types of cancer cells have much less affinity for other cells and so do not form regular monolayers.

In vivo some control system may exist which allows normal cells to divide only so long as they have some freedom of movement. This would mean that the moment this freedom of movement were lost (e.g., through the formation of a continuous monolayer) cell growth would stop. In an obvious way, contact inhibition makes sense. Inside a multicellular organism, it would be disadvantageous for a cell to grow and divide if it had no room to move about.

FIGURE 16–1   *Schematic comparison of the multiplication of a normal cell and of a cancer cell upon a solid surface. The normal cells divide until they form a solid monolayer. Cancer cells, however, often have less affinity for the solid surface and form irregular masses, several layers deep.*

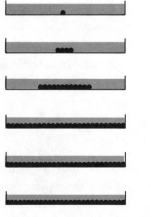
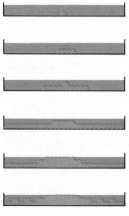

Normal cells   Cancer cells

MALIGNANCY AS A LOSS OF CELLULAR AFFINITIES

The "sticky" quality of cells, observed in contact inhibition, displays considerable specificity. A given type of cell, e.g., a liver cell, prefers to stick to other liver cells and shows very little, if any, affinity for kidney cells. This type of specificity has been elegantly demonstrated in experiments in which small amounts of the proteolytic enzyme trypsin are used to break apart organs such as the liver and the kidney into single cell components. If these isolated cells are then incubated in the absence of trypsin, they reaggregate to form tissue fragments identical to those in the intact organ, e.g., small fragments of liver tissue and small fragments of kidney tissue. When kidney and liver cells are mixed together, small fragments of liver and kidney are again observed. No mixtures of kidney and liver cells are detected. Thus a kidney cell prefers to stick to a kidney cell, and a liver cell to a liver cell. If this experiment is repeated with cancer cells, however, the normal cellular affinities no longer hold. For example, the mixing of cells from a malignant skin cancer with normal kidney cells results in aggregates containing both kidney cells and skin cancer cells. A loss of normal cellular affinities is most likely the reason why many malignant cancer cells invade a variety of normal organs.

The results from both the normal and the cancer cells point to the same important conclusion. The outside surfaces of cells play a very important role in ensuring the correct positioning of cells in a multicellular organism. Moreover, if the current speculation about contact inhibition is correct, the formation of the correct cellular contact is of great importance in determining whether a cell will divide.

SEARCH FOR CHEMICAL DIFFERENCES BETWEEN NORMAL AND CANCER CELLS

Almost as soon as scientists began to describe molecules within normal cells, they also looked to see whether these same molecules were found in cancer cells. Now, when a new chemical reaction (or enzyme) is described in a normal cell, a search is very often made to see if the same reaction occurs in the cancer cell. Often these searches seem to be successful, with the tumor cells containing much more (or less) of a particular component than their normal equivalent. Further analysis, however, has so far invariably resulted in disappointment. One of the difficulties inherent in this type of analysis is that, if we observe a change, the question arises: Should we regard the change as the primary metabolic disturbance or as a secondary response to the changed metabolism caused by the primary changes? Moreover, in many such experiments, it is impossible to select a good control with which to compare the tumor cell, since we cannot be sure in what type of normal cell the cancerous transformation has occurred. Also our only comparison must often be with isolated normal cells growing in tissue cultures. These are not good standards for comparison, however, since normal cells may have undergone a number of genetic changes during their adaptation to growth in the unnatural environment of tissue culture.

CANCER INDUCTION BY RADIATION AND CHEMICALS

It is obvious that a prime requirement for satisfactory chemical analysis of cancer cells is the availability of external agents whose application can change, in vitro (that is, in tissue culture), a normal cell into a cancer cell. We already know of many examples of an externally added agent greatly increasing the incidence of tumors inside living animals. These cancer-causing agents are called *carcinogens*. Among the most potent carcinogens are various forms of radiation. Exposure of the thyroid gland to x rays, for example, greatly increases the occurrence of thyroid cancer. None of the various radiations, however, can be used to cause all the cells in an exposed population to become cancerous. Only a small fraction is affected. Thus radiation does not yet seem to be a useful agent for studying the biochemistry of the primary events accompanying the change-over from the normal to the cancerous state. Similarly, most chemicals which cause tumors in animals transform only a small percentage of the exposed cell population.

A further difficulty in analyzing the biochemical events occurring during either radiation or chemical carcinogenesis is that both types of agents are quite toxic and undoubtedly cause many changes other than the cancerous change. What biochemists need is an agent whose primary effect is connected with the change to unrestrained growth. Fortunately, as we shall soon see, carcinogenesis induced by viral infection fills the requirement. Before we discuss how viruses act, however, we must first enquire how the cancer cell maintains its cancerous property.

CANCER AS A HEREDITARY CHANGE

When a cancer cell divides, the two progeny cells are usually morphologically identical to the parental cell. The factor(s) that gives cancer cells their essential quality of unrestrained growth is thus regularly passed on from parent to progeny cells. These changes persist not only in tumors growing in intact animals, but also in tumor cells growing in tissue culture. Hundreds of generations of growth can occur in tissue culture without appreciable reversion to a normal state. The permanence of such changes is shown not only by perpetuation of a typical morphology, but also by the ability of progeny cells to cause new tumors when injected into a tumor-free animal of genetic composition similar to the one from which the original tissue culture was obtained.

The heritability of the changes allowing unrestrained growth makes us consider the possibility that an alteration has occurred at the chromosomal level. Direct proof of this idea is impossible, however, since we now have no means of studying the genetics of single cells of higher organisms. It is not yet possible to cross two different cancer cells and look for normal segregants. This will be possible only when a means is found to fuse diploid cells, hoping then for mitotic recombination. Currently, much effort is being directed toward that goal, so perhaps we shall soon have clear proof that a specific cancer is caused by chromosomal alterations.

Alternatively, we can imagine that the cancerous change is an example of irreversible differentiation. That is, the mechanism which makes the cancerous transformation permanent may be similar to the devices which, for example, ensure that a nerve cell always multiplies as a nerve cell. We cannot, however, really follow up this hypothesis, for, as we emphasized in the previous chapter, no one yet knows how cells are irreversibly differentiated.

SOMATIC MUTATIONS AS POSSIBLE CAUSES OF CANCER

If the essential changes that make cancer cells are at the chromosomal level, it is possible to imagine two quite different mechanisms for their occurrence. The first mechanism postulates that somatic mutations (mutations occurring in cells not destined to become sex cells) constitute the essential change. Under this scheme, a somatic mutation could cause a cancer if its occurrence upset a normal control device regulating cell division. Proponents of this hypothesis believe that, in general, several somatic mutations are necessary to cause a cancer. This idea is based on the fact that the incidence of cancer greatly increases with age. This phenomenon would be explainable if a particular cell had to accumulate several mutations, each occurring randomly in time, before becoming a full-fledged cancer cell. At present there exists no direct evidence either for or against this theory, which we might best describe as cancer due to loss of an essential gene(s). Even without evidence, however, it is clear that somatic mutations must occur; it would be surprising if at least some did not disrupt the normal control of cell division.

VIRUSES AS A CAUSE OF CANCER

Alternatively, there is the hypothesis that many cancers are caused by viruses. In a sense, this is not really an hypothesis, since there is already convincing evidence that a number of specific cancers in animals, ranging from fish to mammals, are virus-induced. The relevant question is thus not whether viruses can cause cancer, but whether a sizable fraction of cancers are virus-induced.

Until recently, there was no intellectual framework in which to consider how viruses might cause cancer. Now, largely as a result of work with bacterial viruses, we realize that when a virus enters a cell a new piece of genetic material is brought into the cell. Normally we think of viruses as objects whose multiplication inevitably kills cells. Addition of a tumor virus to a cell, however, often does not kill the host cell. It is thus possible, as we shall soon show, to believe that the essential aspect of viral carcinogenesis is *the introduction of new genetic material,* in contrast to somatic mutations which, we suspect, often cause a loss of functional genetic material.

At present it seems most likely that not all tumor viruses act in the same way. For example, a variety of cancers are caused by RNA-containing viruses. The best-known of these RNA viruses is the Rous sarcoma virus, which causes solid tumors in chickens (a sarcoma is a tumor of connective tissue). Certain other RNA viruses most likely cause leukemia in both birds and mammals, probably including man. Acting quite differently are several groups of DNA viruses. One group is responsible for wart-like growths on the skin in many different mammals, ranging from rodents to man. Other closely related DNA viruses, of which the best-known is a mouse virus called "polyoma," can cause a variety of tumors when injected into newborn animals. Below we shall focus attention first on polyoma and then on the Rous virus to show that it is now possible to propose concrete hypotheses, at the molecular level, about how they cause cancerous transformations.

TWO FATES OF A POLYOMA PARTICLE

Polyoma is a virus that normally multiplies in rodents, including mice, rats, and hamsters. It is a relatively small, spherical virus of MW about 25,000,000 (Figure 16–2). The outside is a protein shell containing 72 protein subunits, each one most likely composed of smaller subunits. Inside is a circular molecule of double-helical DNA of MW near 3,000,000 (Figure 16–3). This amount of DNA is sufficient to code for five different proteins at most, so we are dealing with one of the simplest viruses discovered.

When a polyoma virus enters a susceptible cell, it may suffer two possible fates. Most commonly, it multiplies like a conventional virus and produces a very large number of new virus particles. The site of polyoma reproduction within its host cell is the cell nucleus. A single nucleus may become filled with

FIGURE 16–2   *An electron micrograph (courtesy of L. V. Crawford, Institute of Virology, Glasgow) of polyoma virus particles. The viral diameter is about 500 A. Careful observation reveals that 72 subunits are used to construct the external protein coat. Two of the particles (lower left) are held together by an antipolyoma antibody molecule.*

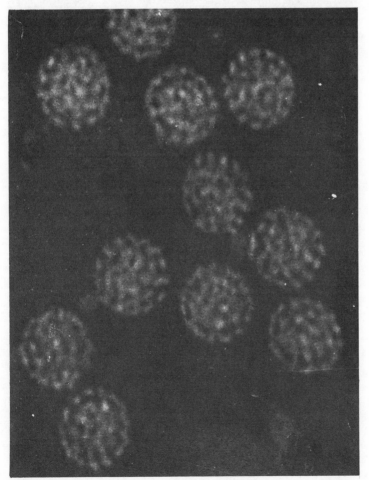

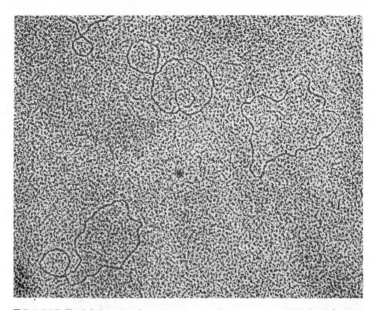

FIGURE 16-3   An electron micrograph (courtesy of W. Stoeckenius, Rockefeller Institute) of several molecules of purified polyoma DNA. All clearly have a circular contour. The DNA contour length is 1.6 μ, corresponding to 3 × 10⁶ daltons.

millions of particles, a process during which the normal nuclear functions are disrupted and the host cell necessarily dies (a lytic infection). Much more rarely, the virus enters the cell and forms no new particles. Instead, the infected cell becomes transformed into a morphologically distinguishable cancer cell.

Both the lytic and transforming responses can be observed outside living animals, in tissue culture. In these experiments, tissue culture cells (usually derived from embryonic mice) are allowed to grow on a glass surface bathed in nutrient solution. A number of polyoma particles are then added. Many of these particles multiply in the cells to produce progeny particles, which then adsorb to nearby cells, producing a circular region of dead cells similar to the plaques formed by bacterial viruses (Figure 16-4). If, on the other hand, the virus transforms one of the tissue culture cells, the transformed cell then begins to multiply in the disorganized and easily identifiable fashion of a cancer cell (Figure 16–5). Particularly noticeable in the case of the transformed cells is their apparent lack of contact inhibition, which results in the formation of groups of cells piled irregularly on top of each other.

ABSENCE OF INFECTIOUS POLYOMA PARTICLES FROM TRANSFORMED CELLS; SEARCH FOR A PROVIRUS

No infectious polyoma particles are present in transformed cells. It is, of course, not surprising that the nuclei of transformed cells are not filled with viral particles. This would probably result in cell death. The fact is, however, that no particles at all can be detected. It appears as if the virus enters the cell and then vanishes. This phenomenon immediately raises the question of whether only the polyoma chromosome is present, perhaps integrated into one of the *host* chromosomes by a crossing over be-

FIGURE 16–4 *Plaques of polyoma virus. Polyoma particles were added to embryonic mouse cells growing on a glass surface. The plaques, which became visible after 25 days of incubation, represent contiguous masses of dead cells which stain differently than growing cells. [From Crawford and Diamond, Virology, 22, 235 (1964), with permission.]*

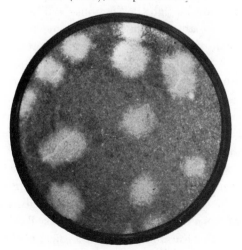

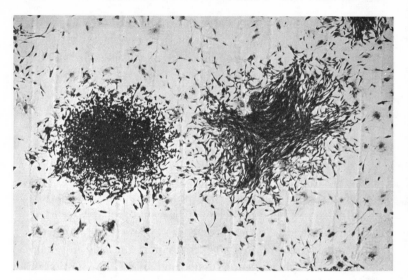

FIGURE 16–5 Clones formed by transformed (left) and normal (right) mouse embryo cells. The transformed cells pile on top of each other, thereby forming a thicker (darker) mass than do normal cells (courtesy of M. Stoker, Institute of Virology, Glasgow, Scotland).

tween the circular polyoma DNA and one of the mouse chromosomes (Figure 16–6). Here it is easy to draw an analogy to lysogenic bacterial viruses (see Chapter 7). Lysogenic phages also have two possible fates. They may multiply lytically or they may become part of the host chromosome by crossing over. The attachment of a lysogenic phage to the host chromosome, however, is not irreversible. Under special conditions, it leaves the chromosome and produces new progeny particles. On this last and crucial point a real analogy between polyoma and the lysogenic phages has not been demonstrated. Despite much effort, no one has been able to induce a polyoma tumor cell to produce virus particles.

Recently, there has been an attempt to prove that polyoma DNA is present in polyoma tumor cells by showing that DNA from transformed cells, but not from normal cells, will form a specific DNA-RNA double helix with polyoma RNA, prepared enzymatically using the enzyme RNA polymerase with polyoma

DNA as the template. So far, these experiments give no evidence that polyoma DNA is present. The experiments are not very sensitive, however, since they would have detected polyoma DNA only if at least five molecules were present. Thus an experiment which will clearly prove whether one polyoma DNA molecule is present is still needed.

TUMOR–SPECIFIC ANTIGENS

A result hinting at the existence of the viral genome within the viral-induced tumor cell comes from experiments which study the immunological properties of tumor cells. The tumors induced by polyoma possess distinctive antigens that elicit the formation of tumor-specific antibodies. These antibodies do not combine with the polyoma virus particle, indicating that the tumor antigen is distinct from the polyoma coat protein. The nature of the tumor specific antigens is still unknown. It most likely is a protein and, if so, we must ask which genetic material codes for its amino acid sequences. Now, a frequently considered possibility is that the antigen is coded for by a section of polyoma DNA itself. If this is the case, all tumor cells must contain at least that section of the polyoma genome.

The presence of the specific antigens explains why polyoma

FIGURE 16–6 *A schematic drawing showing how the circular polyoma chromosome might integrate into a host chromosome.*

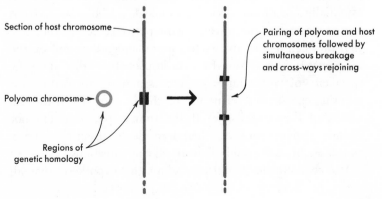

Section of host chromosome

Pairing of polyoma and host chromosomes followed by simultaneous breakage and cross-ways rejoining

Polyoma chromosme

Regions of genetic homology

(and many other tumor viruses) induces tumors only in newborn animals. At the time of birth, most mammals have a very poor ability to make circulating antibodies. The tumor cells arising at birth are not destroyed by newly-produced polyoma tumor-specific antibodies. In fact, the presence of tumor cells often confers immunological tolerance, as the host's immunological system recognizes the tumor cells as normal cells.

In November, 1964, the claim was made that the tumor-specific antigen induced by the virus SV40 [a close relative of polyoma whose natural host is monkeys (and perhaps man)] can also be observed within cells producing infectious SV40 particles. Moreover, the tumor antigen is concentrated within the nucleus in both the tumor cells and the cell producing SV40 virus. This finding, if extended to polyoma, strongly suggests that the metabolism of the tumor cell is closely related to that of the virus-infected cell and thus also argues for the presence of some polyoma DNA within polyoma tumors.

VIRUS—INFECTED CELLS NEED TO SYNTHESIZE NUCLEIC ACIDS

Here we shall try to face up to the heart of the matter. Why should a variety of DNA-containing viruses, many morphologically similar to polyoma, but others of very different structure (e.g., certain adenoviruses), all possess the ability to induce tumors in newborn animals? Our answer will start with the assumption that formation of tumors which *kill* the host is essentially a laboratory accident. Outside a laboratory, animals almost never become infected with polyoma before the time that they can mount an effective immunological assault on the incipient tumors. We further suspect that the antigenic specificity of virus-induced tumors is a necessary feature for ensuring the survival in nature of the host of the virus and, hence, of the virus itself. If the tumors provoked did not contain specific antigens, then host death resulting from a cancer might be the result of nearly all viral infections.

We shall further tentatively adopt the hypothesis that all

transformed cells contain a viral chromosome (provirus) integrated by crossing over into one of the host chromosomes. If we assume a provirus is present, we can then ask whether knowledge of any of the properties of a virus-infected cell could lead to a crucial insight into the metabolism of a cancer cell.

At present, our knowledge of the metabolism of cells infected with the viruses that multiply in higher organisms is scant, so that we must base our argument on our knowledge of bacterial viruses. These systems have yielded the very important generalization that viruses tend to maximize their reproductive potential by altering the host cell so that they can synthesize viral nucleic acid at an extremely rapid rate. In Chapter 12, we discussed several examples in which the nucleic acid of the infecting virus codes for enzymes involved in nucleic acid metabolism. Sometimes, the enzymes involved are unique to the virus-infected cell, but in other cases, the viral-specific enzymes have the same functions as preexisting host enzymes. For example, phage T2 codes for an enzyme similar to *E. coli* DNA polymerase, which allows the infected cell to synthesize DNA much faster than the uninfected cell.

It is likely that many other viruses, in addition to phages, also take active measures to ensure a rapid rate of viral nucleic acid synthesis. The tendency may even be more pronounced for viruses infecting organisms which have a high proportion of nondividing cells, because many nondividing cells (e.g., liver cells) are quite deficient in the enzymes involved in making the deoxynucleoside-triphosphate precursors. When an animal virus enters such a cell, either it must code for all the missing nucleic acid-synthesizing enzymes or it must release the control mechanisms that prohibit a nondividing cell from making these enzymes. Many times, of course, viruses will enter metabolically satisfactory cells. On the other hand, they are likely to enter nondividing cells sufficiently often to confer a marked evolutionary advantage upon those particles which can multiply in either phase of a cell's life.

Thus we must ask whether polyoma is likely to code for a large number of enzymes involved in nucleic acid synthesis. Here molecular genetics says no. Polyoma cannot code for a large number of different enzymes since it contains only 4500 nucleotide base pairs and so codes for only 1500 amino acids. Perhaps 300 amino acids are found in the protein molecule used to construct its protein coat. This would leave 1200 amino acids, enough to code for three or four average-size proteins. The above calculations lead to the conclusion either that polyoma is always restricted to actively dividing cells or that, when multiplying, it uses its specific proteins to unlock its host's normal control mechanisms. It should soon be possible experimentally to distinguish between the alternatives. There are already hints that, in polyoma-infected cells, the level of enzymes involved in DNA synthesis is greatly increased over that in normal cells. If this is true, then further study of the biochemistry of the polyoma-infected cell may provide great insight into the enzymatic mechanisms of converting a non-growing cell into a cell capable of rapid DNA synthesis.

Most importantly, studies of the antigens in tumor cells strongly hint that the distinctive properties of the transformed cell are intimately related to metabolic changes caused by viral multiplication. The observation that the distinctive antigen of SV40 tumors is also found in cells actively producing SV40 virus is very hard to ascribe to chance. Instead, it seems quite possible that the distinctive tumor antigen is an enzyme involved in viral nucleic acid synthesis. It may be coded by a viral gene that continues to function *after* the virus DNA is inserted in a host chromosome. The story would then be almost complete if we were to assume that this enzyme is responsible for the unlocking of the devices that prevent uncontrolled growth.

However, we would still be left with the problem of understanding what advantage there is for the tumor virus to insert itself into a host chromosome as a provirus. It seems hard to believe that insertion is a matter of chance, since it requires that homologies in nucleotide sequence exist between regions of the viral and host chromosomes. Our current failure to answer this enigma should, however, be seen in relation to a similar lack of understanding in bacterial lysogeny. Here also, we are as yet unable to pinpoint any selective advantage for the prophage state.

ROUS SARCOMA IS CAUSED BY A MYXOVIRUS

Not all tumor viruses, however, contain DNA. Many are RNA viruses. Thus we should ask whether the hypotheses we favor for the DNA tumor viruses might hold, with some modification, for the RNA group. The best-known RNA tumor virus is the Rous sarcoma virus (RSV). Though it was discovered over 50 years ago, the state of our knowledge about how viruses multiply did not allow decisive experimentation with RSV until the past ten years. RSV is a medium-size virus, belonging to a group of viruses called *myxoviruses*. These are viruses considerably more complex than the polyoma group. In the center of the virus particle is a *single-stranded RNA chain* combined with a large number of protein subunits (the internal proteins) somewhat in the manner of tobacco mosaic virus.

FIGURE 16–7 *An electron micrograph (by W. Bernhard, Institute of Cancer, Villejuif, France) of an ultrathin cross section of a chick cell infected with both RSV and a helper virus. The virus particles appear as circular bodies about 750 A in diameter. [Reproduced from* Bull. Cancer, 43, 497 *(1956), with permission.]*

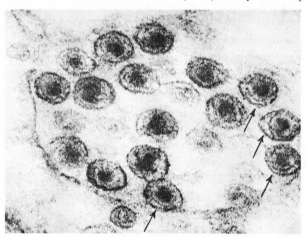

The RNA-protein complex is not rigid as in TMV, but is flexible and is itself contained within a special outer membrane composed of both protein and lipid (Figure 16–7). The presence of the lipid gives the myxovirus the feature of being rapidly destroyed by lipid solvents. Among the best-known myxoviruses are the groups that cause influenza and the mumps.

There appears to be considerable range in the size of myxoviruses. The external diameter of some is as small as 700 A (e.g., influenza), whereas for others (e.g., mumps) it is about 1200 A. Likewise, there is a large spread in the amount of nucleic acid present per particle; it ranges between 2×10^6 and 10^7MW. Nucleotide base analyses show noncomplementary base ratios indicating single-chain structures. Recent measurements of RSV suggest that each particle contains about 10^7 MW units of RNA per particle. The genetic message of RSV (30,000 nucleotides) is thus about six times larger than that of polyoma (4500 base pairs). Approximately 10,000 amino acids are thus coded by the RSV genome. This number is sufficient for at least 25 different proteins, many more than need be found in its coat. This fact suggests that a large number of still unidentified proteins are synthesized during RSV multiplication.

Myxoviruses seem to mature on the surface of susceptible cells (Figure 16–8). After their entrance into cells, the RNA chains of many myxoviruses move to the cell nucleus. There progeny RNA chains, as well as specific internal proteins, are synthesized. RNA-internal protein complexes then move to surface membranes, where they are surrounded by the lipid and protein components that comprise the outer membrane. The newly formed virus particles appear to pinch off from the cell surface, quite possibly acquiring some normal cell components in the process. A distinctive feature of a myxovirus infection is that considerable viral multiplication and release can occur without immediately causing cell death. Though the reproduction of many myxoviruses does eventually lead to cell death, as we shall soon point out in the case of RSV, cell death is very definitely not an obligatory consequence of the large-scale production of a myxovirus by a cell.

INFECTION BY A SINGLE RSV PARTICLE
LEADS TO A CANCER CELL

Infection of a susceptible chicken cell by a *single* RSV particle almost immediately converts the normal cell into a cancer cell. Within 48 hours after attachment of the virus, an RSV-infected cell loses its normal shape, becomes more spherical, and acquires the invasive properties of a malignant cell. This rapid response is easily demonstrated using tissue culture cells derived

FIGURE 16–8 *Diagrammatic view of the life cycle of a typical myxovirus (influenza virus).*

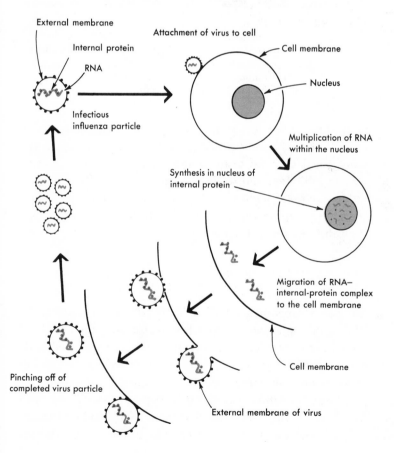

External membrane

Attachment of virus to cell

Internal protein

Cell membrane

RNA

Nucleus

Infectious influenza particle

Multiplication of RNA within the nucleus

Synthesis in nucleus of internal protein

Migration of RNA–internal-protein complex to the cell membrane

Cell membrane

Pinching off of completed virus particle

External membrane of virus

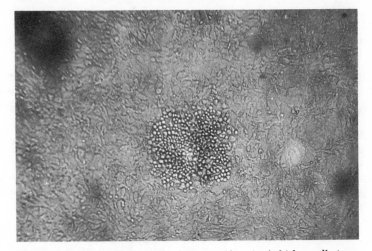

FIGURE 16-9   Photograph of a group (focus) of chicken cells (magnification × 30) transformed by RSV infection (supplied by H. Rubin, Department of Molecular Biology, University of California, Berkeley). The spherical transformed cells are easily distinguished from the background of normal cells.

from chick embryos. When RSV particles are added to a number of normal cells growing attached to a glass surface, the transformed cells are easily scored. They are not subject to contact inhibition and so do not stop growing after the glass surface is covered with cells. Instead, they continue to proliferate and pile up on top of each other to form discrete masses easily distinguishable from normal cells.

CANCER CELLS PRODUCED BY SINGLE INFECTION DO NOT PRODUCE PROGENY RSV PARTICLES

Most early experiments with RSV studied tumors induced by adding, on the average, several RSV particles to each cell. In these cases, it was found that most tumor cells produced RSV particles. RSV virus production and cell growth can go hand in hand without inhibiting each other. Conversely, the seemingly paradoxical situation was observed that, when cells were infected with a single RSV particle, none of the induced tumor cells released any virus (nonproducing cells). The infecting virus had seemingly disappeared without a trace (Figure 16–9). Yet the nonproductive tumor cells had cancerous properties identical to those cells yielding virus.

NONPRODUCING TUMOR CELLS PRODUCE RSV WHEN SUPERINFECTED WITH A RELATED VIRUS

The significance of this bizarre result is shown by experiments in which the nonproducing cells were superinfected with a closely related virus called RAV (Rous associated virus). Within 24 hours, all nonproducing cells began to produce RSV particles.

FIGURE 16–10 *An infection by a single RSV particle introduces RSV genetic information into a normal cell. The cell is transformed and the RNA genome is replicated each time the cell divides. No RSV particles are produced. If the helper virus RAV is added, both RSV and RAV particles are made. (Redrawn from H. Rubin, Sci. Am., June, 1964, pp. 46–52, with permission.)*

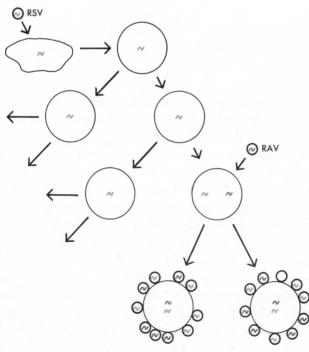

Simultaneously, they began to yield progeny RAV particles (Figure 16–10). Further experiments revealed that all preparations of RSV always contained RAV particles, in fact more RAV particles than RSV particles. It became clear that RSV particles are made only in cells simultaneously infected with a related helper virus.

RSV IS A DEFECTIVE VIRUS

Thus RSV is a defective virus, unable to multiply by itself. Now it appears that the defect of RSV lies in its inability to make a normal protective coat. This characteristic is demonstrated by experiments in which nonproducing cells are converted to RSV-producing cells by superinfection with either RAV or RIF, another closely related virus. RAV can be distinguished from RIF by the rates at which they are inactivated by specific antibodies. It is thus possible to ask whether the RSV particles made in the presence of RAV are different from RSV particles made in cells superinfected with RIF. The answer is very clearly *yes!* The outer membranes of RSV particles are always identical to the outer coat of the helper virus (Figure 16–11), which means that the proteins used to make the outer membrane are always coded for by the genome of the helper virus.

Thus all purified preparations of RSV are, in fact, mixtures of RSV and helper virus genomes, surrounded by outer membranes deriving their specificity from the helper virus. Thus it is very likely that we shall probably never obtain a pure preparation of RSV unless by chance there exists a cell in which the genome is not defective. Furthermore, it will be very difficult to study the biochemistry of cells infected only by RSV. Even if a low ratio of virus to cells is used for infection, at least half the infected cells will be infected by the helper virus.

Whether the fact that RSV is defective is related to its carcinogenic property is not yet clear. It is a tempting speculation, however, to relate the changed surface properties of the RSV cell to the fact that myxoviruses mature at the cell surface. The mere release of a myxovirus from a surface does not, however, convert a cell to a cancer cell, as shown by infecting cells with RAV or RIF. Both viruses permanently convert the host cell and all its descendents to RAV- (RIF-) producing cells without simultaneously making them cancer cells. Thus it is possible that the RSV gene(s) coding for the coat protein(s) produce(s) polypeptide chains unable to aggregate into a normal coat, yet able to move to the cell surface and upset the normal surface organization, thereby preventing contact inhibition.

A DNA PROVIRUS STAGE FOR RSV?

The defectiveness of RSV also poses the question as to the physical form of the RSV genome when it is in a nonproducing cell. Superficially, it seems easiest to believe that its RNA

FIGURE 16–11   *Conversion of a nonproductive RSV cell into virus-producing cells by the addition of helper viruses. When RIF is added, all the virus products have external membranes with specificity to RIF. If the helper is RAV, all the coats have the RAV specificity.*

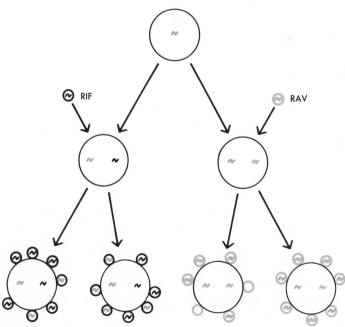

replicates like an RNA phage, using double-helical RNA molecules as intermediates. If this is the mechanism, then the nucleus of all nonproducing cells should contain large numbers of double-helical intermediates. A large number may be needed to ensure that random segregation during mitosis does not occasionally produce a cell lacking an RSV genome. Reversion to normality never occurs. Thus either the number of RSV genomes is large, or those present have a fixed arrangement in the cell so that they are regularly segregated at mitosis to both progeny cells.

Now data are being collected, however, that have suggested to some (but not all) scientists working with RSV that the RSV genome becomes part of one of the host chromosomes (a provirus stage), where it replicates as if it were a set of host genes. The evidence is of several sorts. One set of experiments shows that inhibitors of DNA synthesis prevent RSV from forming nonproducing cells. This can be interpreted to mean that, after entry of the RSV genome into the host nucleus, it is used as template to form a complementary DNA strand. Under this hypothesis, the DNA strand, most likely after subsequent formation of a complementary DNA strand, is inserted into a host chromosome. Supporting this interpretation is the claim that DNA, isolated from RSV-infected cells, contains a small region in which one of its chains is complementary in sequence to RSV-RNA. In contrast, no homology was seen with uninfected cells. If the provirus hypothesis is correct, it is possible that the integrated viral genome then produces progeny RSV-RNA molecules by the same mechanism as the host genes transcribe RNA.

The concept of a DNA provirus for an RNA virus is clearly a radical proposal. If true, it overturns the belief that flow of genetic information always goes in the direction, DNA to RNA, and never RNA to DNA. Much more evidence must be presented before it could gain general acceptance. On the other hand, if true, it offers an even greater variety of ways for cells to exchange genetic information. Considering the enormous complexity of biological systems, it would not be surprising if this device should be uniquely advantageous in some situations.

CAN THE ROUS SYSTEM BE GENERALIZED TO OTHER CANCERS?

When we discussed polyoma we argued that, although in nature it may almost never cause cancer, a study of how it multiplies might nonetheless provide fundamental insights into the normal control of cell growth and division. Polyoma's carcinogenic property, we postulated, is essentially limited to the laboratory, where immunological responses can be avoided. An essential aspect of our argument was that, since polyoma tumors contain a unique antigen, under normal circumstances they will always be destroyed by an immunological response. As yet, evidence for the Rous virus is incomplete. As long as a helper virus is present, Rous tumors are highly antigenic and are often destroyed by an immunological response against the mature virus particles located on the cell surface. This is why most tumors are easily transplanted to young chicks (which have a poor immunological system) and only poorly transplanted to adults. On the other hand, a tumor induced by a defective RSV particle in the absence of a helper does not produce virus particles and is much more resistant to an immunological counterattack by the host.

It is thus possible that many "spontaneous" tumors arising in adult animals are caused by defective virus particles like RSV. Examination of these tumors with the electron microscope is not likely to reveal any virus. For, if a helper virus is present, then an immunological response might be expected to destroy both the virus and the virus-producing cells. Thus the current evidence that most "spontaneous" tumors do not contain any virus particles cannot be used as evidence against induction by a tumor virus. Thus much current research is now being directed toward finding helper viruses that will induce human cancer cells to release cancer viruses.

STUDY OF CANCER AT THE MOLECULAR LEVEL

Until the recent work with polyoma and RSV, the search for chemical differences between normal and cancer cells resembled the search for a needle in a haystack. There may be more than a million different genes in a mammalian cell, of which we now can assign functions to perhaps 1000. Thus, the odds are that a biochemist studying cancer is looking for changes in molecules that have not been discovered. This situation is likely to prevail as long as research is dominated by the concept of somatic mutation.

The increasing use of viruses as carcinogenic agents has greatly changed the picture. Now we can ask how an essential aspect of virus multiplication can be misdirected toward the production of a cancer. Attention can be concentrated on the fact that some of the most potent tumor viruses contain only several genes. A primary goal is thus to assign functions to each of these genes during viral multiplication. In particular, we hope to find a polyoma-specific protein (enzyme?) that releases the normal control of DNA replication. In the case of RSV, we hope to learn the details of how the mature virus particles form at the cell surface, and, hopefully, how the faulty viral proteins made by its defective genome may upset contact inhibition. Naturally, we should not underestimate the difficulties ahead. These viruses multiply in cells that we are only beginning to study at the molecular level. Nonetheless, most important is the fact that at last the biochemistry of cancer can be approached in a straightforward, rational manner.

SUMMARY

A cancer cell is a cell that has lost the ability to control its growth and division. When it becomes a cancer cell, it divides both when and where it should not. Many cancer cells have lost a surface component which restricts the types of cell to which they may attach (loss of "selective stickiness"). Possibly connected with the disappearance of selective stickiness is a parallel loss of "contact inhibition" [inhibition of cell movement (and division?)].

At this time, tissue culture techniques are used in much cancer research. A single cancer cell can be isolated and the properties of all its progeny observed as they multiply in vitro. The technique allows a clear demonstration that the transformation of a normal cell to the cancerous state is a permanent change; all the cancerous properties are passed on to the descendants of a cancer cell. There are three main hypotheses about the origin of human cancers. One states that they are due to the accumulation of somatic mutations. An alternative hypothesis ascribes the occurrence of many cancers to viruses. Supporting this hypothesis has been the discovery of a variety of vertebrate viruses which transform normal cells into cancer cells. The third hypothesis is that the cancerous transformation is an example of irreversible differentiation.

Study of the biochemistry of the cancer cell often suffers from the fact that the original normal cell is not present for comparison. Systems are needed whereby addition of an external agent (carcinogen) will rapidly transform well-defined normal cells into cancer cells. Among the most useful carcinogenic agents known at present are several viruses. One is polyoma, a DNA virus which multiplies in mice; another is the Rous sarcoma virus, an RNA virus which causes solid tumors in chickens.

A polyoma virus particle, when it infects a susceptible cell, may either multiply lytically to produce new virus particles or transform the host cell into a cancer cell. No virus particles are synthesized by the transformed cells. Transformed cells, however, possess a specific antigen which may be present in virus-infected cells. This antigen is not a constituent of the polyoma external coat and so may be an enzyme, involved in the production of polyoma DNA. The crucial question not yet answered about the transformed cells is whether they contain the polyoma genome integrated as a provirus into a host chromosome.

Rous sarcoma virus (RSV) is a defective virus which rapidly transforms normal chicken cells into cancer cells without producing any virus particles. Nonproducing cancer cells can be converted into RSV-producing cells by superinfection with a related helper virus. At the same time as the RSV begins to appear on the surface of an infected cell, the helper virus particles also begin to be made on the cell surface. The function of the helper virus is to provide a protein necessary for the external coat of RSV. These RSV particles are, in fact, an RSV genome surrounded by a helper virus external coat. It is still unclear whether the cancer-causing property of RSV is connected with its defectiveness. Nonetheless, it is tempting to relate the conversion to the cancer state with the appearance of a defective coat protein which disturbs the cell membrane, thereby blocking contact inhibition.

REFERENCES

Huxley, J., *Biological Aspects of Cancer*, Harcourt, New York, 1958. A brief introduction to the cancer problem as seen by a distinguished zoologist.

Burnet, F. M., "Cancer: Biological Approach. I. Processes of Control," *Brit. Med. J.*, I, 779 (1957). A superb appraisal of the complexity of the cancer field with emphasis on the consequences of somatic mutation.

Harris, M., *Cell Culture and Somatic Variation*, Holt, New York, 1964. A very complete summary of how modern tissue culture research is at the heart of both embryological and cancer research.

Ciba Found. Symp., Carcinogensis: Mechanisms of Action, 1959. A series of papers containing speculations about how the various carcinogens—radiation, chemical, and viral—might act.

Burnet, F. M., *Principles of Animal Virology*, 2nd ed., Academic, New York, 1960. A survey of the reproduction of viruses in animal cells. Now going out of date in the molecular aspects—otherwise still very pertinent.

Gross, L., *Oncogenic Viruses*, Pergamon, New York, 1961. A very well documented survey of the various viruses which cause tumors.

"Basic Mechanisms in Animal Virus Biology," *Cold Spring Harbor Symp. Quant. Biol.*, 27 (1962). An excellent collection of articles, many of which deal with tumor viruses.

Dulbecco, R., "Transformation of Cells in vitro by Viruses," *Science*, 142, 932 (1963). A very clear presentation of current ideas about how viruses may cause cancers.

Rubin, H., "A Defective Cancer Virus," *Sci. Am.*, June, 1964, pp. 46–52. A discussion of how the discovery was made that the *Rous sarcoma* virus is defective.

GLOSSARY

A + T/G + C Ratio. An expression of the relative amount of adenine–thymine pairs to guanine–cytosine pairs in a molecule of DNA.

Acidic Amino Acids. Amino acids having a net negative charge at neutral pH.

Activating Enzyme (see *Amino Acyl Synthetase*)

Adaptor Molecules. Small RNA molecules (sRNA) that bind amino acids to their proper positions on an mRNA template during protein synthesis. Each is specific for both an amino acid and a template codon.

Allele. One of two or more alternate forms of a gene.

Allosteric Proteins. Proteins whose biological properties are changed by the binding of specific small molecules (allosteric effectors) at sites other than the active site.

Amino Acids. The building blocks of proteins. There are 20 common amino acids, each present as the L-stereoisomer. All amino acids have the same basic structure, but they differ in their side groups (R):

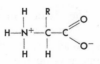

Amino Acid Sequence. The linear order of the amino acids in a peptide or protein.

Amino Acid Side Group(s) (see *Amino Acids*)

471

Amino Acyl Adenylate (AA ~ AMP). In protein synthesis, an activated compound which is an intermediate in the formation of a covalent bond between an amino acid and its sRNA adaptor.

Amino Acyl Synthetase. Any one of at least 20 different enzymes that catalyze (1) the reaction of a specific amino acid with ATP to form amino acyl-AMP (activated amino acids) and pyrophosphate, and (2) the transfer of the activated amino acid to sRNA forming amino acyl-sRNA and free AMP.

Amino Group. $-NH_2$, a chemical group, characteristically basic because of the addition of a proton to form $-NH_3{}^+$.

Amino Terminal. The end of a polypeptide chain that has a free α-amino group.

Angstrom (A). A unit of length convenient for describing atomic dimensions; equal to 10^{-8} cm.

Antigen. Any object which, upon injection into a vertebrate, is capable of stimulating the production of neutralizing antibodies.

Aromatic Amino Acids. Amino acids whose side chains include a derivative of a phenyl group. The aromatic amino acids found in protein are phenylalanine, tyrosine, and tryptophan.

Autoradiographs. When a photographic emulsion is placed in contact with radioactive material (e.g., thin sections of a cell), the radiation exposes the film, revealing details of the location and geometry of the radioactive components.

β-Galactosidase. An enzyme catalyzing the hydrolysis of lactose into glucose and galactose; in *E. coli*, the classic example of an inducible enzyme.

Backbone. The atoms in a polymer that are common to all its molecules (e.g., the sugars and phosphates in RNA).

Bacterial Viruses. Viruses that multiply in bacteria.

Bacteriophages (*Phages*) (see *Bacterial Viruses*)

Base Analogs. Purines and pyrimidines which differ slightly in structure from the normal nitrogenous bases. Some analogs (e.g., 5-bromouracil) may be incorporated into nucleic acids in place of the normal constituent.

Base-Pairing Rules. The requirement that adenine must always form a base pair with thymine (or uracil) and guanine with cytosine, in a nucleic acid double helix.

Basic Amino Acids. Amino acids having a net positive charge at neutral pH.

Breakage and Reunion. The classical model of crossing over by physical breakage and crossways reunion of completed chromatids during meiosis. This model has recently been shown to be applicable in at least one case on the molecular level—crossing over between phage-DNA molecules proceeds by breakage and reunion.

^{14}C. A radioactive carbon isotope emitting a weak β particle (electron). Its half-life is 5700 years.

Calorie. A measure of energy, defined as the amount of energy necessary to raise 1 cc of water 1°C.

Cancer. The name given to a group of diseases that are characterized by uncontrolled cellular growth.

Carboxyl Group. —C—OH. A chemical group, characteristically acidic, as a result of the dissociation of the hydroxyl H to

form C—O⁻.

—COOH ⇌ —COO⁻ + H⁺

Carboxyl Terminal. The end of a polypeptide chain which has a free α-carboxyl group.

Carcinogen. An agent that induces cancer.

Catalyst. A substance that can increase the rate of a chemical reaction without being consumed (e.g., enzymes catalyze biological reactions).

Cell. The fundamental unit of life; the smallest body capable of independent reproduction. Cells are always surrounded by a membrane.

Cell Differentiation. The process whereby descendants of a common parental cell achieve and maintain specialization of structure and function.

Cell-Free Extract. A fluid containing most of the soluble molecules of a cell, made by breaking open cells and getting rid of remaining whole cells.

Central Dogma. The basic relationship between DNA, RNA, and protein: DNA serves as a template for both its own duplication and the synthesis of RNA; and RNA, in turn, is the template in protein synthesis.

Chromatids. The two daughter strands of a duplicated chromosome which are still joined by a single centromere.

Clone. A group of cells all descended from a single common ancestor.

Coat Protein(s). The external structural protein(s) of a virus.

Codon. A sequence of three adjacent nucleotides that code for an amino acid (or chain termination?).

Colony. A group of contiguous cells, usually derived from a single ancestor, growing on a solid surface.

Complementary Base Sequences. Polynucleotide sequences that are related by the base-pairing rules.

Complementary Structures. Two structures, each of which defines the other; for instance, the two strands of a DNA helix:

$$
\begin{array}{c}
\text{A- - -T} \\
\text{G- - - C} \\
\text{T- - - A}
\end{array}
$$

Complementation Test. The introduction of two mutant chromosomes (or sections of chromosomes) into the same cell for the purpose of seeing whether their respective mutations occurred in the same gene.

Conditional Lethal Mutations. A class of mutants whose viability is dependent on growth conditions (e.g., temperature-sensitive lethals).

Constitutive Enzymes. Enzymes that are synthesized in fixed amounts, irrespective of the growth conditions.

Contact Inhibition. The cessation of cell movement (division?) which is often observed when freely growing cells from a multicellular organism come into physical contact with each other.

Coordinated Enzyme Synthesis. Enzymes whose rates of production are observed to vary together. (For example, in *E. coli* cells growing in the absence of β-galactosides, the addition of lactose to the medium causes the coordinated induction of β-galactosidase and β-galactoside permease.)

Copolymer. A polymeric molecule containing more than one kind of monomer unit.

Corepressors. Metabolites which, by their combination with repressors, specifically inhibit the formation of the enzyme(s) involved in their metabolism.

Coupled Reaction. A thermodynamically unfavorable reaction, which by association with a thermodynamically favorable reaction is driven in the direction of product formation.

Crossing Over. The process of exchange of genetic material between homologous chromosomes.

Dalton. A unit of weight equal to the weight of a single hydrogen atom.

Defective Virus. A virus that by itself is unable to reproduce itself when infecting its host, but which can grow in the presence of another virus.

Degenerate Codons. Two or more codons that code for the same amino acid.

Deletions. Loss of a section of the genetic material from a chromosome. The size of the deleted material can vary from a single nucleotide to sections containing a number of genes.

Denaturation. The loss of the native configuration of a macromolecule resulting, for instance, from heat treatment, extreme pH changes, chemical treatment, or other denaturing agents. It is usually accompanied by loss of biological activity.

Deoxynucleoside. The condensation product of a purine or pyrimidine with the five-carbon sugar, 2-deoxyribose.

Deoxyribonucleotide. A compound which consists of a purine or pyrimidine base bonded to the sugar, 2-deoxyribose, which in turn is bound to a phosphate group:

Diploid State. The chromosome state in which each type of chromosome except for the sex chromosomes is always represented twice (2N).

DNA (Deoxyribonucleic Acid). A polymer of deoxyribonucleotides. The genetic material of all cells.

DNA Polymerase. The enzyme that catalyzes the formation of DNA from deoxyribonucleoside triphosphates, using DNA as a template.

DNA–RNA Hybrid. A double helix which consists of one chain of DNA hydrogen bonded to a chain of RNA by means of complementary base pairs.

Electron Microscopy. A technique for visualizing material which uses beams of electrons instead of light rays and which permits greater magnification than that possible with an optical microscope. Resolutions of ~10 A are attainable with biological materials.

Electronegative Atom. An atom with a tendency to gain electrons.

End Product. A chemical compound which is the final product of a sequence of metabolic reactions.

Enzymes. Protein molecules capable of catalyzing chemical reactions.

Episome. A genetic element that can exist either free or as part of the normal cellular chromosome. Examples of episomes are the sex (F$^+$) factor and lysogenic phage DNA.

Feedback (End-Product) Inhibition. Inhibition of the enzymatic activity of the first enzyme in a metabolic pathway by the end product of that pathway.

Fertility Factor (F$^+$). An episome which determines the sex of a bacterium. The presence of this factor in the cell makes it a male. (Female cells are called F$^-$.)

Genetic Information. The information contained in a sequence of nucleotide bases in a DNA (or RNA) molecule.

Genetic Map. The arrangement of mutable sites on a chromosome as deduced from genetic recombination experiments.

Genotype. The genetic constitution of an organism (to be distinguished from its physical appearance or phenotype).

Group (Functional). Covalently bonded groups of atoms that behave as a unit in chemical reactions.

Group-Transfer Reactions. Reactions (excluding oxidations or reductions) in which molecules exchange functional groups.

Growth Curve. The change in the number of cells in a growing culture as a function of time.

Growth Factor. A specific substance which must be present in the growth medium to permit a cell to multiply.

^3H *(Tritium).* A radioactive isotope of hydrogen, a weak β emitter, with a half-life of 12.5 years.

Haploid State. The chromosome state in which each chromosome is present only once.

Heavy Isotopes. Forms of atoms containing greater than the common number of neutrons, and thus more dense than the commonly observed isotope (e.g., ^{15}N, ^{13}C).

Helix. A spiral structure with a repeating pattern described by two simultaneous operations—rotation and translation. It is the natural conformation of many regular biological polymers.

Helper Virus. A virus which, by its infection of a cell, is able to supply one or more functions that a defective virus lacks, thus enabling the latter to multiply.

Hereditary Disease. A pathological condition whose cause is a gene mutation and which can therefore be transferred from one generation to the next.

Hfr (High Frequency of Recombination). Strains of *E. coli* which show unusually high frequencies of recombination. In these cells the F factor is integrated into the bacterial chromosome, where it is thought to play some part in the transfer of the chromosome from Hfr to F⁻ cells. (See also *Fertility Factor.*)

High-Energy Bond. A bond that yields a large (at least 5 kcal/mole) decrease in free energy upon hydrolysis.

Homologous Chromosomes. Chromosomes that pair during meiosis, have the same morphology, and contain genes governing the same characteristics.

Host Cell. A cell whose metabolism is used for the growth and reproduction of a virus.

Hydrocarbon Side Groups. Amino acid side chains consisting of carbon and hydrogen only.

Hydrogen Bond. A weak attractive force between one electronegative atom and a hydrogen atom that is covalently linked to a second electronegative atom.

Hydrolysis. The breaking of a molecule into two or more smaller molecules by the addition of a water molecule:

$$H_2O + A-B \rightarrow H-A + HO-$$

Hydrophilic. Pertaining to molecules or groups that readily associate with H_2O.

Hydrophobic. Literally, water hater. Used to describe molecules or certain functional groups in molecules that are, at best, only poorly soluble in water.

Hydrophobic Bonding. The association of nonpolar groups with each other in aqueous solution, arising because of the tendency of water molecules to exclude nonpolar molecules.

Inducers. Molecules that cause the production of larger amounts of the enzymes involved in their uptake and metabolism, compared to the amounts found in cells growing in the absence of an inducer.

Inducible Enzymes. Enzymes whose rate of production can be increased by the presence of inducers in the cell.

Infectious Viral Nucleic Acid. Purified viral nucleic acid that can infect a host cell and cause the production of progeny viral particles.

Intergenic Suppression. Restoration of a lost function by a second mutation which is located within the same gene as the primary mutation.

Intermediary Metabolism. The chemical reactions in a cell that transform food molecules into molecules needed for the structure and growth of the cell.

Intragenic Suppression. Restoration of a lost function by a second mutation which is located within the same gene as the primary mutation.

In Vitro (*Latin:* in glass). Pertaining to experiments done in a cell-free system. Currently, the term is sometimes modified to include the growth of cells from multicellular organisms under tissue-culture conditions.

In Vitro Protein Synthesis. The incorporation of amino acids into polypeptide chains in a cell-free system.

In Vivo (*Latin:* in life). Pertaining to experiments done in a system such that the organism remains intact, either at the level of the cell (for bacteria) or at the level of the whole organism (for animals).

Label (*Radioactive*). A radioactive atom, introduced into a molecule to facilitate observation of its metabolic transformations.

Leaky Protein. A protein coded by a mutant gene which shows some residual activity.

Linked Genes. Genes which are located on the same chromosome and which therefore tend to be transmitted together.

Lysis. The bursting of a cell by the destruction of its cell membrane.

Lysogenic Bacterium. A bacterium that contains a prophage.

Lysogenic Viruses. Viruses that can become prophages.

Lytic Viruses. Viruses whose multiplication leads to lysis of the host cell.

Macromolecules. Molecules with molecular weights ranging from a few thousand to hundreds of millions.

Map Units. A number proportional to the frequency of recombination between two genes. One map unit corresponds to a recombination frequency of 1 per cent.

Messenger RNA (mRNA). RNA that serves as a template for protein synthesis.

Metabolic Pathway. A set of consecutive intracellular enzymatic reactions that converts one molecule to another.

Micron (μ). A unit of length convenient for describing cellular dimensions; it is equal to 10^{-4} cm or 10^4 A.

Missense Mutation. A mutation that changes a codon coding for one amino acid with a codon corresponding to another amino acid.

Mitotic Recombination. Crossing over between homologous chromosomes during mitosis, which leads to the segregation of heterozygous alleles.

Molecular Weight. The sum of the atomic weights of the constituent atoms in a molecule.

Monolayer. A layer of cells which is uniformly one cell thick.

Monomer. The basic subunit from which, by repetition of a single reaction, polymers are made. For example, amino acids (monomers) condense to yield polypeptides or proteins (polymers).

Mutable Sites. Sites along the chromosome at which mutations can occur. Genetic experiments tell us that each mutable site can exist in several alternative forms.

Mutagens. Physical or chemical agents, such as radiation, heat, or alkylating or deaminating agents, which raise the frequency of mutation greatly above the spontaneous background level.

Mutation. An inheritable change in a chromosome.

Nitrogenous Base. An aromatic N-containing molecule having basic properties (tendency to acquire an H atom). Important nitrogenous bases in cells are the purines and pyrimidines.

Nonsense Mutation. A mutation that converts a codon which specifies some amino acid into one which does not specify any amino acid (a nonsense codon). Nonsense codons may have the function of terminating the polypeptide chain.

Nucleic Acid. A nucleotide polymer. (See also *DNA* and *RNA*.)

Operator. A chromosomal region capable of interacting directly (or indirectly?) with a specific repressor, thereby controlling the functioning of an adjacent operon.

Operon. A genetic unit consisting of adjacent genes that function coordinately under the joint control of an operator and a repressor.

32P. A radioactive isotope of phosphorus which emits strong β particles and has a half-life of 14 days.

Pairing. The sideways attachment of two homologous chromosomes prior to crossing over.

Peptide Bond. A covalent bond between two amino acids in which the α-amino group of one amino acid is bonded to the α-carboxyl group of the other with the elimination of H_2O:

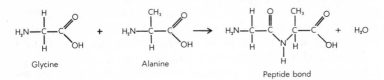

Phage (see *Bacteriophage*)

Phage Cross. Multiple infection of a single bacterium by bacteriophages that differ at one or more genetic sites. This leads to the production of recombinant progeny phage, which carry genes derived from both parental phage types.

Phenotype. The observable properties of an organism; produced by the genotype in cooperation with the environment.

Phosphodiester. Any molecule that contains the linkage

$$R-O-\overset{\overset{\displaystyle O}{\|}}{\underset{\underset{\displaystyle O^-}{|}}{P}}-O-R'$$

where R and R' are carbon-containing groups (e.g., nucleosides), O is oxygen, and P is phosphorus.

Plaques. Round clear areas in a confluent cell sheet which result from the killing or lysis of contiguous cells by several cycles of virus growth.

Polymer. A regular, covalently bonded arrangement of basic subunits (monomers) which is produced by repetitive application of one or a few chemical reactions.

Polynucleotide. A linear sequence of nucleotides in which the 3' position of the sugar of one nucleotide is linked through a phosphate group to the 5' position on the sugar of the adjacent nucleotide.

Polypeptide. A polymer of amino acids linked together by peptide bonds.

Primary Protein Structure. The number of polypeptide chains in a protein, the sequence of amino acids within them, and the location of inter- and intrachain disulfide bridges.

Prophage. The provirus (see below) stage of a lysogenic phage.

Provirus. The state of a virus in which it is integrated into a host cell chromosome and is thus transmitted from one cell generation to another.

Radioactive Isotope. An isotope with an unstable nucleus that stabilizes itself by emitting ionizing radiation.

Reading Mistake. The incorrect placement of an amino acid residue in a polypeptide chain during protein synthesis.

Recombination. The appearance in the offspring of traits that were not found together in either of the parents.

Regulatory Genes. Genes whose primary function is to control the rate of synthesis of the products of other genes.

Renaturation. The return of a protein or nucleic acid from a denatured state to its "native" configuration.

Repressible Enzymes. Enzymes whose rates of production are decreased when the intracellular concentration of certain metabolites increases.

Repressor. The product of a regulatory gene, now thought to be a protein and to be capable of combining both with an inducer (or corepressor) and with an operator (or its mRNA product).

Reverse (Back) Mutation. A heritable change in a mutant gene which restores the original nucleotide sequence.

Ribonucleotide. A compound that consists of a purine or pyrimidine base bonded to ribose, which in turn is esterified with a phosphate group.

Ribosomal Proteins. A group of proteins that bind to rRNA by noncovalent bonds to give the ribosome its three-dimensional structure.

Ribosomal RNA (rRNA). The nucleic acid component of ribosomes, making up two-thirds of the mass of the ribosome in *E. coli,* and about one-half the mass of mammalian ribosomes. Ribosomal RNA accounts for approximately 80 per cent of the RNA content of the bacterial cell.

Ribosomes. Small cellular particles ($\sim$200 A in diameter) made up of rRNA and protein. Ribosomes are the site of protein synthesis.

RNA (Ribonucleic Acid). A polymer of ribonucleotides.

RNA Polymerase. An enzyme that catalyzes the formation of

RNA from ribonucleoside triphosphates, using DNA as a template.

^{35}S. A radioactive isotope of sulfur, a β emitter with a half-life of 87 days, very useful in studying protein systems, since it can be incorporated into proteins via the sulfur-containing amino acids.

Soluble RNA (sRNA). Any of at least 20 structurally similar species of RNA, all of which have a MW $\sim$ 25,000. Each species of sRNA molecule is able to combine covalently with a specific amino acid and to hydrogen bond with at least one mRNA nucleotide triplet. Also called *adaptor RNA* or *transfer RNA.*

Somatic Mutation. A mutation occurring in any cell that is not destined to become a germ cell.

Spontaneous Mutations. Mutations for which there is no "observable" cause.

Stereoisomers. Molecules that have the same structural formula but different spatial arrangement of dissimilar groups bonded to a common atom. Many of the physical and chemical properties of stereoisomers are the same, but there are differences in their crystal structures, in the direction in which they rotate polarized light, and, very importantly for biological systems, in their ability to be used in an enzyme-catalyzed reaction.

Steric (Stereochemical). Pertaining to the arrangement in space of the atoms in molecules.

Suppressor Gene. A gene that can reverse the phenotypic effect of a variety of mutations in other genes.

Suppressor Mutation. A mutation that totally or partially restores a function lost by a primary mutation which is located at a genetic site different from the primary mutation.

Svedberg. The unit of sedimentation (S). S is proportional to the rate of sedimentation of a molecule in a given centrifugal field and is thus related to the molecular weight and shape of the molecule.

Synthetic Polyribonucleotides. RNA made in vitro without a nucleic acid template either by enzymatic or chemical synthesis.

Tautomeric Shifts. Reversible changes in the localization of a proton in a molecule, which alter the chemical properties of the molecule.

Template. The macromolecular mold for the synthesis of another macromolecule.

Template RNA (see Messenger RNA)

Tertiary Structure (of a Protein). The three-dimensional folding of the polypeptide chain(s) which characterizes a protein in its native state.

Three-Factor Crosses. Mating experiments involving three distinguishable genetic markers (e.g., $a^+b^+c^+ \times abc$).

Tissue Culture. The growth and maintenance of cells from

higher organisms in vitro, outside the tissue of which they are normally a part.

Transcription. A process involving base pairing, whereby the genetic information contained in DNA is used to order a complementary sequence of bases in an RNA chain.

Transduction. The transfer of bacterial genes from one bacterium to another by a bacteriophage particle.

Transferases. Enzymes that catalyze the exchange of functional groups.

Transfer RNA (See *Soluble RNA*)

Transformation. The genetic modification induced by the incorporation into a cell of DNA purified from cells or viruses.

Translation. The process whereby the genetic information present in an mRNA molecule directs the order of the specific amino acids during protein synthesis.

Tumor Virus. A virus that induces the formation of a tumor.

Turnover Number (of an Enzyme). The number of molecules of a substrate transformed per minute by a single enzyme molecule, when the enzyme is working at its maximum rate.

Two-Factor Cross. A genetic recombination experiment involving two markers (e.g., $a^+b^+ \times ab$).

Ultracentrifuge. A high-speed centrifuge that can attain speeds up to 60,000 rpm and centrifugal fields up to 500,000 times gravity and thus is capable of rapidly sedimenting macromolecules.

van der Waals Force. A weak attractive force, acting over only very short distances, resulting from attraction of induced dipoles.

Viral-Specific Enzyme. An enzyme produced in the host cell after viral infection from viral genetic information.

Viruses. Infectious disease-causing agents, smaller than bacteria, which always require intact host cells for replication and which contain either DNA or RNA as their genetic component.

Weak Interactions (also called Secondary Bonds). The forces between atoms that are less strong than the forces involved in a covalent bond (includes ionic bonds, hydrogen bonds, and van der Waals forces).

Wild-Type Gene. The form of gene (allele) commonly found in nature.

X-Ray Crystallography. The use of diffraction patterns produced by x-ray scattering from crystals to determine the 3-D structure of molecules.

Zygote. The result of the union of the male and female sex cells. The zygote therefore has a diploid number of chromosomes.

INDEX

A + T/G + C ratios, 265
Acetyl-CoA, fatty acid biosynthesis
    and, 96, 148
    formation from pyruvate, 53, 54
    high-energy bond in, 148
    as important metabolic intermedi-
        ate, 95
Activated state, 143, 144
Activating enzyme (see Amino-acyl
    synthetases)
Activation, of amino acids for pro-
    tein biosynthesis, 154
    group-transfer reactions and, 151,
        152
    of nucleotide monophosphates for
        nucleic acid biosynthesis,
        155, 156
Activation energy, 143, 144
    effect of enzymes on, 145
Adaptor-RNA (see Soluble-RNA)
Adenosine diphospate (ADP), as
    high-energy compound,
    147, 151
    principal phosphate group accep-
        tor, 49, 50, 58
Adenosine triphosphate (ATP), in
    amino acid activation for
    protein synthesis, 154,
    322, 323

donor of high-energy phosphate
    groups, 49
energy donor in biosynthetic re-
    actions, 150–154
generation by Krebs cycle, 55
generation during photosynthesis,
    58
in group-transfer reactions, 152,
    153
Alleles, 20
Allosteric proteins, 411, 412
Alpha-helix (α-helix), atomic di-
    mensions, 129
    disruption by proline and disulfide
        bridges, 175
    and secondary protein structure,
        64
Amino acid replacements, in human
    hemoglobin mutants, 245
    in TMV protein, 377
    in tryptophan synthetase mutants
        of E. coli, 248
Amino acids, activation for protein
    biosynthesis, 154, 322–324
    attachment to specific sRNA
        molecules, 316–318
    formulas, 88
    in vitro incorporation into pro-
        tein, 365, 367

483

sequences in proteins, genetic
control of, 244–246
stereoisomeric configurations, 123
Amino-acyl adenylates, as high-
energy compounds, 147
as intermediates in protein
biosynthesis, 154
Amino-acyl sRNA, amino acid
activation and, 322–
324
diagrammatic structure, 318, 319
Amino-acyl synthetases, 154, 316,
317, 322–324
Antibodies, 422
denaturation and renaturation,
427
specificity of, 426–429
structure, 425, 426, 429
Antibody biosynthesis, as defense
mechanism, 422–424, 427
model system for cell differentiation, 422–424
plasma cell site of, 429–433
Antibody formation, clonal selection
theory of, 434–436
instructive theories of, 427, 428
selective theories of, 428
Antigen, 424
absence from antibody-producing
cells, 433, 434
diagrammatic view, 425
effect of repeated injections of,
433, 434
stimulation of antibody production, 423, 429, 430
tumor-specific, 455, 456, 458
Arginine biosynthesis, in E. coli,
237, 238

Backbones, of biologically important
polymers, 90
Bacteria, advantages, for genetic
research, 194
colony formation by, 75, 76
haploid nature, 8
Bacteriophage λ, circular DNA
from, 277, 278
crossing over during multiplication, 226
diagram of structure, 202

insertion of DNA into host cell
chromosome, 206
as lysogenic phage, 204–207
Bacteriophage φx174, life cycle, 355,
356
single-stranded circular DNA
from, 277
Bacteriophage R17, diagram of
structure, 202
life cycle, 355–358
subunit structure, 343
Bacteriophage T2, chromosome,
autoradiograph, 276
demonstration of DNA as genetic
material of, 259–260
DNA, electron micrograph, 256
electron micrograph, 345
life cycle, 352
plaque morphology mutants of,
221, 224
structure, 202, 345
unusual components of, in DNA,
352–354
Bacteriophage T4, as complex virus,
360, 361
crossing over during multiplication, 226
fine-structure genetic analysis of,
231–234
genetic analysis of, 193
genetic map, 225
protein coat components, genetic
control of, 243
structure, 202, 345
unusual components of, in DNA,
352–354
Bacteriophage T6, structure, 202,
345
unusual components of, in DNA,
352–354
Bacteriophages, conditional lethal
mutations in, 222
of E. coli, 202, 203
mutations affecting plaque morphology, 220, 221
plaque formation by, 203, 204
transduction by, 217, 218
Base analogs, as mutagens, 289, 290
Base pairs, in DNA double helix,
264, 288

β-Configuration, of polypeptide
    chains, 174
β-Galactosidase, hydrolytic action on
    lactose, 392
    as inducible enzyme, 393, 394,
        396–399
    levels, in E. coli, 391, 393
    mRNA, 405, 406
Biosynthesis of small molecules, ser-
    ine and uridine-5′-phosphate
    as examples, 161–164
Biosynthetic pathways, in E. coli,
    96, 97
Breakage and reunion, as mecha-
    nism of genetic recombina-
    tion, 281–285
5-Bromouracil, as mutagen, 291, 292

Cancer, 442
    and control of cell division, 442–
        444
    as hereditary change, 448, 449
    induction, by radiation and
        chemicals, 447, 448
    by viruses, 449–468
    as loss of specific cellular affinities,
        446
    somatic mutations and, 449
Carcinogens, 447
Cell differentiation, 416, 417
    control of gene action in, 418–
        421
    embryonic inducers and, 422
    irreversibility of, 417
    model system for study of, 421,
        422
Cell theory, 2
    universal applicability, 8
Cells, as fundamental units of life, 2
    lower size limit for, 357–359
    mammalian and E. coli, DNA
        content of, 415
Central dogma, 297, 298, 315
Centromere, 5
Chain growth, direction, in poly-
    peptide synthesis, 333,
    335–337
    in RNA biosynthesis, 311, 312
    of polypeptides, start and stop
        signals and, 376–379

Chlorophyll, biosynthesis of por-
    phyrin ring, 166, 167
    role in photosynthesis, 58
    structure, 165
Chloroplasts, as plant cell con-
    stituents, 4
    role in photosynthesis, 58
Chromatids, 6
    behavior during meiosis, 21, 188
Chromosomes, 4
    bacterial, circularity of, 209, 215
    behavior, during meiosis, 7–9, 188
    during mitosis, 6
    constancy of DNA content of,
        259
    crossing over and, 21, 187, 188
    of E. coli, 77–79, 209–215, 274,
        277, 278
    location of genes on, 210–214,
        216
    genes as parts of, 18
    of higher organisms, electron
        microscopy, 186
    of leopard frog, light micro-
        graph, 5
    location of gene position, by
        genetic crosses, 186,
        189
    mapping, 189–191, 193
    mutant, complementation of,
        236, 237
    recombination, 187, 188
    sex, 18, 19, 22, 23
    sex determination and, 18
    single DNA molecules as, 276,
        277
    synapsis of, 21
    of viruses, 198, 199
Chymotrypsinogen, amino acid
    sequence of, 170, 171
Clonal selection, theory of, and an-
    tibody biosynthesis, 434–436
Coat protein, of viruses, 343, 344
Codons, 321, 324, 333, 335, 337
    changes in, and amino acid re-
        placements, 376, 377
    determination of nucleotide
        sequences in, 369–373
    misreading, and suppressor genes,
        381, 383

64 possible, 367
tentative assignment of nucleotide order in, 374
Coenzymes, 42
relation to vitamins, 59
Colinearity, of gene and its polypeptide product, 244–247
Complementary structures, in
antigen-antibody complexes,
114, 116
in DNA structure and replication,
262, 266, 267
and weak binding forces, 119
Complementation test, 235–237,
240
revealing adjacent genes with related functions, 242
Constitutive enzyme synthesis, 395,
401, 407, 408
Contact inhibition, 444–446, 453,
462
Coordinated enzyme synthesis, 399
Copy choice, as mechanism of genetic recombination, 281–
285
Corepressors, and regulation of protein synthesis, 393, 397, 398,
404
Coupled reactions, free-energy
changes in, 150, 151
oxidation-reduction, 54, 56
oxidative phosphorylation as, 56,
57
Covalent bonds, definition and
characteristics, 103
energy and formation, 106
free-energy change in formation,
109
Crossing over, 21
and DNA replication, 284, 285
within gene, 231–234
molecular mechanisms of, 281–
285
during virus multiplication, 226
Cysteine residues, in formation of
disulfide bonds, 170–174

Degeneracy, of genetic code, 324,
373, 374
Degradative pathway, 45, 46, 98

Deletion mutants, in rII region of
bacteriophage T4, 235
Denaturation, of macromolecules,
60, 134
thermal, of DNA, 266
Density gradient centrifugation, 273
3′-Deoxyadenosine, and direction of
RNA chain growth, 311
Deoxyribonuclease, 257
Deoxyribonucleic acid (DNA),
A + T/G + C ratios in
diverse organisms, 265
amount, constancy in chromosomes, 259
in E. coli, 99
in mammalian cells, 415
of bacteriophage T2, electron
micrograph, 256
glucose in, 353, 354
base pairing in structure of, 264,
288
circular molecules of, as chromosomes, 277–279
density-gradient sedimentation of,
273
double-helical structure, 66, 131,
132, 261, 262
enzymatic synthesis of, 269–271
formation of hybrid molecules of,
266
genetic role, proof of, 65, 218–
220, 257–261
hydrogen bonding in, 131–133,
264
model of 3-D structure, 262
mutagenic effect of nitrous acid,
290
nucleotide building blocks of, 89
opposite directions of polynucleotide chains in, 263, 264
replication, 66, 67, 266–270,
351–356
accuracy of, 268
of circular forms, 280
strand separation and, 273, 274
single-stranded, 273, 275, 276
replication of, 273, 275, 276,
355
strand separation in, experimental
evidence for, 271–273

structural stability, 131–133
template for RNA synthesis, 299, 302, 305–313, 329
thermal denaturation, 266
transformation by, 218, 219, 257, 258
Watson-Crick structure, 66
x-ray diffraction by, 263
Diphosphopyridine nucleotide (DPN; *see* Nicotinamide adenine dinucleotide)
Diploid state, 8
and sexual cycle, 10
Disulfide bonds, in antibody structure, 425
arrangement of, in chymotrypsinogen, 173
behavior during protein denaturation and renaturation, 176, 177
structural feature in proteins, 173
DNA biosynthesis, alterations in T2-infected cells, 352–354
deoxynucleoside triphosphates as precursors, 155
DNA polymerase, 269, 270
and single-stranded DNA virus replication, 355
DNA-RNA hybrids, 307–310
in demonstration of DNA template for sRNA and rRNA synthesis, 329
for determining which DNA strand is copied, 309, 310
Dominant traits, 12, 15, 16
Drosophila melanogaster,
advantages in use of, 20
eye color of, as multigenic character, 24
genetic map, 192
inheritance of sex-linked gene in, 22, 23
mutant genes of, 24, 25
salivary gland chromosomes, "puffing" and mRNA synthesis, in 419–421
sex determination in, 19

Embden-Meyerhof pathway of glycolysis, 45–48

End products, effect on enzyme activity, 409–412
effect on enzyme synthesis, 393
Enol phosphates, as high-energy compounds, 147
Enzymatic activity, unique amino acid sequences and, 251, 252
Enzyme-substrate complex, formation, 52
weak secondary bonds and, 126
Enzymes, and activation energy of a chemical reaction, 145
crystalline proteins as, 33
effect on position of chemical equilibria, 145
inducible, 393–396
repressible, 393, 396–399
specificity of, 50, 51
synthesis, genetic control of, 237, 239
Episomes, definition, 209
F factor and lysogenic phage chromosomes as, 209
Equilibrium constant, 107, 144
and free-energy change, 108, 109
Escherichia coli, approximate chemical composition, 85
"average cell," properties, 74, 80
bacteriophage resistance in, 195, 196
bacteriophages infecting, 202, 203
chromosomes, 77–79
growing point in, 274
circularity of chromosome, 209, 215, 274
DNA of, 75, 83–85, 99
electron microscopy, 75, 81
extracts, and in vitro protein synthesis, 363–365
generation time, 73
genetic map, 210–214, 216
growth curve, 77
growth-factor requirements, 195
inducible β-galactosidase synthesis in, 393, 394, 397–400
insertion of chromosome of phage λ into chromosome of, 206
main metabolic pathways, 96, 97
mutants with specific growth factor requirements, 196

488

pathway of arginine biosynthesis in, 237, 238
ribosomes, structure, 326
sexual cycle in, 207–209
sexuality, demonstration, 197, 198
synchronized growth of, 77, 78
tryptophan biosynthesis in, 246
tryptophan synthetase, 245
mutants of, 244–252
Evolution, theory of, 1, 2
hereditary variation as basis of, 26
Exponential (logarithmic) growth, of bacteria, 77, 78

F₁ generation, 12, 16, 17
Feedback inhibition, allosteric proteins and, 411, 412
and regulation of protein function, 408–412
Fermentation, 44, 45, 58
cell-free extracts in study of, 45
phosphorylated intermediates in, 48
Fertility factor (F factor), cause of sexuality in E. coli, 207–209
Fertilization, 8
First law of thermodynamics, 106
Flavin adenine dinucleotide (FAD), as hydrogen-transfer coenzyme, 45
Flavin mononucleotide (FMN), as coenzyme, 43
Free energy, definition, 107
and reactions at equilibrium, 107, 108
variation during chemical reaction, 143
Free-energy change, and equilibrium constant, 108, 109
metabolic pathways and, 145, 146
Free rotation, about single bonds, 104

Galactose, 391, 392
Gene-enzyme relationship, 28, 237, 238
Genes, "average," number of nu-

cleotide pairs in, 279–281, 294
chromosomal location, 25
control of amino acid sequences in proteins by, 244–252
of E. coli, arrangement on chromosome, 210–214, 216
fine-structure analysis of, 231–234
historical definition, 13
inheritance of sex-linked, in Drosophila, 22, 23
linked, 20
mutant, 20
in D. melanogaster, 24, 25
regulatory, 395, 396
with related functions, adjacent location of, 241–243
self-duplication, 28
suppressor, and code-reading mistakes, 378–381, 383, 385
effect on repressor synthesis, 395
mechanism of action, 380, 383, 385
wild-type, 20
Genetic code, alteration by chemical mutagens, 289–291
degeneracy of, 373, 374
misreading of, and suppressor genes, 378–381, 383, 385
and nucleotide base sequence, 285, 371–374
reading of, 291–294
universality, 386, 387
Genetic crosses, 12, 20, 186, 187, 189–193
Genetic fine structure, of rII region of phage T4, 231–234
reflecting base-pair arrangement, 286
Genetic map, 191
of D. melanogaster, 192
of E. coli, 216
of phage T4, 225
Genetic recombination, in crosses with genetically distinct phage particles, 222–224
and crossing over during meiosis, 187, 188

within gene, in rII region of bacteriophage T4, 231–234
mechanisms of, 281–285
and sexuality in bacteria, 197, 198
and transduction, 217, 218
and transformation, 218, 219
Genotype, 14, 17
Glucose, breakdown, 43–47
as energy source, 142
importance in intermediary metabolism, 94–97
Glycogen, biosynthesis, 168, 169
as storage form of glucose, 96, 97
structural organization, 87, 90
Glycolysis, 45
Group activation, 152
Group-transfer reactions, and activation, 151, 152
Growth curve, 77, 78
Growth factors, 195
Guanidinium phosphates, as high-energy compounds, 147
Guanosine triphosphate (GTP), formation, 152
in peptide-bond formation, 337

Haploid state 8, 10
Helper virus, in RSV infection, 463, 464
Heme, as prosthetic group, 174
Hemoglobin, human, amino acid substitutions in, 245
mutations affecting structure of, 240, 244, 375, 376
subunit structure, 134, 135, 137
Hereditary disease, amino acid metabolism and, 28
sickle-cell anemia, 240
Heredity, chromosomal theory, 11, 16
Heterozygotes, and gene-enzyme relationship, 241
Heterozygous gene pair, 14
High-energy bonds, and free energies of hydrolysis, 146, 147
important classes of, 147
requirement for, in biosynthetic reactions, 148, 149
High frequency of recombination

(Hfr) bacteria, 208, 209
Histidine biosynthesis, adjacent grouping of genes controlling, 243
pathway, 239
regulation, 393, 394, 396–399
Histones, protein component of chromosomes, 185
Homozygous gene pair, 14, 25
"Hot spots," 234
Hybridization, of DNA molecules, 266
of DNA and RNA molecules, 307–310, 329
Hydrocarbons, aliphatic, 34
aromatic, 34
Hydrogen bonds, 103, 115–118
approximate lengths, 116
determining specificity of base pairing in DNA, 288
and double-helical structure of DNA, 131–133
formation by water molecules, 119–121
and solubility in aqueous medium, 122
strength of, 109
Hydrolytic reactions, 93
Hydrophobic bonding, 124, 125

Immunological tolerance, 436
"Inborn errors of metabolism," 29
Independent assortment, 16
Independent segregation, 12–14
Inducers, embryonic, 422
and regulation of protein synthesis, 393, 396–399, 404
Information, genetic, 10, 33, 99, 255, 342
and ordering of amino acid sequences in proteins 244
pathway for transfer, 297, 298
Insulin, beef, amino acid sequence of, 168, 170
Intergenic suppression, 379
Intermediary metabolism, 38
in E. coli, 94–97
Intragenic suppression, 379
"In vitro protein synthesis," experi-

mental details, 364–367
Ionic bonds, 103
  relation to hydrogen bonds, 118, 119
  strength of, 109

Krebs cycle, 53, 55

Lactose, and β-galactosidase induction, 391, 393
Linkage groups, 21, 25
Lipids, structural organization, 82, 83
Lymphocytes, 430
Lysis, during phage multiplication, 203
Lysogenic bacteria, 204–206
Lysogenic bacterial viruses, 204–206
  analogy of polyoma virus to, 454
  life cycle, 205
Lytic viruses, 205, 206

Macromolecules, biological, structural organization, 87, 90
  molecular weights, by ultracentrifugation, 61
  structure of, by x-ray crystallography, 62–64
Magnesium, and mRNA binding to ribosomes, 326
  and ribosome structure, 326
  in vitro coding mistakes and, 378
Meiosis, 7–9
  gene-exchange during, 21
Membrane, as cell constituent, 2, 3
  of E. coli, appearance by electron microscopy, 81, 82
  phospholipids as constituents of, 82
Mendel's laws, 11–14
Messenger-RNA (mRNA), amount, and enzyme levels, 394
  β-galactosidase, 405, 406
  differential reading of a single molecule, 403, 404
  direction of reading, 331, 332
  metabolic stability, 404–406
  ribosome attachment to, 330, 331

sizes, 330
  synthesis on insect salivary gland chromosomes, 419–421
  template for protein synthesis, 326, 327, 330–336
Metabolic pathways, branch points in, 95
  degradative, 98
  free-energy changes and, 145, 146
  major, of E. coli, 96, 97
Mitochondria, electron micrograph, 300
  role of DNA in, 298
  sites of oxidative phosphorylation, 57
Mitosis, 5, 6
Mitotic recombination, 448
Monolayer, 444, 445
Mutable sites, 247–251
Mutagens, for increasing spontaneous mutation rate, 195, 196
  mechanism of action, 289–291
Mutation rate, spontaneous, 289
Mutations, 26
  addition and deletion, and genetic code, 291–294
  affecting plaque morphology in bacteriophage, 220–222
  classes, 287
  conditional lethal, in bacteriophage, 222
  deletion, within rII region of bacteriophage T4, 235
  in E. coli, bacteriophage resistance as, 195
  growth-factor requirements as, 195
  tryptophan synthetase, 244–252
  induction by x rays, 28
  insertion and deletion, effect on code reading, 380, 385
  location in same gene, by complementation test, 235–237
  missense, 374–376, 381, 382
  nonsense, 374, 375
  "reverse," in E. coli tryptophan synthetase, 251, 252

single deletion, effect on reading genetic message, 380, 385
somatic, and cancer, 449
suppressor, effect on repressor synthesis, 395
and misreading of genetic code, 378–381, 383, 385
Myoglobin, 3-D structure, 172
Myxovirus, life cycle, 461
RSV as, 459, 460

Nicotinamide adenine dinucleotide (NAD), as hydrogen-transfer coenzyme, 44
Nonpolar molecules, 111
Nucleolus, 3, 6
Nucleus, 2–4
site of RNA synthesis, 299

Operator, controlling β-galactosidase synthesis, 399–402
Operon, controlling β-galactosidase synthesis, 398–400
definition, 399
function, control of, 399–401
Oxidation-reduction reactions, coupled, in respiratory chain, 54, 56
role of coenzymes in, 42, 43
Oxidative phosphorylation, 56

Paper chromatography, 62
Peptide bond, hydrolytic breakdown, 92
partial double-bond character, 104, 105
planar shape, 104
as structural feature of proteins, 87, 90
Peptide bond formation, enzymes required for, 337
free-energy change during, 149, 150
on ribosomes, 324, 325, 333, 335–338
Phages (see Bacteriophages)
Phenotype, 14, 15, 17
Phosphate esters, in energy storage, 48

Photosynthesis, generation of ATP during, 58
over-all chemical reaction, 39
Phytol, chlorophyll constituent, 165
Plaques, formation, mutations affecting, 220–224
phage multiplication and, 203, 204
from polyoma-infected cells, 452, 453
Plasma cell, antibody production in, 429–433
developmental stages, 429–431
electron micrograph, 433
Polar molecules, 111
Polynucleotide phosphorylase, in synthesis of synthetic polyribonucleotides, 368, 369
Polyoma tumors, tumor-specific antigens of, 455, 456
Polyoma virus, absence from transformed cells, 453–455
circular DNA of, 277
DNA, electron micrograph, 452
integration into host chromosome, 455
electron micrograph, 451
life cycle, 451, 452
metabolism of infected cells, 456–458
physical properties, 450–452
as simplest known animal virus, 360, 450
Polypeptide chains, α- helical folding of, 129
addition of amino acids to, 154
β-configuration, 174
Polyphenylalanine, poly U directed synthesis, 369
Polyribonucleotides, synthesis by polynucleotide phosphorylase, 368, 369
synthetic, and genetic code, 369–371
Polyribosomes, electron micrograph, 334
sites of protein synthesis, 301, 332–334
Polysaccharides, structural organiza-

tion, 87, 90, 93
Polyuradylic acid (Poly U), coding
for polyphenylalanine, 369
Porphyrin biosynthesis, 166, 167
Primary structure of proteins, 173,
174
Prophage, relation to host cell
chromosome, 204–207
Proteins, chemical objections to self-
duplication of, 180–182
constitutive, 395
structure, primary, 173, 174
secondary, 174, 175
subunit, 134, 135
tertiary, 175, 176
synthesis of, template requirement in, 178
viral-specific, 350, 355
of viruses, demonstration of nongenetic role of, 259–261
Provirus, in polyoma-transformed
cells, 453–455, 457, 458
in RSV infection, 465, 466
Purines, bases, nucleic acid constituents, 90–92
biosynthesis, initial steps, 161,
162, 164
formula, 34
Pyrimidines, bases, nucleic acid constituents, 90–92
biosynthesis of, uridine-5′-phos-
phate as example, 161–164
formula, 35
Pyrophosphatase, importance for
biosynthetic reactions,
156, 157
Pyrophosphate, as high-energy compound, 147, 156
hydrolysis of, as biosynthetic
driving force, 156, 157

Recessive traits, 12, 14
and gene-enzyme relationship,
241
Renaturation, nucleic acids, 266
of protein after urea denaturation,
177

Replicative form (RF), 355
in φx174 infection, 355, 356
of phage M13, electron micrograph, 357
Repressors, and regulation of
enzyme synthesis, 395–
400, 402, 407
regulation of synthesis of, 408
Resistance inducing factor (RIF),
helper virus in RSV infection, 464, 465
Respiration, over-all chemical reaction, 39
Respiratory chain enzymes, 54, 56
Ribonuclease, lack of effect on transforming principle, 257, 258
Ribonucleic acid (RNA), base
composition of enzymati-
cally synthesized, 307
base composition of, from various
sources, 302
base ratios, noncomplementarity
of, 309, 310
chemical formula of chain segment, 304
double-stranded, as viral replicative form, 356, 357
enzymatic synthesis, fidelity of
DNA-template copying, 307
movement from nucleus to cytoplasm, 299
relation of cellular amount and
protein synthesis, 299
ribonucleotide building blocks of,
303
role in protein synthesis, 338
structural organization, 87, 302
synthesis on DNA template, 302,
305–313, 329
template in protein synthesis,
297, 326, 327, 330–336
viral, as mRNA in protein synthesis, 366
as viral genetic material, 345–
348, 355–357
of viruses, replication, 355–357
Ribosomal-RNA (rRNA), 325
function, 328

lack of genetic role, 325
size classes, 327
synthesis on DNA template, 329
Ribosomes, association with mRNA, 326, 327, 330–332
E. coli, structure, 326
and protein biosynthesis, 324–327, 330–336
structural changes in, and codon misreadings, 385
structural proteins, 392
Rickettsiae, 201, 359
RNA biosynthesis, direction of chain growth, 311, 312
ribonucleoside triphosphates as precursors, 155, 308
starting points, 312, 313
RNA polymerase, 306, 307, 311–313
of host cell, in T2 infection, 353
RNA synthetase, and viral RNA replication, 355–357
Rous associated virus (RAV), helper virus in RSV infection, 463–465
Rous sarcoma virus (RSV), cell transformation by, 461–463
defectiveness, 464, 465
DNA provirus stage, 465, 466
as myxovirus, 459, 460
physical properties, 459, 460

Salmonella typhimurium, histidine biosynthesis in, 239
Secondary structure of proteins, 174, 175
Second law of thermodynamics, 107
Segregation ratios, 18
Self-assembly, 136, 137
Serine, biosynthesis in E. coli, 161, 162
Sex linkage, 20, 22, 23
Sexual cell cycle, 10
Sickle-cell anemia, 240
Soluble-RNA (sRNA), as adaptor, 318
alanine-specific, structure, from yeast, 319, 320

and amino acid activation, 154, 322–324
base-paired regions in, 318, 319
binding to trinucleotide-ribosome complexes, 371, 372
leucine-specific, degeneracy and multiple forms, 374
structure, 318, 319
synthesis on DNA template, 329
unique component, in suppressor bacteria, 385
Spindle, 6
Streptomycin, and misreading of genetic message, 385, 386–387
mutant E. coli resistance, 195
Subunit construction, advantages, 135, 136
of viruses, 343, 344
Suppressor genes, 378–381, 383, 385
Synapsis, 21

Tautomeric shifts, 264
Template, requirement for, in protein synthesis, 178
Template-RNA (see Messenger-RNA)
Template surface, in formation of polymeric molecule, 179
Tertiary structure of proteins, 175, 176
Thioesters, as high-energy compounds, 147
Three-factor crosses, and gene order, 190
Tobacco mosaic virus (TMV), amino acid replacements in mutants of, 377
electron micrograph, 347
formation of virus from RNA and protein, 349
RNA as genetic material of, 346, 348
subunit structure, 134, 343
Transcription, of RNA, on DNA template, 305–312
Transduction, 215–218

Transfer-RNA (tRNA; *see* Soluble-
    RNA)
Transformation, of bacteria by
    DNA, 218–220, 257, 258
  of mammalian cells by viruses,
    452–468
Transforming agent, chemical isola-
    tion, 258
Translation, of nucleotide sequence
    into amino acid sequence,
    298
Tryptophan biosynthesis, pathway in
    E. coli, 246
Tryptophan synthetase, of *E. coli*,
    244, 245
  colinearity and, 244–247
  mutant forms, 244–252
Tumors, 443
Two-factor crosses, and tentative as-
    signment of gene order, 189,
    190

"Unity of biochemistry," 48
"Unusual bases," in DNA of phage
    T2, 352–354
  in yeast-alanine sRNA, 319–321
  structures, 321
Urea, as denaturing agent, 135, 137,
    176
Uridine-5′-phosphate, biosynthesis
    in *E. coli*, 161–164

van der Waals bonds, 103, 112–
    115, 122, 124, 125, 180,
    317, 397, 412
  hydrophobic interaction between
    nonpolar groups, 124, 125
  strength, 109
van der Waals radii, of atoms in
    biological molecules, 113
Viral-specific proteins, control of
    synthesis, 404
Viruses, bacterial (*see* Bacterio-
    phages)
  as cause of cancer, 449–468

control of heredity in, 198, 199
  effect on host cell metabolism,
    350, 351, 353, 354
  electron microscopy, 344–347
  infection and multiplication, 200,
    201
  infectivity of nucleic acids of,
    261, 345
  lower size limit, 359, 360
  as parasites, 201
  single-stranded RNA of, as
    mRNA, 366
  size and shape, 200
  structural organization, 343–347
  subunit construction, 343, 344
"Vitalism," 32
Vitamins, relation to coenzymes, 59

Water, lattice structure, 120
Weak chemical interactions, in anti-
    gen-antibody interaction,
    425–427
  and complementary molecular
    surfaces, 119
  as determining molecular shape,
    126–128
  and enzyme-substrate affinities,
    126
  and feedback inhibition, 411, 412
  in interaction between repressor
    and inducer, 397
  kinds, 102, 103
  strengths, 109
  and template activity, 180
  and virus structure, 349

x-ray crystallography, attempts to
    solve RNA structure, 327
  and determination of DNA
    structure, 263
  myoglobin structure as deter-
    mined by, 172
  of proteins, hemoglobin, and
    myoglobin, 62–64